# Marine Microbial Ecology

# Marine Microbial Ecology

E. J. FERGUSON WOOD

*Professor of Marine Microbiology*
*Institute of Marine Science*
*University of Miami, Florida*

## MODERN BIOLOGICAL STUDIES

LONDON: CHAPMAN AND HALL LTD
NEW YORK: REINHOLD PUBLISHING CORPORATION

*First published* 1965
© *Chapman and Hall Ltd.,* 1965
*Printed in Great Britain by*
*Richard Clay (The Chaucer Press), Ltd.,*
*Bungay, Suffolk*

# Editor's Foreword

This volume inaugurates a new series of Modern Biological Studies. The purpose of this series is twofold. First, to place before the world of biological scholarship a group of outstanding monographs: second, to present these important monographs at a price within the means of both the student and the research biologist.

The present work should fill a rather large gap in the existing literature of oceanography and marine ecology. There are abundant works on the broad bases of this subject but marine microorganisms, save possibly as they affect petroleum production, have been largely ignored. Professor Ferguson Wood brings to this subject not only a deep knowledge of all its aspects but also an unusual ability to present this knowledge clearly and succinctly. While discussing the results of his own researches and those of workers from many parts of the world he has highlighted the problems still awaiting solution as well as the places where our basic knowledge is still scanty. The book serves to bring out the intricate relationships of the whole subject and its vital bearing on the unravelling of marine ecosystems and thus on productivity in the sea. A terminal chapter on methods both clarifies what has gone before and should render easier the task of those who follow.

We therefore welcome this book as a fine inaugural volume for the new series and as an outstanding monograph in its own right.

PETER GRAY
*Professor of Biological Sciences*
*University of Pittsburgh*

J. D. CARTHY
*Department of Zoology*
*Queen Mary College, London*

# Author's Preface

When I was asked to write this book, I had just returned to Woods Hole after an exciting day on a *Zostera* bank at Martha's Vineyard, and was, no doubt, inspired by the enthusiasm of the Ecology group at the Summer School of the Marine Biological Laboratory. I had the basis in some lectures I had prepared, some years previously, and considered their revision as rather an interesting exercise. I had not realized the tremendous effort currently being put into various aspects of marine microbiology, nor the enormity of the gaps in our knowledge that still remained to be bridged. When I began seriously to undertake the work of revision, I was shocked at my temerity.

It is only because I believe that a book should be written now, trying to integrate our knowledge of marine microbial ecology that I have continued.

I have tried to review the literature, and to give a series of references, not perhaps the best, and certainly not a complete list, but such as will give the seeker a chance to complete his own bibliography and forward his own studies. I have also tried to link isolated bits of information by quoting my own and others' experience, often snippets not worth publishing in themselves but confirmative of other work or bridging two ideas. I have not hesitated to give my own ideas and interpretations, and to quote the ideas of others where I deemed them apposite. I once worked with a brilliant colleague who had many ideas daily. Most of them were, like nearly all of mine, of little use, but some were will o' the wisps which had to be followed, correct or not, and others were gems of thought. It taught me that ideas are not things for scientists to be ashamed of but that even in their wrongness may excite others to disprove them and so achieve positive results.

In marine microbiology, our facts are so discrete and disconnected that they do not form a story, and the most important truths of our discipline are still unknown. Disconcertingly, too, there are few marine microbiologists, though the importance of this branch of oceanography is now being realized. This book is therefore for the student rather than the professor or the senior research worker. It is intended to interest, and, if I am not too ambitious, to excite him, to suggest projects and the means of studying them, and perhaps to give the specialist some general information, and the bibliographies to enable him to follow it up.

At the moment, we need marine biologists in the grand tradition, men of breadth and vision rather than specialists, men who can integrate rather than dissect. We have to envisage the ocean as an entity, an ecosystem if you like, and whenever we separate its components be ready to put them back. Details of course are necessary too, but we must see the wood through the trees.

If I can stimulate one researcher to devote his life to marine microbial ecology, or to any aspect thereof, I believe I shall have achieved my purpose in presenting this book.

The first person is used, not because I am egotistical but because I wish to take full responsibility for my ideas. Science is never objective because we can never stop thinking. Even a routine experiment is planned, and true objectivity disappears with the planning.

I should like to thank my colleagues at the Institute of Marine Science for assistance and constructive criticism, in particular, Dr Carl H. Oppenheimer, and my assistants for their co-operation. I shall always remain indebted to the late Professor L. G. M. Baas Becking for ideas and suggestions during the earlier months of preparation of the book, and to Dr Claude E. ZoBell for encouragement in the days when we were both struggling to maintain marine microbiology as an essential discipline within marine biology.

E. J. F. W.

*Miami,*
  *October 1964*

# Contents

## Plates

CHAPTER I

# Introduction

The recent trend in biological sciences has been away from general biology and towards specialization and the study of one usually limited facet such as the physiology of cell walls, cytochemistry, biochemical study of a small group of enzymes or taxonomic studies of a small group of animals or plants. To be a biologist in the sense of studying life as it is in nature has become unfashionable and this is perhaps why this book has not been written before.

Microbes are so small, have such a large surface–volume ratio, are so intimately associated with their environment and with each other that the widest possible scope must be given to the microbiologist if he is to understand the microscopic world. Individual organisms in this world are very short-lived, their rate of metabolism is roughly in inverse ratio to their body size (Odum [1]) and their rate of reproduction exceedingly rapid in terms of human time scales, so the study of individuals is virtually impossible. Some marine bacteria have been recorded as having a generation-time of 10 minutes, and even the diatoms may reproduce once in every 3 to 4 hours in certain circumstances in their natural environment. Because of the intimate relations between the microbes and their environment, they possess wide physiological potentialities and biochemical activities, but in nature, many of these potentialities and activities will never be used. This limits the value of *in vitro* studies; and other properties of the microbial world such as the excretion of external metabolites including exocrines, and the great importance of adsorption of organisms and chemical substances on particulate matter in the seas, make the task of the marine microbiologist a very difficult one. For these reasons, as will be seen in the following pages, there are sad gaps in our knowledge, and in the adequate interpretation of the facts we do know. The student of marine microbial ecology is hampered at the outset by these difficulties; moreover, the tremendous importance of microbiology at various trophic levels in the biological cycle in the water, and the major part played by microbes in chemical processes in the oceans and estuaries and in the geochemistry of the sediments has been only tardily recognized. Dr Claude E. ZoBell [2] was the first microbiologist to maintain marine microbiology as a separate discipline in oceanography, and to state his faith as he did in his book, *Marine Microbiology*, which he published in 1946. ZoBell, however, was primarily interested in the bacteria which he believed play such an important part in the economy of the sea from the tidal edge to the deepest abyss and to the remotest part of the ocean. Planktologists meantime had been stressing the part played by 'phytoplankton' in trophic chains in the sea, though, because of their association with the North Atlantic Ocean, their interest centred in the diatoms, which they called 'the grass of the sea', and to a lesser extent in the Dinoflagellates which Jörgensen [3] called the 'protistplankton'. Later, Bernard [4] and others suggested that the coccolithophores are important among the plankton, and Raymont and Gross [5], Parke [6], and Knight-Jones [7] showed that other flagellates such as the Chrysomonads must be considered. It is only recently that Vishniac [8] has suggested that we have not paid sufficient attention to the possible importance of the fungi.

Thus, the number of groups of micro-organisms which must come within our purview has steadily increased. It was not so very long ago that a plant was a plant and an animal remained an animal, except for such inconvenient micro-organisms as the dinoflagellates, which were called plant-animals and relegated by the botanists to zoology, and by the zoologists to botany. Nowadays, the findings of people like Joyce Lewin [9] that even the 'true plant' diatoms have a number of facultatively heterotrophic species leave us no option but to consider these microbes independently of their mode of nutrition which so many of them can change with changing circumstances. We now find ourselves concerned with a number of trophic levels, and with photoautotrophy, chemoautotrophy, heterotrophy, and phagotrophy, as well as the complication of auxotrophy, terms which will be defined later.

The importance of microbes, or as they were fashionably known a century ago, *infusoria*, will be recognized when one considers that the macroscopic algae or seaweeds cover about 2% of the sea bottom (though they make up considerably more of the plant biomass), and the rest of the photosynthetic material in the sea, apart from the sea-grasses in estuaries and on shallow continental shelves, is microscopic. Thus, the first trophic level in the oceans is controlled by the activities of micro-organisms. At the next trophic level, colourless flagellates, ciliates, and sarcodina are very important, although there seems to have been no attempt to estimate *how* important they are, except for a very small amount of work done by the author. Again, at the final trophic level, bacteria, fungi, and other heterotrophs transform organic matter into its inorganic constituents to start another cycle. The microbes then have three functions in the sea, to provide most of the energy required by the animals by means of the autotrophs, to short-circuit food chains by means of the phagotrophs, and to complete the trophic cycle by means of the heterotrophs. For this reason, the scientific rewards of the marine microbial ecologist must be high.

## Some Definitions

In defining a subject, there is always a difficulty in deciding just where to set the limits. The saying *natura non facit saltem* becomes dismayingly evident, and forces the author to give a full explanation for the arbitrary limits which he sets. Human beings cannot envisage a continuum, but tend to put things and ideas into pigeon-holes, and this tendency must be resisted to the utmost. Discontinuities in nature are usually due to a break in time or space such as ice ages, changes in levels of the earth's surface, or to some catastrophe. So, to begin with, it must be decided how far from the sea one should go in defining the word 'marine'. In the environment which would normally be excluded, we have two extremes, fresh water and salt lakes. Biologically, there is a gradual transition from fresh water to saturated brine environments with the same processes occurring in each. Many of the organisms, however, change at certain salinity levels, depending on their 'salt tolerance'. Organisms which are restricted by salinity changes are called *stenohaline*, those with a wide range, *euryhaline*. For the present, those organisms will be considered as marine which grow in the open ocean (*oceanic*), close to shore (*neritic*), and in salt or brackish, tidal waters (*estuarine*). The limits of estuarine organisms are somewhat arbitrary, and there will be some reference to fresh water influences in this connexion. It may be necessary also to refer now and then to brines for comparison.

It is unfortunate that the term 'microbiology' has so often been used as a synonym for 'bacteriology'. This is partly due to a conceit that the bacteria were the only micro-organisms worth studying, or that they were unique in their properties. By derivation, *microbiology* should apply to the study of all small organisms, and this meaning will be adopted here. In biology, however, size is often misleading as a criterion, as closely related organisms can vary greatly, e.g. in the diatom *Coscinodiscus*, small forms of about $20\,\mu$ can be found, while *Coscinodiscus rex* may reach 1 to 2 mm in diameter and is often larger than some of the crustacea (e.g. copepods) which occur in the sea. As these copepods are relatives of the lobster and crayfish, they are conveniently left to the macro-zoologist, while the diatoms are claimed as part of the province. *Rhizosolenia castracanei* is another diatom which can be seen with the naked eye and yet comes within our purview, while *R. delicatula* is only a few microns long. The field may be defined by considering as micro-organisms living creatures which are either unicellular or colonial but normally undifferentiated, and which generally require a microscope for their identification. This will include both the *autotrophic* (capable of existing in inorganic media), *heterotrophic* (requiring dissolved organic constituents to supply carbon), and *phagotrophic* microbes which ingest particulate organic matter including other organisms. The term *autotrophy* cannot, in the light of present evidence, be used without qualification because, firstly, many organisms which do not require organic carbon to form their protoplasm do require organic constituents such as auxins or vitamins for normal function; such organisms are known as *auxotrophs*. Secondly, many organisms formerly thought to be autotrophic are now known to be able to live partly or wholly as heterotrophs or phagotrophs and are known as *myxotrophs*. Up to now, the 'plants' in the seas, i.e. the micro-organisms which contain chlorophyll, were known as 'phytoplankton' if free in the water, and the animals which do not contain chlorophyll were called *zooplankton*. The bacteria, because of their mode of nutrition, using dissolved organic substances, were considered separately. Occasionally, the dinoflagellates, which were known to combine autotrophy and phagotrophy, were ascribed to the 'protistplankton' as has been mentioned. Now that we know that many diatoms, flagellates (phytomastigina), unicellular green algae and other potential *photosynthonts* (photosynthetic micro-organisms) can also live partly or wholly on dissolved organic matter to supply their carbon, the separation of the bacteria is unwarranted on nutritional grounds, though some of them do possess peculiar nutritional aspects. Wood [10] suggested the term *protoplankton* to include both protophyta and protozoa of the planktonic communities we are going to study. In the protoplankton, I would include the bacteria, unicellular plants (diatoms and phytomastigina), and the rest of the protozoa, i.e. the zoomastigina, ciliata, and sarcodina. As well as the floating organisms or *plankton*, the *periphyton*, i.e. the micro-organisms attached to floating or fixed surfaces also come within the field (*epontic* from Greek, ἐπι – on and οντος – being, if attached to any substrate or *epiphytic* from ἐπι – on and φητον – plant, if attached to plants), and those which live on or in the sediments and are called *benthic*.

I shall consider *ecology* in the sense so well defined by Clarke [11] who states:

'The organisms interact with each other and also with the physical conditions which are present. Thus, organisms and the physical features of the habitat form an *ecological complex* or, more briefly an *ecosystem*.

'The concept that organisms and their environment form a reciprocating system represents the viewpoint of most modern ecologists. In every natural situation, the environment affects the organisms present, and, to a greater or lesser extent, the organisms affect the environment.'

Ecology, in this wide sense, becomes the ultimate aim of biological research. It can answer most of the questions that a scientist or an interested layman is likely to ask. The scientist is interested in why the organism is there, and what are its relationships to the other organisms present and to the environment. This is the fundamental problem. The layman is interested in the economic or social effect of the organism's existence upon himself or on the community of which he is a member. The organism can act in two ways; it can assist in some process which is desirable for humanity, i.e. serve as food, as a link in the food chain, produce something of economic value; or it can be deleterious, it can compete with useful forms, destroy a desirable substrate or render an environment unsuitable for a desired purpose. Because these processes are usually complex, it is essential that a large collection of fundamental data should be made, and some interpretation attempted, before the commercial aspects of the problem are exploited too far. Many of the processes involved are irreversible if allowed to proceed beyond a certain point.

**The Land and the Sea**

Water covers over 70% of the earth's surface and receives that portion of the light and heat energy from the sun. Primary production, which is the *sine qua non* of animal populations, depends on plant growth, and this makes use of solar energy for *endothermic* (energy-requiring) reactions, forming biological material with this external energy source. Thus, plants store solar energy and convert it to biological energy, much of which is later used by the animals which feed on the plants. On land, most plants are macroscopic, while, in the water, the greater number are microscopic and come within the scope of this inquiry. In comparing the land and the waters, it is found that essentially the same processes go on: photosynthesis, sulphur, nitrogen, and phosphorus cycles, the synthesis and degradation of organic matter, and the formation and dissolution of inorganic materials. The great difference in the two environments is the rate of change. On land, trees may live for a thousand years or more, while, in the water, one may see vast blooms of microscopic plants which colour the water but live only a few days or weeks. Land plants are differentiated into roots, stems, and leaves, which take over different functions and share their labours. Marine plants, except for the sea-grasses (*Zostera, Posidonia, Ruppia,*

B

*Diplanthera, Thalassia,* etc.), which are land plants returned to an aqueous habitat, are little differentiated, and each cell works for itself. Even the sea-grasses have a much simpler anatomy than their terrestrial relations, and the algae all have a very slightly differentiated structure. Apart from the kelp forests which fringe the land in cooler latitudes, and the smaller sargassums and coralline algae of warmer waters, the aquatic forests consist mainly of unicellular plants which grow to an effective depth of 10 to 150 metres and move with the currents. Each of these cells is a complete unit with a large surface–volume ratio, and production, storage, and elimination of waste products occur in the same cell. Supporting and translocation tissues are thus eliminated, increasing the efficiency of the plant as a whole, and also its rate of metabolic turnover. In the sea, as on land, nutrients and temperature can become limiting factors in the increase of plant material, but moisture is no longer limiting. The non-photosynthetic micro-organisms are concentrated in the substrate (soils or sediments) both in terrestrial and aquatic environments, though the micro-organisms dispersed through the vast volume of water below the *photic zone* (or zone of light penetration) are probably comparable in quantity with those in the photic zone, and perhaps more numerous.

## Methods of Approach

In the beginning of a study of a new environment, the first essential is taxonomy. By this I do not mean a mere listing of the genera and species and larger groups to be found in the ecosystem, but also a thorough understanding of the principles and limitations of the taxonomy of each group. van Niel [12], Paulsen [13], Wood [14, 15] have discussed the limitations of taxonomy of the bacteria and dinoflagellates and have suggested a variability pattern or spectrum rather than a series of rigid divisions. This is further discussed in the next section. Because of this lability, the environment must have a greater effect on micro-organisms than it will on higher forms which are more stable in their characters and less liable to external influences. Because each individual micro-organism is so intimately connected with the environment and has no specialized cells to deal with awkward situations, one must expect the relationships between micro-organisms and their environment to be extremely close, while, at the same time, the organisms should have considerable resilience to changes in the environment. It is not possible here to give a detailed classification of all the thousands of organisms to be found in the aqueous environment, or even in environments where the aqueous phase is continuous. Moreover, until a great deal more critical work has been done on taxonomy, including pure culture studies to determine variability patterns and relations of these labile organisms to changes in the milieu, taxonomic study of micro-organisms as an ultimate study has limited use. However, it is necessary for the ecologist to know within reasonable limits the identity of the organisms in the environment he is studying, so that changes in their biology or even their morphology can be correlated with changes in the environment.

The second step in the study of an environment is ecological. *Autecology* is the study of the distribution of individual organisms or species within a given environment and the relation of these organisms to that environment; *synecology* is the grouping or *association* of organisms in an environment and their relation to the environment and to each other. It is possibly easiest to study first the autecology of individual microbes, e.g. the bacteria of the various phases of the sulphur cycle, and then to integrate the information gained in order to obtain a knowledge of the synecology of organisms in the ecosystem. A considerable amount of information can be gleaned by qualitative or descriptive work because, frequently, the presence or absence of a particular form or group of forms has significance. For instance, the presence of the diatom *Pleurosigma angulatum* or *P. balticum* in plankton is indicative of turbulence affecting the bottom in shallow water; or the appearance of the true Antarctic species *Rhizosolenia chunii* or *Biddulphia weissflogii* off the coast of New South Wales in temperate waters is an excellent indicator of the upwelling of Antarctic water in that region, though such water may not reach the surface. Because species and associations of species may vary considerably in a given region, it may be convenient to determine the 'affinity' or lack of 'affinity' between species or groups of species by a mathematical analysis as has been attempted by Fager [16] and Fager and McGowan [17]. This method of assessment has been little used in planktology, but can give a mathematical interpretation to fix what are known as *indicator species*. This term has been used in the past to designate species which are associated with certain water masses, e.g. the diatom *Rhizosolenia curvata*, which is stated by Hart [18] to be confined to the waters of the Antarctic convergence and therefore to act as an *indicator* of that water mass. By a suitably designed punched-card system, it is possible to designate associated and distinct species groups, and to assign them to certain water types, or to certain temperature or salinity regimes (Wood [19]).

Quantitative work becomes necessary when we wish to study the horizontal and vertical distribution of organisms, diurnal and seasonal differences and so on. It can be done by counting the organisms, by chemical or physical estimations based on microbial reactions, e.g. in 'productivity' studies.

Problems in hydrobiology may be attacked in two ways, by analysis or by synthesis or preferably by analysis followed by synthesis. Synthesis is often difficult because all the factors are not recognized, while analysis usually breaks down eventually for technical reasons. Furthermore, what appears on analysis to be a simple factor may be found by a synthetic approach to be complicated. Microbiologists dating from Koch have regarded pure culture analysis to be the most desirable method of approach, and there is a whole literature of microbiology devoted to experimental research with pure cultures. Winogradsky, on the other hand, regarded mixed cultures in a controlled milieu as the most productive way of investigating microbial phenomena. While the former method has produced excellent results, especially in medical bacteriology and taxonomy, it has led to many false assumptions in other fields. The study of the physiology and biochemistry of micro-organisms in pure cultures is fraught with many dangers, for micro-organisms, like their macro-counterparts, can be trained even by the very artificiality of their laboratory environment to perform strange tricks which they would scorn to do in their natural state. One might equally regard as a natural phenomenon the jumping of lions through blazing hoops because all circus lions have been observed to do so. Studies of type cultures of bacteria, for example, have often shown both morphological and physiological differences from the original descriptions, due no doubt to the progressive influence of unnatural conditions on the organism. I have found stock cultures in my laboratory gradually changing their fermentative and proteolytic characters over the years. Again, bacteria attached to fouling plates appear thereon as pleomorphic spirilla, but later become stable coccobacilli in subcultures (Wood [20]).

**Variation and the Species Concept**
In the microbial world, one can study the biology only of strains, because individuals have an evanescent existence. This applies not only to the bacteria, but also to the flagellates, diatoms, and other unicellular forms, and to morphological as well as to physical characters. Size is meaningless, or nearly so, although many authors (Kofoid and Skogsberg [21], Steemann Nielsen [22], Bohm [23]) have used it to determine species. It is well known that certain diatoms gradually decrease in size in successive generations owing to their pill-box formation. Similar size-variation has been recorded in the dinoflagellates *Goniodoma polyedricum* and *Ceratium symmetricum*, where there was no question of a specific difference (Wood [15]). Shape does have a degree of constancy in many cases, although there is, at times, a considerable variation, e.g. in the dinoflagellates *Ceratium tripos* and *Dinophysis caudata*, or the bacterium *Mycoplana*. In the latter case, the type culture in the American Collection of Type Cultures has become morphologically a

*Pseudomonas*, although a culture obtained by me from the British National Collection has the morphology originally ascribed to it by Gray and Thornton [24]. Physiological characters, as would be expected, are even less constant, at least in the bacteria and the flagellates. Many of the latter are holozoic (either heterotrophic or phagotrophic) or holophytic (auto-trophic) according to conditions, or may be myxotrophic, i.e. use both means of nutrition at the same time. Bacteria are, with their smaller size and lesser differentiation, even more variable. Most people who have worked extensively with the non-pathogenic bacteria have great difficulty in classifying them. Some workers have merely given tables of reactions of the strains, others have worked out divisions to suit their own purposes, while still others have described large numbers of new species or tried to fit their strains between the covers of Bergey's *Manual of Determinative Bacteriology*. None of these expedients seem satisfactory to me though I have tried them all. I have now come to the conclusion that bacteria possess great potentialities for variation, and that, being closely contiguous with the environment, they are capable of being influenced by that environment far more readily than the higher forms can ever be. As examples may be quoted changes induced in the fermentation of certain strains of *Escherichia coli* (Wood, unpublished) and in the temperature and salinity relationships of the sulphate-reducing bacterium *Desulphovibrio desulphuricans* recorded by Baas Becking and Wood [25]. In the case of *E. coli*, both Type 1 *coli* and *Alkaligenes* types were cultured from a single cell of a slow-lactose-fermenting strain by repeated selection on lactose broth. Baars [26] and Littlewood and Postgate [27] showed that *Desulphovibrio* could adapt to varying salinities, and that *D. aestuarii*, *D. desulphuricans*, and *D. rubents-chiki* could not therefore be maintained as separate species. Baas Becking and Wood [25] and Wood (unpublished) have isolated *Desulphovibrio* from aquatic sediments with pH from 6·8 to 8·4, salinity of 19 to 30 p.p.mille and a temperature range from 14° to 23°C and grown them in culture at pH from 3·8 to 11·0, salinities from 1 to 24 p.p.mille and temperatures from 10° to 65°C with or without bivalent cations. It must be assumed that, under the original conditions, the strains contained potential variants, or a potential for variation which they could never exhibit in their natural habitat, but which became dominant as soon as conditions were appreciably altered. The same kind of variability can be shown to exist among both heterotrophic and autotrophic bacteria, so to generalize it could be said that it is the rule rather than the exception in aquatic bacteria. There are, however, strains which are not nearly so adaptable to changed conditions, strains of coliform organisms which did not vary appreciably after many attempts to change them, and strains of *Desulphovibrio* which were sensitive to very small changes in salinity or temperature. This suggests that the variability is inherent in the strain, and is not imposed from without. In this view, each strain of a primary culture would have a norm about which the population is gathered; alterations of conditions would increase the probability of survival of variants in that strain adapted to the new conditions, thus forming a new norm for the population. This concept is supported by the work of Hughes [28] and Hata [29]. The degree of variability of a given strain would depend on the difference of the extremes from the norm in regard to the property being tested. The difference of opinion regarding the three 'species' of *Desulphovibrio*, *D. desulphuricans*, *D. aestuarii*, and *D. rubentschiki* is due to the variability of the strains encountered by different workers. Postgate [30] isolated a hydrogenase-free strain of this genus from El Agheila and regarded it as unique in his collection. Baas Becking and Wood [25] found similar strains dominant in the estuarine environment in Port Hacking and Botany Bay, near Sydney, Australia, but some of these after prolonged cultivation yielded a hydrogenase-positive strain. On the other hand, hydrogenase-containing strains predominated in Lake Macquarie some 100 miles to the north. This lagoon, while estuarine in character, has properties somewhat different from those of Port Hacking and Botany Bay, and these differences seem sufficient to select different strains of *Desulphovibrio*. In the absence of genetic evidence, it is impossible to say whether variations in salt-tolerance, hydrogenase activity, etc., are significant in designating species (cf. Flannery [31]).

This leads to the species-concept in bacteriology, and, indeed, in microbiology generally, in cases where the sexual process of reproduction is inadequately known. Because of the inherent variability in such forms, the bacteria cannot be considered subject to the Linnean species concept. It is true that, even in the species of well-defined higher plants and animals, there are intergrades which cast doubt on the value of certain specific distinctions, but in such cases one can usually use two or more defining characters to assist the diagnosis. With the saprophytic bacteria, however, one rarely finds two well-correlating characters, and when one does it is often coincidence. Liston and his colleagues [32, 33] have applied the Adansonian principle to certain marine bacteria, but this does not solve the problem of variability in response to changes in the natural environment. Wood [14] accepted the bacterial species as a useful concept which does not necessarily have objective validity. He did not go as far as van Niel [12] who considered that the only satisfactory way to identify bacteria is by a series of cross-indices; for one thing, this procedure is too time-consuming, and for another, arbitrary species are quite useful to the ecologist provided the species-limits are carefully defined. Wood [14] condemned the practice of creating genera on the basis of environment or origin, e.g. *Corynebacterium-Arthrobacter*, *Actinomyces-Streptomyces*, *Pseudomonas-Phytomonas*. For one reason, the obvious derivation of the pathogenic form from the non-pathogenic counterpart is obscured by such nomenclature, and for another, the possibility of one strain belonging to two categories is excluded. If, for example, a diphtheria culture becomes non-pathogenic, as does happen, and is 'trained' to an optimum temperature of 25°C by careful selection, does it become *Arthrobacter*? The case of *Pseudomonas-Phytomonas* is even more serious because *Pseudomonas* has strains which appear to become pathogenic to plants and animals and then to lose their pathogenicity. This is especially true of aquatic strains which are sometimes found to be pathogenic to fish; in fact, most fish pathogens belong to *Pseudomonas* and are very variable in their degree of pathogenicity. If *Phytomonas* is used for plant pathogens, why not create a genus *Zoomonas* for animal pathogens? This would be consistent if futile.

Among the dinoflagellates, too, the species concept is very difficult, and Paulsen [13] and Wood [14] have drawn attention to the fact. We do not know of a sexual process in many or most of the species of the group. Further, in some species, e.g. *Ceratium tripos*, *Peridinium grani*, and *P. divergens* there is a wide variation in morphology as well as in the potentialities for either holozoic or holophytic nutrition. Some authors have split these species groups, e.g. *Ceratium tripos*, *C. semipulchellum*, *C. tripodioides*, while others have reunited them. Locality-species too have been created among the dinoflagellates, e.g. *Peridinium antarcticum* distinguished from *P. depressum* by Schimper on account of its habitat. A difficulty here is that there is often a slight or gradual change in morphology as one proceeds from the equator to the poles as in *Peridinium piriforme*, *Dinophysis tripos*, and *D. ovum*; but even man changes his nutrition and also his morphology according to whether he dwells in equatorial or boreal regions. Another difficulty which applies more generally is that, with the movement of oceanic water masses, closely related species may be found brought together by different currents. Wood [15] observed that species such as *Dinophysis ovum*, *Peridinium grani*, *P. ovatum*, and *P. depressum* occur with morphological differences in the Antarctic and in estuarine environments. The question arises, are these to be regarded as eco-forms or as different species? Taxonomically, the question is subjective – to split or not to split; ecologically, the answer is vitally important in regard to the bi-polarity of species, for these species occur also in the Northern Hemisphere but are not truly oceanic in tropical or sub-tropical waters.

The diatoms exhibit considerable variation in morphology, especially the planktonic species which have appendages, such as *Corethron, Bacteriastrum,* and *Chaetoceros*. One frequently sees chains of *Chaetoceros* which have the characters at one species at one end of a chain and those of another species at the other (Crosby and Wood [34]). Further, in blooms of *Chaetoceros*, a number of species of the same group or sub-genus are frequently recorded in the same catch, an ecological implication that many of these 'species' are not valid genetically. The existence of two valves of the same diatom frustule with the characters used to distinguish two genera (and maybe assigned to different families) suggests that the shape and structure of the siliceous frustule may not be a valid specific character for this group of organisms. I have found *Coscinodiscus-Asteromphalus* frustules in the Antarctic (Wood [35]) and in the Timor Sea [36], and *Coscinodiscus-Actinocyclus* frustules in the Texas Bays. There is considerable variation among the pennate diatoms also, e.g. in *Navicula granulata* and *N. brasiliensis* which Hendey [37] separates on the type material, but which Hustedt unites because of its numerous intergrades. There are intergrades and consequent taxonomic confusion in the *Navicula lyra* and *N. hennedyi* complexes also. In the case of the diatoms, it is difficult to suggest an alternative to the siliceous tests as specific characters, especially as these are all that is left of these organisms in the geological record, and they do allow comparisons of that record with present day species or groups.

Taxonomic difficulties can prevent the ecologist from appreciating the relationships between two environments of the changes in environment indicated by changes in morphology or physiology of a species. A case in point is the *Dinophysis tripos-caudata* assemblage (fig. 1). The form of this dinoflagellate appears to be related to water temperature, angular forms of *caudata* being related to tropical occurrences in both Indian and Pacific Oceans, rounded *caudata* forms to the sub-tropics, smooth *tripos* forms to warm-temperate estuaries, and lobed *tripos* to cool-temperate estuaries (Wood [15]); in fact, in the Dinophysidae generally, the protuberances are associated with colder waters. The position of *Dinophysis tripos-caudata* is made more difficult by the existence in New South Wales waters of an overlap zone between Newcastle and Port Hacking. In this zone, both *D. tripos* and *D. caudata*, as well as the closely associated and probably transitional form known as *D. diegensis*, may be found in the same water mass.

It would be ideal if one could decide taxonomic relationships by cultures, but unfortunately it has not so far been possible to grow most of the tropical oceanic species of diatoms or dinoflagellates in the laboratory, despite many years' work by many workers including myself. This leaves

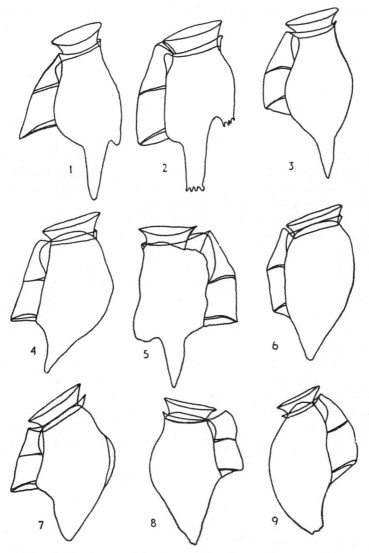

FIG. I. *Dinophysis tripos-caudata-diegensis* showing eco-forms and intergrades.
I. *D. tripos,* Sydney form; 2. *D. tripos,* south Tasmanian form; 3. *D. caudata* (Sydney form); 4, 6, 7, 8, 9. *D. caudata-diegensis* intergrades; 5. *D. caudata* (tropical form).

the matter of classification very much in the hands of the observer, and is the reason for so many differences of opinion in regard to details of marine and estuarine ecology. In the case of the naked flagellates, cultures from a single cell can be different enough to be ascribed to different species by a protozoologist ignorant of their origin, but, in their case, cultures can be and are being used to establish the limits of variability. There is no ready solution to the taxonomic problem, but if progress is to be made, taxonomy must have a certain amount of lability and must be pragmatic. If it forms a regular pattern and gives us a logical explanation of observed phenomena, that is all we can hope with our present knowledge. Type specimens in museums and culture collections are or can be far too restricting, as they take no account of natural variation. A good ecologist must remember that the pigeon-holes of taxonomy have been made for convenience only, and have not necessarily any objective existence.

The physiological activity of many micro-organisms also varies considerably, for example, many agar-digesting bacteria will not attack agar in the presence of a more readily available carbon source; ammonia or nitrate restrict the fixation of nitrogen by some microbes; the end products of sulphur oxidation by the purple sulphur bacteria depend on the oxidation-reduction potential (redox or Eh) of the environment. Thus, the presence of potential agar-digesters, nitrogen fixers, or sulphide oxidizers does not mean that agar will be digested, dissolved nitrogen fixed, or sulphate formed. All too frequently potentialities such as these are lost during successive sub-cultures, and we may get an *Agarbacterium* which will not hydrolyse agar, or a *Photobacterium* which has lost the property of bioluminescence. The adaptation of many species to holophytic or holozoic growth has been mentioned. This implies that they can assist productivity or degradation in the same milieu with only slight alteration of the conditions. Therefore, the function of various members of an association of micro-organisms can be known only if we have determined the physico-chemical characters of the environment, and if we know the behaviour of each group of organisms under the prevailing conditions.

## Characterization of the Environment

A considerable amount of work has been done on the physico-chemical characteristics of marine and fresh water environments, and somewhat less on estuarine ones, but the correlation between hydrology and biology leaves a great deal to be desired. This means that the biologist and the hydrologist have been living in their separate ivory towers without a really determined effort to understand each other's problems. For example, a great deal is known about bacterial enzymes, or at least about those of *Escherichia coli* and *Staphylococcus aureus*, but little about the influence of the physico-chemical conditions on marine environments or bacterial metabolism. Likewise the hydrologist can tell us accurately, though perhaps not accurately enough, the nitrate and phosphate content of the water, but knows little about the dynamics of the nitrogen or phosphorus cycles of the region he is studying. Waksman and his co-workers showed that the diatoms and other phytoplankton organisms can use nitrate, nitrite, and ammonia, but the ratio of these that is actually being assimilated by various plankton organisms is not assessed. In this case, important energy changes are involved, which could have considerable effect on the oceanic ecosystem. The position is gradually improving, but there is still a rather deplorable attitude of *laissez faire* in many marine laboratories. The gaps in our knowledge can best be bridged by closest collaboration between the microbiologist and the hydrologist, with a considerable amount of overlapping in the interests of both.

Baas Becking and Wood [25] made an attempt to correlate hydrogen-ion concentration (pH) and oxidation-reduction potential (Eh) with the microbiology of estuaries and other aqueous systems. They drew up a diagram (fig. 2) showing the pH/Eh relationships of a number of microbial processes such as the sulphur cycle and photosynthesis. Each participant organism has its own limits, but there are points or areas where these limits overlap, and where many of the reactions can proceed together. However, a change in hydrogen-ion concentration or in redox potential favours one or another of the organisms. This work has given us clues regarding the taking up and release of phosphorus (Baas Becking and Mackay [39]), on the ferrous–ferric system (Baas Becking, Wood, and Kaplan [40]), and other reactions in the estuarine system which will be discussed later. The potential milieu can be outlined and the governing chemical reactions indicated. The actual milieu lies well within the potential limits, because other reactions and biological processes intervene, e.g. the sharp decrease of bicarbonate ion above pH 9·4 in sea water and 10·5 in fresh water. The pH of the ocean is controlled by the $CO_2 \rightleftharpoons HCO_3$ equilibrium, except in certain shallow waters where $CO_3^=$ is precipitated. These equilibria are altered by photosynthesis and respiration. We have little knowledge yet of the biological–physico-chemical interactions of the nitrogen cycle in the sea, despite much work on the enzymes and pathways of strains of *Azotobacter*, because these have been studied without serious thought of the way in which such knowledge could be applied in the natural environment. There is hardly any information on organic transformations or ion exchange in muds or silts.

In the ocean, the problem is simpler, as there are not so many factors,

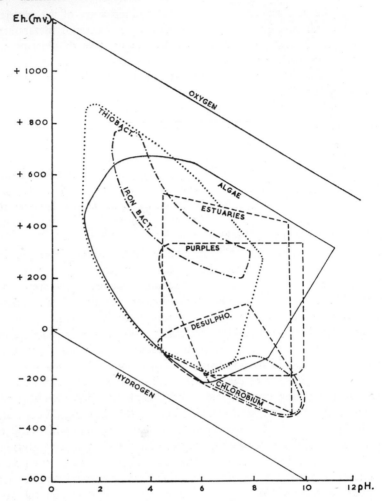

FIG. 2. The range of bacterial groups and algae in aqueous systems with respect to pH and Eh (after Baas Becking and Wood, 1955).

and the milieu is not so subject to change, but the problem of sampling is exceedingly difficult and it is almost impossible to sample the same body of water twice. We shall have to wait until someone has designed a sort of 'Kon-Tiki' raft, unaffected by wind, which can be borne along by an ocean current and stay for days and if necessary for weeks in the same body of water. Otherwise, we are merely making a grab at oceanic phenomena as they pass by.

# REFERENCES

[1] ODUM, H. T. (1956), 'Efficiencies, size of organisms and community structure', *Ecology*, 37, 593–97.

[2] ZOBELL, C. E. (1946), *Marine Microbiology*, Chronica Botanica Press, Waltham, Mass., 240 pp.

[3] JÖRGENSEN, E. (1905), 'The protist plankton and diatoms in bottom samples', *Bergens Mus. Skr.*, 23.

[4] BERNARD, F. (1948), 'Réchérches sur le cycle de *Coccolithus fragilis* Lohm. flagellé dominant des mers chaudes', *J. Cons. Int. Expl. Mer*, 15, 177–88.

[5] RAYMONT, J. E. G. and GROSS, F. (1942), 'On the feeding and breeding of *Calanus finmarchicus* under laboratory conditions', *Proc. Roy. Soc. Edin.*, B67, 267–87.

[6] PARKE, MARY (1949), 'Studies on marine flagellates', *J. Mar. Biol. Ass. U.K.*, 28, 255–86.

[7] KNIGHT-JONES, E. W. and WALNE, P. R. (1951), '*Chromulina pusilla* Butcher, a dominant member of the ultraplankton', *Nature*, 167, 445.

[8] VISHNIAC, HELEN S. (1956), 'On the ecology of the lower marine fungi', *Biol. Bull.*, 111, 410–14.

[9] LEWIN JOYCE, C. (1963), 'Heterotrophy in marine diatoms', *Symp. Marine Microbiol.*, Ch. 23, C. H. Oppenheimer, ed. Thomas, Springfield, Ill.

[10] WOOD, E. J. F. (1963), 'The relative importance of groups of algae and protozoa in marine environments of the Southwest Pacific and East Indian Oceans', *Symp. Marine Microbiol.*, Ch. 24, C. H. Oppenheimer, ed. Thomas, Springfield, Ill.

[11] CLARKE, G. L. (1954), *Elements of Ecology*, Wiley, New York, 534 pp.

[12] VAN NIEL, C. B. (1946), 'The classification and natural relationships of bacteria', *Cold Spring Harb. Symp. Quant. Biol.*, XI.

[13] PAULSEN, O. (1949), 'Observations on dinoflagellates', *Kgl. Dansk. Vidensk. Selsk. Biol. Skr.*, 6, 4, 1.

[14] WOOD, E. J. F. (1950), 'The classification of bacteria', *Proc. Linn. Soc. N.S.W.*, 57, 195–213.

[15] WOOD, E. J. F. (1954), 'Dinoflagellates of the Australian region', *Aust. J. Mar. Freshw. Res.*, 5, 171–351.

[16] FAGER, E. F. (1957), 'Determination and analysis of recurrent groups', *Ecology*, 38, 586–95.

[17] FAGER, E. F. and MCGOWAN, J. A. (1963), 'Zooplankton species groups in the Northern Pacific', *Science*, 140, 453–60.

[18] HART, T. J. (1937), '*Rhizosolenia curvata* Zacharias, an indicator species in the Southern Ocean', *Discovery Repts.*, 16, 2, 415–46.

[19] WOOD, E. J. F. (1964), 'Studies in the microbial ecology of the Australasian region', *Nova Hedwigia*, 7, 1–2, 3–4.

[20] WOOD, E. J. F. (1953), 'Heterotrophic bacteria in marine environments of Eastern Australia', *Aust. J. Mar. Freshw. Res.*, 4, 160–200.

[21] KOFOID, C. A. and SKOGSBERG, T. (1928), 'Dinoflagellata; The Dinophysoidea', *Mem. Mus. Comp. Zool. Harv.*, 51.

[22] STEEMANN NIELSEN, E. (1934), 'Untersuchungen über die Ceratien im Südlichen Stillen Ozean', *Dana Rept.*, 4, Carlsberg Foundation.

[23] BOHM, A. (1931), 'Distribution and variability of *Ceratium* in the Northern and Western Pacific', *Bernice P. Bishop Mus. Bull.*, 57.

[24] GRAY, P. H. H. and THORNTON, H. G. (1928), 'Soil bacteria that decompose certain aromatic compounds', *Z. Bakt.*, II, 73, 74–96.

[25] BAAS BECKING, L. G. M. and WOOD, E. J. F. (1955), 'Biological processes in the estuarine environment, I, II', *Kon. Ned. Akad. Weten. Proc.*, B58, 160–81.

[26] BAARS, J. K. (1930), 'Over Sulfatreduktie door Bakterien', Dissert. Delft, 164 pp.

[27] LITTLEWOOD, DOROTHY and POSTGATE, J. R. (1957), 'On the osmotic behaviour of *Desulphovibrio desulphuricans*', *J. Gen. Microbiol.*, 16, 596–603.

[28] HUGHES, W. H. (1954), 'On the individuality of micro-organisms', *J. Gen. Microbiol.*, 11, proc. ii.

[29] HATA, Y. (1960), 'Relations between the activity of marine sulphate-reducing bacteria and the oxidation-reduction potential of the culture media', *J. Shimonoseki Coll. Fish.*, 19, 57–77.

[30] POSTGATE, J. R. (1958), 'Biochemistry and physiology of the sulphate-reducing bacteria', *Producers' Month.*, 22, 12–16.

[31] FLANNERY, W. L. (1956), 'Current status of the knowledge of halophilic bacteria', *Bact. Rev.*, 20, 49–66.

[32] LISTON, J. (1957), 'The occurrence and distribution of bacterial types on flatfish', *J. Gen. Microbiol.*, 16, 205–16.

[33] COLWELL, R. R. and LISTON, J. (1961), 'Taxonomic relationships among the pseudomonads', *J. Bact.*, 82, 1–14.

[34] CROSBY, L. H. and WOOD, E. J. F. (1958), 'Studies on Australian and New Zealand diatoms', *Trans. Roy. Soc. N.Z.*, 85, 482–530.

[35] WOOD, E. J. F. (1959), 'An unusual diatom from the Antarctic', *Nature*, 184, 1962–1963.

[36] WOOD, E. J. F. (1963), 'Studies on Australian and New Zealand diatoms, VI', *Trans. Roy. Soc. N.Z., Botany*, 2, 15, 189–218.

[37] HENDEY, N. I. (1953), 'Taxonomic studies on some *Naviculae punctatae*', *J. Roy. Micro. Soc.*, 73, 151–61.

[38] HUSTEDT, F. (1956), 'Marine littoral diatoms from Beaufort, North Carolina', *Duke Univ. Mar. Sta. Bull.*, 6, 1–67.

[39] BAAS BECKING, L. G. M. and MACKAY, MARGARET (1956), 'Biological processes in the estuarine environment, V', *Kon. Ned. Akad. Weten. Proc.*, B59, 109–23.

[40] BAAS BECKING, L. G. M., WOOD, E. J. F., and KAPLAN, I. R. (1956), 'Biological processes in the estuarine environment, VIII', *Kon. Ned. Akad. Weten. Proc.*, B59, 398–407.

CHAPTER 2

# The Marine Environment

The marine environment is distinguished from the fresh water environment primarily by its higher salt content. In the oceans, the salt content varies from about 33 to 38 p.p.mille, but close to land the salinity will drop below the former figure if there is much run-off or if there are rivers in the vicinity. In estuaries, there is still further dilution by fresh water, though, if an estuary in a region of low rainfall becomes closed for a long period, it may have a higher salinity than the ocean. This has been recorded from such coastal lagoons as Lake Illawarra in New South Wales and portions of the Laguna Madre such as Baffin Bay in Texas. Because the estuaries are so much more easily affected by climate, by the juxtaposition of water and sediment and by their shallowness relatively even to the continental shelf, the oceanic and estuarine environments will be treated separately.

## The Oceanic Environment

The oceanic environment differs from most terrestrial, fresh water, and estuarine environments in its comparative constancy. There are, of course, differences between Arctic and equatorial water in temperature and salinity, and between surface water and that at 10,000 metres at the bottom of the ocean abysses, in temperature, salinity, pressure, and other essentials, and with such differences go concomitant differences in other properties. But the changes take place over vast distances and long periods of time. Not only is oceanic salinity relatively constant as we have stated, but true ocean waters contain remarkably constant proportions of the nine ions that make up 99·5% of the total salts in solution: sodium 30·4%, magnesium 3·7%, calcium 1·16%, potassium 1·1%, strontium 0·04%; and the negative ions chloride 55·2%, sulphate 7·7%, bromide 0·19%, and borate 0·07%. In addition, carbonate and bicarbonate ions make up 0·35%. The boric acid is mostly undissociated, and it and the carbonate–bicarbonate ions act as efficient buffers keeping the pH of sea water relatively constant at pH 8·0 to 8·3, the alkalinity being produced by the excess of cations. Oceanic environments are thus efficiently buffered to render them stable for biological systems.

The salt content is expressed in two ways, as salinity and chlorinity, the latter being determined by titration of chloride, and the former by the now more usual conductivity method. Salinity is defined as:

$$S\%_0 = 0.030 + 1.8050 \ Cl\%_0$$

and tables and nomograms for conversion from one to the other are readily available.

As well as these major constituents, sea water contains a very large number of trace elements in quantities which are, in some cases, exceedingly minute and which may yet prove to be of great importance for the biological regime in the oceans. For example, iron is considered to be a limiting factor in the growth of phytoplankton, e.g. by Menzel and Ryther [1], and silica may, at times, be limiting to diatom blooms, while cobalt in the form of cyanocobaltamine is believed to be an important factor in the production of 'red tides' off the west coast of Florida. Many sea plants and animals concentrate some of the rarer elements, and it is possible that the presence of minute traces of these elements conditions the occurrence of such species. Thus, the *trace* elements may be as important as the major ones in the biology of the oceans.

The factors affecting the concentration of salts in the oceans include evaporation, precipitation, and movement, both horizontal and vertical. Evaporation is greatest in the tropics where insolation is highest, and results in an increase in density of equatorial and sub-equatorial surface waters. Precipitation is greatest in the polar regions and in the vicinity of land masses such as the equatorial island chains of the Indonesian and Polynesian regions. This causes dilution of Arctic and Antarctic waters in the summer. The land mass effect is essentially a surface one, and causes the low salinity of the surface water of the Java, Arafura, and Timor Seas during the monsoonal rains. In the Antarctic, the winter freezing of the ice causes an increase in salinity of the water below because freezing water leaves its dissolved salts in the solution. Low salinity waters tend to float on top of water of higher salinity because of lower density and the slow rate of diffusion of salts. Moreover, increase in temperature also causes a decrease of density and thus low salinity surface waters become more buoyant. The junction of low salinity and high salinity water masses is known as the *thermocline*. Such boundaries occur due to temperature or salinity differences between two water masses. The density or specific gravity of water is expressed as the ratio of its weight to that of an equal volume of distilled water at maximum density, i.e. 4°C. This is expressed by the Greek letter sigma, and the variation of the density with salinity and temperature is expressed as $\sigma_t$. Another factor which comes into the density equation is pressure. Hydrostatic pressure increases by 1 atmosphere (roughly 15 lb) per 10 metres depth, so that the pressure at 10,000 metres is about 1,000 atmospheres or 15,000 lb/in$^2$. Although water is relatively incompressible, there is a pressure effect which can also be found in tables and nomograms.

The general picture is one of high salinity and density waters in low latitudes (i.e. near the equator), and low salinity and density waters in high latitudes at the surface, except for the Antarctic winter water. Water movements are produced by density differences, wind, and the earth's rotation. The less dense water masses will tend to flow over the more dense ones, direction of flow being governed largely by land contours, wind direction and velocity, and the density differences themselves. An important factor in the direction of movement is a component due to the earth's rotation. This is called the Coriolis force and tends to deflect currents to the right in the Northern Hemisphere and to the left in the Southern Hemisphere. This force is proportional to the rate of the current and at right angles to the direction of flow. This results in the deepening of a moving body of water on its right side in the north and on its left in the south, i.e. the thermocline will slope down in the direction of the Coriolis force. Run-off from the land is also affected by this force, which may considerably alter the direction of the current systems when run-off is large as in big river systems.

As the water moves away from an area it forms a current bounded by waters of different characteristics. Such a current is known as a *water mass*. A current as known to navigators may consist of one to several water masses and a water mass may be ascribed to different currents during its flow. The water moving away must be replaced and this often causes denser water to move upward from below, till ultimately it reaches the surface as an *upwelling*. Water may also be caused to upwell by the bottom topography. As examples, the floor of the Tasman Sea between Tasmania and New Zealand is very level at about 2,500 fathoms. Farther north, a series of ridges occur, running roughly north-north-east, and a large, shallow area occurs west of North Island of New Zealand, deflecting the bottom waters and causing an upward movement. In addition, the south-moving East Australian Current causes upwelling off the south-east coast of Australia, aided by the Coriolis force, and the configuration of the slope of the continental shelf, together with submarine canyons, bring Antarctic water close to the surface, replacing the warm water derived from the Coral Sea. This brings not only nutrients to the surface, but also Antarctic species of phytoplankton.

It is not my intention to discuss in detail the configuration of current

C

systems in the oceans, as this information is readily available in other text-books, and would divert interest from the main theme, the interaction of the organisms with the environment. In the Antarctic winter, the denser water below the ice sinks below the relatively light sub-Antarctic water especially in the Weddell Sea and the South Indian Ocean. The Antarctic bottom water gains inorganic nutrients by bacterial decomposition of organic matter and moves along the bottom of the oceans, gradually turning northward. It is this water which adds fertility to areas where it is forced to the surface in upwellings. The Arctic does not show a similar pheno-menon due to the extent of the Asian and European and American land masses and to the configuration of the bottom. In the south, there is a circumpolar surface current moving east and north, bounded by the Antarctic convergence. A *convergence* may be defined as a region in which the net movement of the water is downward. This downward-moving water will be replaced by inward-moving water so that organisms con-tained therein will move towards the convergence and down into the lower layers. The downward movement also causes considerable turbulence and mixing. A *divergence* on the other hand has a net upward movement so that organisms will tend to move away from a divergence. North of the Antarc-tic convergence, the sub-Antarctic water also moves eastward, turning to the south near the Antarctic convergence and to the north near its northern boundary which is known as the sub-tropical convergence. This, in the Australian region, is extremely ill-defined by physico-chemical parameters, and its actual position is the subject of some discussion. It is probably a diffuse movement spread over some 5 degrees of latitude. North of this convergence, the waters in the Indian, Pacific, and Atlantic Oceans tend to form an anti-clockwise system flowing west along the equatorial current and south along the east coasts of the continents. Just north of the equator in the Pacific is the east-flowing equatorial counter-current, and, in the Northern Hemisphere, the rotation is clockwise so that the north-equatorial current also flows west, the water moving north in the Kuro-Sio Current in the Pacific and the Gulf Stream in the Atlantic. From the Arctic come the Oro-Sio and Labrador Currents flowing south-east in the Pacific and Atlantic Oceans respectively. These surface Currents, and the upward and downward movements associated with divergences and convergences, have a tremendous bearing on protoplankton populations in the oceans. This aspect will be discussed in more detail later.

In addition to the substances mentioned previously, the dissolved gases in ocean waters are of great importance to plant and animal life. Oxygen is important to the normal plant and animal inhabitants of the ocean for respiration. On the rare occasions when a complete lack of oxygen occurs, e.g. due to large concentrations of biological matter or to volcanic eruptions, nearly all the normal inhabitants of the water will die, and their decomposition will tend to reduce the oxygen tension still further. The oxygen content of the oceans is maintained by contact with the surface and diffusion as well as the photosynthesis of plants. The degree of saturation at the surface is increased by wind and wave action stirring the surface layers. The amount of oxygen in the water is dependent on the history of the water. If surface water sinks close to a convergence, it will carry down considerable oxygen, while upwelling water will be lower in oxygen than the surrounding surface water. If there is a considerable amount of respiration by plants and animals without a chance of restoration, the oxygen will fall rapidly and, as in the intermediate waters of the oceans, may be used as an index of the rate of biological activity. In surface water, supersaturation may occur due to photosynthesis of sessile algae or plankton. In deep waters such as the closed areas of the Mediterranean or the Black Sea, the layers below the sill separating the sea from the outside water will become stagnant and may completely lack oxygen. In the open oceans, however, oxygen is present even at the greatest depths, probably due to the slow metabolic rate of organisms at such depths, i.e. respiration is less than the rate of replenishment by the slow-moving bottom currents. Organisms which can live only in a milieu containing oxygen are known as *aerobes*, those which cannot tolerate oxygen as *anaerobes*, but many organisms, especially microbes, can live as aerobes or anaerobes by varying the type of metabolism. These are known as *facultatives*. Organisms which prefer a low concentration of oxygen are known as *microaerophiles*. Oxygen tension in a given body of water will be affected by changes of salinity, temperature, and pressure, so movement or mixing may be important in controlling the plant and animal associations in the ecosystem.

Nitrogen is also important in the oceans, especially as there are many species of microbe which can, in theory at least, fix dissolved nitrogen. The fact that the oceans are frequently unsaturated with nitrogen does suggest that such fixation may be an important factor in the natural fertilization of the oceans.

Carbon dioxide is important for the photosynthesis of plants in the sea. It is present as carbonate ($CO_3^=$ ions), bicarbonate ($HCO_3^-$ ions), and as undissociated $CO_2$, these being in equilibrium with each other and with hydrogen ions. At the pH of ocean water, the ratio of $CO_3^=$ to $HCO_3^-$ ions is about $1 : 5 : 1 : 2 \cdot 5$. This means that, with rising pH, the formation of calcium carbonate is enhanced, an important factor in shallow waters in warmer climates such as the Great Barrier Reef of Australia or the Bahama Banks; where such waters are clear and the bottom reflective such microbial processes as photosynthesis and bacterial denitrification can cause the precipitation of calcium carbonate. The formation of calcareous skeletons by a number of marine organisms, such as the coccolithophores and the foraminifera, is due to their ability to make use of these equilibria. With increase of pressure due to depth, the pH is lowered, excess base and bicarbonate increased while carbon dioxide and carbonate are decreased.

In addition to the inorganic matter in the oceans, there is a considerable amount of both dissolved and particulate organic matter, the quantity and availability of which has been disputed by a number of workers. Dissolved organic matter is available to bacteria, and those other organisms which can adapt themselves to heterotrophic nutrition. There is some recent evidence that some aquatic animals can also use dissolved organic matter, thus partly confirming the theory of Putter. This will be discussed in a later section. Particulate organic matter is often an order of magnitude greater than the protoplankton, and is certainly available as an adsorbent. Though much of it appears to be refractory, it can probably be slowly decomposed by bacteria.

This brief and rather sketchy account of the oceanic environment will be expanded in discussing the effect of this environment on the organisms living in it and that of the organisms on the environment. For further details of the hydrology of the oceans, the reader is referred to Sverdrup, Johnson, and Fleming [2] and to Harvey [3].

## The Sediment as an Environment

Although the sediments are in contact with the waters of the oceans, and are formed from materials partly derived therefrom, they form a separate biocoenosis. There is considerable exchange of inorganic salts between the sediments and the water above, but the former act selectively owing partly to sorption phenomena and partly to microbial activity. In shallow waters, turbulence causes a relatively rapid interchange of chemical substances and micro-organisms, but in the oceans generally, where there is little or no turbulence, the exchange is through diffusion and animal movement. Except in calcareous sediments, the pH is generally lower than that of the water above, and the Eh is also lower, in some cases much lower as in the Black Sea where hydrogen sulphide actually penetrates the lower part of the water system. The change in Eh means a change in the microbial flora and in the mode of nutrition of many of the organisms common to both. Thus, benthic diatoms change from autotrophy to heterotrophy, and the aerobes to microaerophilic conditions. Because the microbial populations are much more concentrated in the sediments, the organic matter is much higher and nitrate, phosphate, and ammonia tend to be removed from the water and stored in the sediments. Particulate inorganic matter tends to sink through the water and settle out.

The ocean bottom is carpeted by contributions from the land, volcanic and tectonic activity, cosmic material, and the inorganic residues of marine microbes such as diatoms, radiolaria, foraminifera, and coccolithophores. As the greatest ocean depths are close to land masses, it is probable that the material of these sediments is largely derived from the land by way of run-off and rivers. Much of the deep ocean bottom is covered by so-called red clay, which has a low lime content, but is rich in ferric hydroxide and manganese dioxide, and also contains volcanic material, skeletons of diatoms, radiolarians, and the calcareous remains of animals. This red clay covers about 40 million square miles. A peculiar aspect of these sediments is the presence of manganese nodules consisting of manganese dioxide and ferric hydroxide which form concretions around a nucleus such as a shark's tooth. This environment is an oxidized one in which anaerobes could play only a very small part in micro-environments. It has been suggested that microbial activity plays a part in the formation of these manganese nodules, but there is no evidence on the matter.

Calcareous ooze, formed largely from the casts of foraminifera, covers about 50 million square miles of the ocean floor, especially in lower latitudes. I have found foraminifera containing protoplasm in oozes collected from ocean abysses by the Danish research ship *Galathea*, and believe that these oozes are formed from organisms living at or close to the sediment rather than in the upper waters. The fact that carbonate ion gives place to bicarbonate ion as pressure increases means that frustules composed of calcium carbonate would tend to dissolve as they sank, even if the water at the surface were in equilibrium with respect to carbonate–bicarbonate ions. Organic matter associated with such carbonate would not last long enough to maintain protection of the carbonate throughout the sinking. The sponge spicules which form a large part of the sediments in higher and lower latitudes are almost certainly autochthonous as *Galathea* found numerous sponges growing on the sediments.

Diatom oozes occur in higher latitudes and form about 12 million square miles of ocean floor. Wood [4] gave reasons why the 'rain' theory for the deposition of these is untenable except in shallow waters.

The fact that ZoBell [5] found so many instances of sulphate-reducing bacteria occurring in the deep sediments implies that reducing conditions must be present, but he did not isolate any sulphide-oxidizing bacteria, nor did I from a number of cores taken in the Coral Sea.

There is little information regarding the oceanic sediments as an environment for micro-organisms, probably due to the fact that, until the *Galathea* expedition, it was considered doubtful that such organisms existed at the greater ocean depths. The most useful studies on the microbial ecology of sediments has been made by Rittenberg, Emery, and Orr [6], who examined the California Basins. These basins are less than 2,000 metres deep and are separated by a shelf from the continental slope, so they may not be representative of true ocean sediments. However, from the picture drawn by ZoBell of the *Galathea* sediments, and the general similarity of the microbial floras of sediments wherever obtained, it may be assumed that the ecology of similar types of sediment would be essentially similar, whether estuarine, neritic, or oceanic. In the California Basin sediments, the pH of the overlying water was higher than that of the overlying sediments, but below the surface, the pH ranged between 7·3 and 8·3, at times increasing, at others decreasing or remaining constant as the depth of the sediment increased. The redox potential ranged from about $+$ 300 mV to about $-$ 250 mV. In some cores, the Eh remained positive to the bottom (2,000 m), while in others it became negative at various levels; negative Eh was almost invariably associated with sulphate-reduction and the presence of hydrogen sulphide. Where the Eh was positive, sulphate could usually be demonstrated; thus Eh gave a good indication of the oxidation state of sulphur. The silica content of the sediments rose as the depth increased; this is probably due to increase of pH and consequent increase in the solubility of silica. The nitrogen content of the sediments is related to the particulate organic matter, i.e. is organic in origin. Nitrogen decreases sharply in the first few inches of the sediment due to biological activity; below this, the quantity varies, but is apparently linked to the water content which again is linked to the grain-size of the sediment. The decrease of nitrogen with depth is due to the decomposition of organic matter, and this is accompanied by a concentration of ammonia near the surface. In the lower layers, the inorganic nitrogen is present as ammonia because of the low redox potential and consequent anaerobic digestion by the bacteria concerned. In the upper layers, nitrification is important, so nitrate is found in surface sediments unless the surface redox is negative. We can thus conclude that the nitrogen cycle in the sediments is biological; it will be discussed in greater detail later.

The organic matter in the surface sediments was shown to have a higher carbon–nitrogen ratio than the plankton, showing that decomposition with release of nitrogen occurs above the surface sediments and in the upper layers thereof. Lignins, humus, proteins, carbohydrates, fats, waxes, and degenerated plant pigments have been shown to occur in the sediments. In calcareous oozes, such as Globigerina ooze, the carbon–nitrogen ratio rises until the stable oozes have a very low nitrogen content.

The question of interchange of materials by direct or indirect microbial agency will be discussed when dealing with specific groups of micro-organisms.

## The Estuarine Environment

Estuaries lie biologically and physico-chemically as well as topographically between the fresh water environment and that of the open sea. Reid [7] discusses in some detail the geology and chemistry of the estuarine environment as well as the macro-ecology. However, his discussion is not adequate for the requirements of microbial ecology owing to the intimate relationships of microbes to their physical and chemical environment. A convenient, if quite arbitrary division of estuaries is into marine-dominated and river-dominated, and there should perhaps be a third group including such estuaries as the Laguna Madre and other Texas Bays in regions of low rainfall and little interchange with the sea where the estuary is more or less self-contained for most of the time; these may be called evaporite estuaries. Another separation which is quite useful ecologically is into river estuaries, drowned valleys, and lagoons. These three are not, of course, mutually exclusive, as rivers frequently debouch into drowned valleys and sometimes into lagoons, while lagoons may be formed by the partial submergence of drowned valleys, with perhaps a trough fault at their entrance as at Mourilyan Harbour, Queensland, by a sand-bar built up across what was once a wide-floored valley, e.g. Lake Macquarie, or by a silted-up river mouth as at Crookhaven, Old Bar at the mouth of the Manning River, or Stewarts Point in the Macleay River, all in New South Wales. In the last three estuaries mentioned, the effect of the Coriolis force turning the river waters to the left, i.e. the north (since these rivers flow east), is seen in the gradual translation of the river mouth up to 15 miles north of its original site. This has, of course, vitally affected the rate of discharge of the river, and the ecology of the whole estuarine system. Where rivers flow through plain country in regions of low rainfall, and the coastal waters are shallow, one finds chains of coastal lagoons with low barrier islands; this is typified by the lagoons of South Texas, the Gippsland Lakes of Victoria, and Lake Alexandrina of South Australia.

The origin of the estuary is important as it determines the character of the water and the sediment. Drowned valleys are usually marine in character and fairly deep with steep shores and rocky bottom, which usually becomes partly silted, forming basins separated by rock outcrops and ledges. Silted river mouths are usually shallow, and have a sandy surface except in the channels which are usually silted. Open estuaries have mainly silted bottoms, while meandering rivers with barred estuaries usually have sandy bottoms.

The drowned valleys in Australia usually have *Sargassum*, *Hormosira*, or *Cystophyllum* as the main seaweeds, while *Fucus* predominates in the Northern Hemisphere, growing along the shores and on the rocky outcrops. The meandering river, lagoon, or silted entrance types are usually characterized by sea-grasses such as *Zostera*, *Thalassia*, *Diplanthera*, or *Cymadocea*, while, in Australia, *Posidonia* usually occurs in deeper waters. This is largely a matter of substrate, the Sargassums occurring on rocky formations or on rock overlain by recent muds, and the sea-grasses on sand and silt overlying mud which is frequently reducing in character. The brown alga *Cystophyllum* and certain red algae such as *Gracilaria* can attach to pebbles or shells and thus become established in the *Zostera* formation or on shingle beds.

The characteristics of an estuary can be determined by measurement of salinity range, temperature range, excess base, oxygen- and hydrogen-ion concentration. The Eh ranges from $+ 150$ to $+ 500$ mV in Australian estuarine water with a maximum of $+ 600$ mV in fresh to brackish water. The lowest Eh was $- 120$ mV associated with high phosphate, free $H_2S$ and colloidal hydrotroilite giving conditions described by Baas Becking and Mackay. Temperature, oxygen, and pH will vary throughout the day, temperature because of insolation, and the others because of the continuous alteration in the photosynthesis–respiration relationship. From sunrise until some time in the afternoon, depending on light and turbidity, the pH and oxygen will rise, and the carbonate–bicarbonate ratio increase because of photosynthesis; at times the pH will reach 9·3 or 9·4 and calcium carbonate will precipitate. This reduces the amount of bicarbonate available to the plants, thus limiting photosynthesis, and the pH does not exceed 9·4 in waters high in Ca ion such as sea water. After photosynthesis has reached its maximum, the pH and oxygen will fall, the carbonate–bicarbonate ratio decrease as carbon dioxide is evolved by the plants and utilization falls off, while the pH will consequently drop. The extent of fluctuation will depend on the amount of sunlight, influence of external water, e.g. tide or river flow, and the amount of plant material capable of assimilation. The greatest fluctuation will therefore occur on the shallower banks or channels which are completely bedded with sea-grasses together with their epiphytes. On these shallow flats, the temperature may rise considerably, altering the oxygen solubility and thus the saturation, and in warmer regions, the water may become so hot as to limit the growth of certain plants. At Stewarts Point, for example, where the water is at most 18 inches deep for about 15 miles, and there is no water movement, the red alga

*Gracilaria confervoides* is killed off by heat in late November and the water is too hot to walk in. Stratification of the water with respect to salinity and temperature is absent or infrequent in shallow estuaries or in those with much tidal exchange or river dilution, but is more common in the drowned valley types where there is little or no interchange of water in the deeper portions. Here a *thermocline* (essentially a boundary region between the lower-temperature, higher-salinity water below and the higher-temperature, lower-salinity water above) is developed in the summer, and, as the surface water cools in the autumn and thus becomes more dense, overturn occurs as in lakes. Stratification will often cause a very different microbial population in the *epilimnion* (i.e. the region above the thermocline), and the *hypolimnion* (the region below the thermocline), and further changes will occur after the overturn. The rate of dilution of the estuarine water by the river water, and the extent of tidal flushing, as well as the rate of evaporation, will determine the salinity of different parts of the estuary, which may vary from fresh water to more than $50\%_0$ in evaporite regions. In fine, each estuary has its own characteristics and should be studied as a separate ecosystem; there is no typical estuary.

The marine plants play a large part in the life of the estuary. The killing of *Zostera marina*, in eastern American and European waters, presumably by the myxomycete *Labyrinthula*, ruined the oyster industry in most of northern Europe and the Atlantic coast of America. This was due to the lack of opportunity for the sedentary forms of the *Zostera* community to grow and thus protect the environment for the free-swimming forms which live in this community. In addition, water movements across the flats normally occupied by the *Zostera* increased and siltation decreased owing to the lack of *Zostera* to act as a mechanical strainer. The same chain of events, this time due to the hand of man, caused the destruction of *Zostera* beds and the loss of certain fisheries in the Gippsland Lakes of Victoria, Australia. In other coastal lagoons of eastern Australia, hundreds of black swans descend on *Zostera* beds to feed on the stolons. They have denuded whole areas in a number of lagoons, turning over the sediments and completely destroying the *Zostera* community. In these cases the mullet and shrimp fisheries also failed completely until the sea-grasses grew again, a process which may take a generation. Associated with the *Zostera* and *Posidonia* are reducing substances such as an organic hydrazine or dimethyl sulphide associated with a pigment (Wood [8]), and these substances no doubt affect the environment, especially the sediment. It is usual for the removal of *Zostera* to be accompanied by an increase in the redox potential of the sediments, and the silt fraction appears to be eluted due to increased water movements. The roots of *Zostera* prefer a reduced environment, especially one with free hydrogen sulphide, so the change in the sediment prevents or seriously delays the return of the *Zostera*, as has happened in Port Hacking. Unfortunately, not much is known of the physiology of the sea-grasses. In the late summer, these grasses flower, die, and rot down, the rotting being accompanied by a rapid growth of micro-organisms, particularly flagellates, bacteria, and ciliates. According to Imai and Hatanaka [9], this appears to act together with a temperature rise, as a stimulus for the spawning and larval growth of the Japanese oyster *Ostrea gigas*, for which the micro-organisms serve as food prior to the settlement of the spat. Generally speaking, *Posidonia* grows in deeper waters than the other grasses with the exception of the less important *Halophila*. *Zostera*, *Thalassia*, and *Diplanthera* occur in shallow water below low tide mark, *Cymadocea* in shallow water in Florida, in deeper water in western Australian estuaries, while *Ruppia* is more tolerant of fresh water, though Baas Becking has found it in more saline environments. I have, on several occasions, found *Ruppia*, *Zostera*, and *Posidonia* growing in association in Australian coastal lagoons; occasionally, *Diplanthera* and *Ruppia* may be found together in the Texas Bays.

Baas Becking and Wood [9] consider that in the estuaries it is the sediments which control the ecosystem, due to the intense microbial activity, the close association of the photic zone with the sediments and the relation of the sea-grasses with the substrate.

We have already considered the origin of estuaries. Their hydrological characters are governed by the rate of inflow of fresh water and the tidal flushing with sea water. In areas with a heavy terrestrial rainfall, the upper and middle reaches of the estuary will be dominated by fresh and brackish water influences and this will affect the community. The same effect is obtained in areas of less run-off in the drowned valley type of estuary with little outlet to the ocean. In both, stratification will occur for much of the year in the deeper parts, i.e. below the sill, and the waters below the thermocline may be marine in type and are frequently archaic and little altered by time. In estuaries that are wide open to the sea, and to an extent in shallow evaporite types, the oceanic components of the community tend to dominate. Floods may bring a certain amount of stratification or even a fresh water environment for a time which will depend on the flushing rate or on evaporation.

# REFERENCES

[1] MENZEL, D. W. and RYTHER, J. H. (1962), 'Occurrence of iron in the Sargasso Sea off Bermuda', *Limnol. and Oceanog.*, 7, 155–59.
[2] SVERDRUP, H. U., JOHNSON, M. W., and FLEMING, R. H. (1949), *The Oceans*, Prentice Hall, New York, 1,024 pp.
[3] HARVEY, H. W. *The Chemistry and Fertility of Sea Water* (1955), Cambridge University Press, Cambridge, 244 pp.
[4] WOOD, E. J. F. (1956), 'Diatoms in the Ocean Deeps', *Pac. Sci.*, 10, 377–81.
[5] ZOBELL, C. E. (1952), 'Bacterial life at the bottom of the Philippines Trench', *Science*, 115, 507–8.
[6] RITTENBERG, S. C., EMERY, K. O., and ORR, W. L. (1955), 'Regeneration of nutrients in sediments of marine basins', *Deep Sea Res.*, Suppl., 3, 23–45.
[7] REID, G. K. (1961), *Ecology of Inland Waters and Estuaries*, Reinhold, New York, 373 pp.
[8] WOOD, E. J. F. (1953), 'Reducing substances in *Zostera*', *Nature*, 172, 916.
[9] IMAI, T. and HATANAKA, M. (1949), 'On the artificial propagation of the Japanese oyster *Ostrea gigas* fed by non-coloured naked flagellates', *Bull. Inst. Agr. Soc. Tohoku Univ.*, 1, 1, 33.
[10] BAAS BECKING, L. G. M. and WOOD, E. J. F. (1955), 'Biological processes in the estuarine environment. I, II', *Ned. Akad. Weten. Proc.*, B58, 160–81.

# CHAPTER 3
# The Micro-organisms

The microbes we have to consider as important denizens of the marine environment include bacteria (fig. 3), fungi, flagellates (or Phytomastigina)

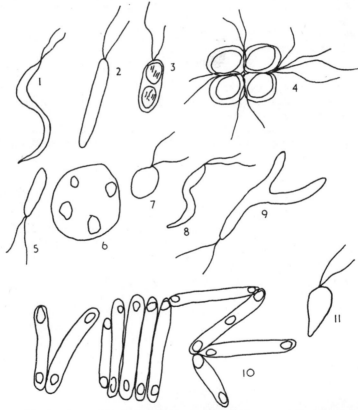

FIG. 3. Marine bacteria. 1. *Spirillum*, 2. *Pseudomonas*, 3. *Pseudomonas*-like form of *Mycoplana* usually seen in cultures, 4. *Sporosarcina ureae*, 5–9. *Pseudomonas-Spirillum*, branched form and 'cystite' of *Mycoplana*; all these forms may be seen in the one strain when freshly cultured, 10. *Corynebacterium*, 11. *Vibrio*.

32

including coccolithophores, dinoflagellates, silicoflagellates, chrysomonads, cryptomonads, xanthomonads, chlamydomonads, and euglenids (fig. 4), colourless flagellates (Zoomastigina), ciliates (including tintinnids), Sarcodina (including Radiolaria and Foraminifera), diatoms and unicellular and multicellular algae. Of these, the diatoms, tintinnids, radiolaria, foraminifera, silicoflagellates and, to a lesser extent, the coccolithophores, are of geological significance owing to their possession of calcareous or siliceous skeletons or 'tests' which can persist after death of the organism, and may form bottom oozes. Such oozes are at times of great thickness and are important constituents of marine and fresh water sediments. This will be discussed in greater detail in a later chapter. Dinoflagellate skeletons have also been identified, though it has not been possible to homologize fossil species with present-day forms. Bacteria, and, to a lesser extent, fungi have also great geological significance, but theirs is an active rather than a passive role. We get few identifiable fossil bacteria, as, except perhaps for the iron bacteria, they have no hard parts, but the bacteria are the chief micro-organisms that assist chemical changes of a permanent character. Apart from the photosynthetic bacteria, the chemical role is one of catalysing at low temperatures reactions which occur without bacteria only at higher temperatures or at greater pressures. Coal is in part due to bacteria, and oil is almost certainly due in some measure to the activity of bacteria, possibly related to the action of sulphate-reducers and fat-splitters. Not so well recognized are the roles of bacteria in the formation of laterites, sedimentary sulphur deposits, in ore formation and nitrogen fixation, which, in the early days of our planet, must have played a great part in the lush growth of plants in the Carboniferous period. As these reactions occurred in marshes, bogs, shallow seas, and estuaries, they come within the purview of the hydrobiologist.

## Bacteria in Hydrobiology

There is no doubt that bacteria play the most important biological part of any micro-organisms (or macro-organisms for that matter) in aqueous environments. They loom largely in bulk only in the anaerobic zone of the sediments, where few other organisms can live and reproduce, but even here they may be outweighed by the ciliates which feed on them and can rove rapidly through the environment as they exhaust the food supply. In all other areas, the photosynthetic plants and animals greatly outweigh the bacteria, except on rare occasions, though ZoBell [1] considers that the paucity of bacteria in upper waters of the ocean is due to grazing. I think there is sufficient indirect evidence to confirm this, but it is difficult to estimate grazing rates in the oceans. Chemically speaking, the bacteria can

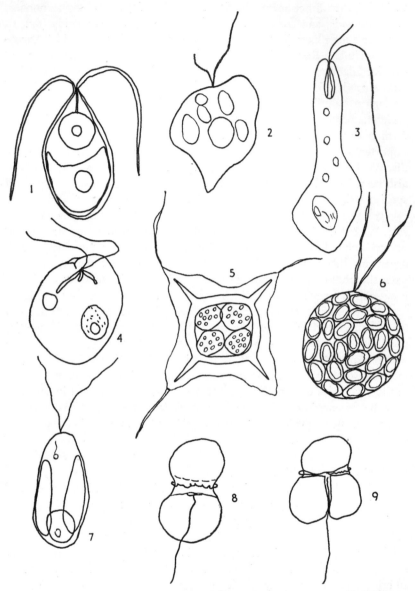

FIG. 4. Marine flagellates. 1. *Dunaliella* (Phytomonad), 2. *Chloramoeba* (Xanthomonad), 3. *Eutreptia* (Euglenid), 4. *Protochrysis* (Cryptomonad), 5. *Dictyocha* (Silicoflagellate), 6. *Pontosphaera* (Coccolithophore), 7. *Isochrysis* (Chrysomonad), 8. *Gymnodinium simplex*, 9. *G. marinum* (Dinoflagellates).

build and destroy Neptune's kingdom, convert and translocate minerals, transform organic materials to inorganic, inorganic to organic, and alter the physical properties such as pH and Eh with great abandon. Bacteria also assist in the attachment of animal larvae in the littoral and sub-littoral zones. Wilson [2] suggested that bacteria in moderate numbers are an aid to the settlement of *Ophelia* larvae, but in excess they are repellent. ZoBell [1] believed that bacteria were necessary for the attachment of animal larvae to ships and other subjects, though Wood [3] did not find them essential for this.

The classification of bacteria is, as was discussed in Chapter 1, in a very indefinite state. It is based primarily on morphology, followed by physiology, and, as different groups perform different functions in the marine environment, a brief outline will be given. Bacteria occur as spherical, or near-spherical forms or *cocci*, as *rods*, *commas*, spiral forms, and as forms of less regular shape. Sometimes they adopt a number of shapes in the same culture, and are called *pleomorphic or polymorphic*. These pleomorphic forms are very common in the seas, and may be said to be characteristic of the marine environment, though they do occur in other habitats.

The main genera we shall meet are *Micrococcus* and *Sarcina* (both spherical forms, the latter forming 'packets' or groups of 4, 8 or more), *Vibrio* (commas), *Bacillus*, *Bacterium*, *Pseudomonas*, *Corynebacterium* (rods), *Spirillum* (spiral forms), *Mycoplana*, *Nocardia*, and *Streptomyces*. Some of these genera are split further on physiological grounds, and there is argument as to the validity of others such as *Mycoplana*. The *Gram* stain, at first used arbitrarily, has been found to depend on the nature of the cell walls, and it does serve a useful purpose to separate groups which differ for other, not so well-defined reasons. Most of the cocci, and the rods *Bacillus*, *Corynebacterium*, *Nocardia*, and *Streptomyces* are gram positive, the genera *Bacterium* (including *Achromobacter* and *Flavobacterium*), *Pseudomonas*, *Vibrio*, and *Spirillum*, and others which do not concern us as marine bacteriologists, are gram negative. Motility is characteristic of the most frequent and important species of marine bacteria, though some of the micrococci, sarcinas, and corynebacteria isolated from marine sources are not motile (Wood [4]). The most important single group of bacteria in the sea is the pleomorphic, gram-negative, usually motile assemblage which that author ascribed to Gray and Thornton's genus *Mycoplana*, but which, from their morphological stability in stock cultures, are usually ascribed to *Achromobacter* and *Flavobacterium*. These organisms seem to bridge the gap between the pseudomonads and the corynebacteria of which the former seem to characterize fresh water, the latter soils and certain lakes (Henrici [5]). Pleomorphism of gram-negative rods is far more frequent in the sea than in fresh water and in soils. It seems a pity that marine bacteria are still characterized by their cultural characters rather than by their actual morphological attributes in their natural habitat. This is an instance where the natural peculiarities of organisms are masked by laboratory oceanography.

Fig. 5 shows the relative proportions of gram-positive and gram-negative rods and cocci in certain marine and terrestrial environments. It will be seen that the sea contains a large number of gram-negative rods compared with soils in which gram-positive forms predominate. Wood's studies showed far more cocci in the sea than other workers except Venkataraman and Sreenivasan [6], but in both cases the cocci were isolated from waters of the continental shelf. Those found by Wood were off the ports of Ulladulla and Eden on the south-east coast of Australia, where there is little run-off from the land, but considerable upwelling of Antarctic water and heavy wind and wave action causing frequent turbulence; the peculiar spore-forming *Sarcina* (*Sporosarcina*) *ureae* was found on one occasion (Wood [7]). The pleomorphic gram-negative forms were recorded from the oceans by Fischer [8], Russell [9], and ZoBell [1] as characteristic

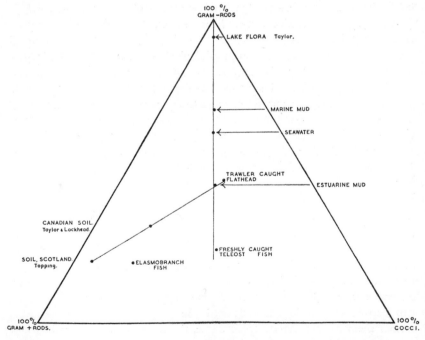

FIG. 5. Distribution of heterotrophic bacteria in marine environments.

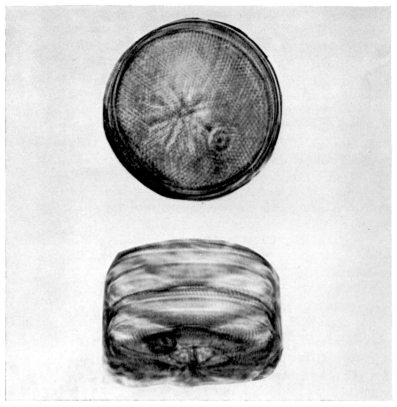

PLATE I. Diatom frustule with one valve belonging to the genus *Coscinodiscus*, the other to *Asteromphalus*.

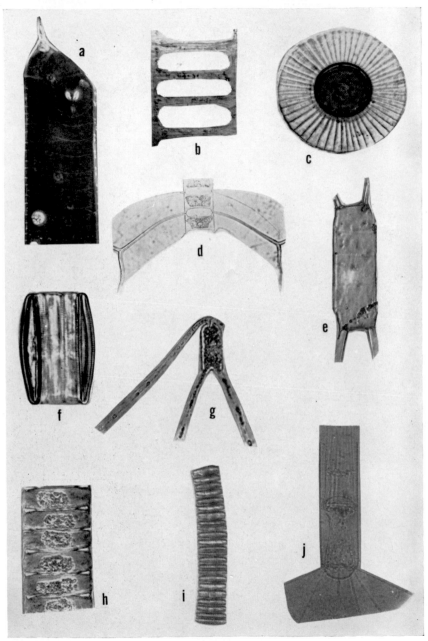

PLATE 2. Flotation mechanisms of diatoms. a. *Rhizosolenia*; b. *Climacodium frauenfeldianum*; c. *Planktoniella sol*; d. *Chaetoceros messanense*; e. *Biddulphia chinensis*; f. *Pseudoeunotia doliolus*; g. *Chaetoceros concavicorne*; h. *Bellerochea malleus*; i. *Fragilariopsis antarctica*; j. *Corethron criophilum*.

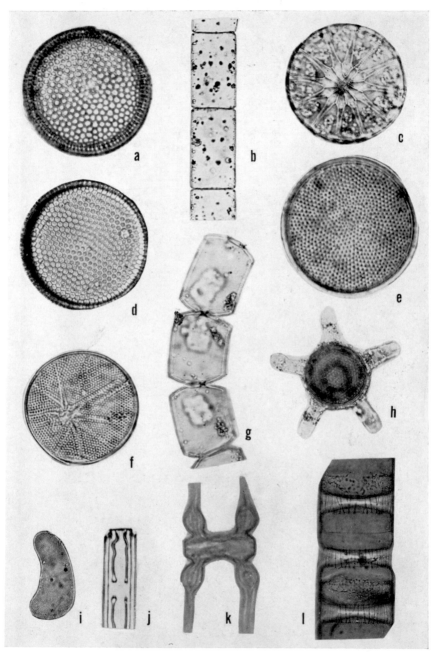

PLATE 3. Planktonic diatoms. a. *Coscinodiscus marginatus*; b. *Guinardia flaccida*;
c. *Asteromphalus grevillei*; d. *Cosc. excentricus*; e. *Cosc. africanus*; f. *Asteromphalus heptactis*; g. *Cerataulina curvata*; h. *Cosc. lineatus* (with processes);
i. *Cosc. reniformis*; j. *Grammatophora marina*; k. *Chaetoceros bulbosus*;
l. *Stephanopyxis palmeriana*.

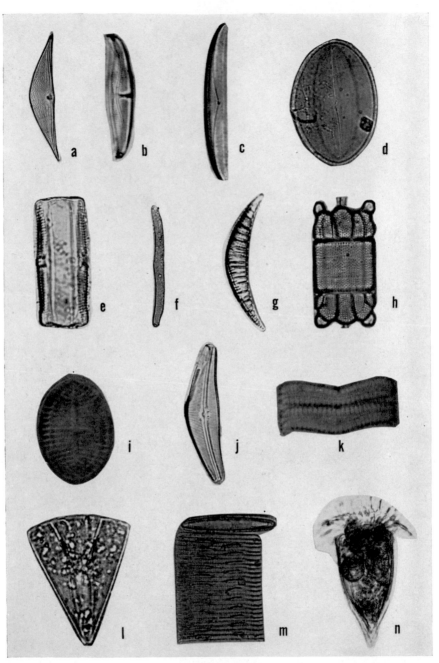

PLATE 4. Epiphytic diatoms and a tintinnid. a. *Amphora rhombica*; b. *A. littoralis*; c. *A. proteus*; d. *Cocconeis heteroidea*; e. *Plagiogramma* sp.; f. *Eunotia* sp.; g. *Rhopalodia gibberula*; h. *Biddulphia pulchella*; i. *Cocconeis imperatrix*; j. *Cymbella cistula*; k. *Achnanthes longipes*; l. *Licmophora abbreviata*; m. *Rhabdonema adriaticum*; n. a Tintinnid.

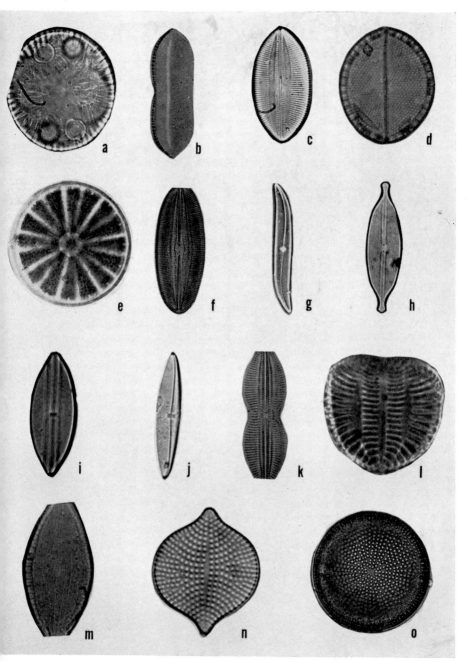

PLATE 5. Benthic diatoms. a. *Auliscus compositus*; b. *Nitzschia panduriformis*; c. *Navicula hennedyi*; d. *Mastogloia horvathiana*; e. *Actinoptychus splendidus*; f. *Diploneis smithii*; g. *Pleurosigma hippocampus*; h. *Anomoeneis sphaerophora*; i. *Navicula lyra*; j. *Trachyneis aspera*; k. *Diploneis crabro*; l. *Campylodiscus undulatus*; m. *Mastogloia quinquecostata*; n. *Rhaphoneis amphiceros*; o. *Aulacodiscus beeveriae*.

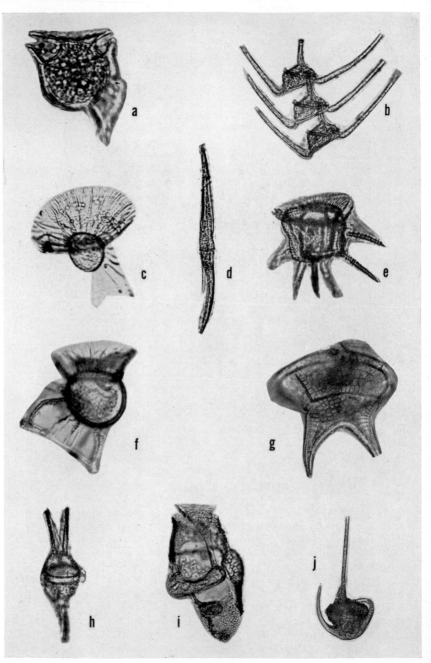

PLATE 6. Dinoflagellates. a. *Parahistioneis gascoynensis*; b. *Ceratium vultur*; c. *Ornithocercus splendidus*; d. *Ceratium incisum*; e. *Certatocorys horrida*; f. *Ornith. heteroporus*; g. *Heterodinium blackmani*; h. *Goniaulax birostris*; i. *Histioneis schilleri*; j. *Ceratium gibberum*.

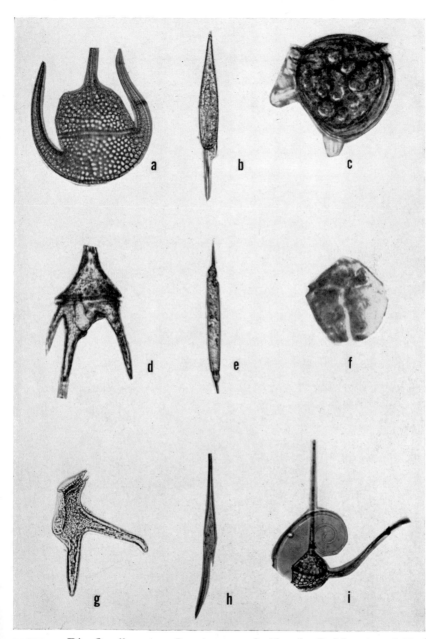

PLATE 7. Dinoflagellates. a. *Ceratium paradoxides*; b. *Podolampas spinifer*;
c. *Phalacroma doryphorum*; d. *Ceratium hirundinella*; e. *Oxytoxum
elongatum*; f. *Gymnodinium* sp.; g. *Dinophysis miles*; h. *Ceratium fal-
catum*; i. *C. hexacanthum*.

of marine bacteria. On a large number of occasions, these appear as spirilla on first isolation and more especially on direct examination of slides or membrane filters. In culture on agar, they occur as coccoid forms, branched or unbranched rods and 'cystites' in conformity with the description by Gray and Thornton [10] of their genus *Mycoplana*. They are fatter and larger than the *Pseudomonas* species which I have isolated from fresh water and spoiling teleost fish, and have a granular appearance that the *Pseudomonas* lack. In subculture, however, they revert to a stumpy short rod with bipolar granulation, which again is unlike the normal pseudomonad. The thiobacilli and sulphate-reducing bacteria have similar morphology, though I have not observed branching in these forms. The pleomorphic morphology of sulphate-reducers is recorded in the names *Spirillum*, *Vibrio*, and *Desulphovibrio* that have been accorded to them. A study of these and other organisms with polar flagella makes it very doubtful whether there is any validity for the two genera *Pseudomonas* and *Vibrio* and even *Spirillum* seems doubtful.

Many of the gram-positive rods which occur in marine environments are also pleomorphic, being similar to the soil corynebacteria. They show 'snapping' cell division, contain metachromatic granules, and form typical 'palisades' and 'chinese characters' (see also Venkataraman and Sreenivasan). Some marine corynebacteria were non-motile, and others frequently reverted to coccoid forms, especially *C. erythraeum*. The corynebacteria were present in sediments, especially in estuarine sediments, but dominated only in the elasmobranch fishes where they occur on the skin as well as in the flesh of spoiling sharks and rays. Apparently their association with elasmobranchs occurs only in certain parts of the world. The sporing aerobes of the genus *Bacillus* (which are facultatively anaerobic) were present in continental shelf sediments and more frequent in estuarine sediments. A bright pink *Bacillus* with central spores was particularly frequent in the Australian region. The Actinomycetes are frequent in estuarine sediments though not so important in the sediments of the continental shelf or the oceans.

Bacteria may be either *autotrophic* in their nutrition, using only inorganic components to synthesize their cell substance and obtain their energy, or *heterotrophic*, requiring organic substances to build their cells, and getting their energy from the oxidation of organic matter. Some groups of bacteria may employ either of these modes of nutrition according to conditions, and many, including both autotrophs and heterotrophs, require the assistance of organic components, e.g. *auxins* or growth factors, *vitamins* or reducing substances if they are to function freely, i.e. they are *auxotrophs*. In discussing the nutrition of aquatic micro-organisms, Henrici [5] states:

D

'Heterotrophic bacteria must be listed as consuming organisms, auto-trophic bacteria as producing organisms. Both heterotrophic and auto-trophic bacteria may serve as food for part of the zooplankton.

'A consideration of the importance of bacteria as producers and con-sumers does not however adequately represent the role of bacteria in the economy of lakes. Heterotrophic and autotrophic bacteria together are *transformers* of materials.'

This, of course, applies equally well to marine environments. Bacteria metabolize in the presence of air (oxygen) or in its absence, i.e. are *aerobic* or *anaerobic*, though many have an optimum oxygen tension between the two extremes, and some change their nutrition with changes in oxygen tension, e.g. the Athiorhodaceae. The bacteria which grow best at reduced oxygen tensions are known as *microaerophiles*. There are bacteria which can function and reproduce at low temperatures (*psychrophilic*) and others at high temperatures (*thermophilic*), those with an intermediate optimum being called *mesophilic*. Some bacteria can form spores which resist the temperature of boiling water for some time, e.g. *Clostridium botulinum*, *Sarcina ureae*, *Bacillus subtilis*. Many bacteria can under certain circum-stances stand a great range of pressures, both osmotic and hydrostatic, i.e. up to about 24% salt and 1,000 atmospheres. They can even stand desic-cation, though only in the resting state. Some species and strains can with-stand poisons such as hydrogen sulphide, copper, mercury, and arsenic as well as organic toxins and antibiotics. Certain types can exist at negative pH, others at pH 10, and at Eh values from − 300 mV to upwards of + 650 mV. Thus, bacteria are the most versatile organisms in nature, and it is in this versatility that their importance lies. In addition, individuals are short-lived and, when they die some of their enzymes are liberated, so that certain activities are continued after the death of the organisms. I have found that Seitz filtrates of cultures of the sulphate-reducing *Desulphovi-brio* added to sterile sea water enriched with sodium sulphate and reduced with metallic iron will reduce sulphate to sulphide, although the reduction is not as rapid as it is when the living organisms are present. I also used Seitz filtrates of corynebacteria to split urea, though once again the filtrates were not as active as the living bacteria. Because certain enzymes can con-tinue to operate after the death of the cell, the estimation of live microbial populations cannot always be relied on to give an accurate picture of the biochemical activity of the milieu. *Thiobacillus thiooxidans* can produce negative pH values in suitable media, but Baas Becking and Wood could not cultivate these strains in sea water media at a pH below 2·5 at which pH the cells appeared to lyse, although strains have been recorded to grow below this value. This could be a case where the enzyme outlived the organism, as viability was not recorded.

## The Diatoms in Hydrobiology

Diatoms have long been recognized as one of the most important groups of micro-organisms in the water environment. Their importance lies in the fact that, especially in high latitudes and close inshore, they form enormous blooms of plant material, and remove vast quantities of nutrient material from the water, depleting it to a greater or lesser extent of phosphate, nitrogen, and silica, and causing rapid alternations in the carbon-dioxide equilibrium. Diatoms are not, however, nearly so important in the warmer parts of the open ocean. The aquatic fauna is of course dependent on plant life for its existence (the autotrophic bacteria are for the moment included as plants) since it is only the plants which can make use of a completely or predominantly inorganic milieu, and thus renew the supply of nutrients to the animal world. The other important role of diatoms is that of indicators of water masses, although Wood [11] does not consider them as important as the dinoflagellates in this respect. He considers the phytoplankton superior to the zooplankton for showing water movements because of the greater and more immediate response of the former to the environment. This is contrary to the opinion of Sverdrup, Johnson, and Fleming [12]. In Bass Strait, for instance, the zooplankton is often continuous from Cape Everard in the east to Cape Otway in the west, but both diatoms and dinoflagellates indicate a complete break between the east and west of Bass Strait with a flora peculiar to this area and to south-east Tasmania (Wood [11]).

Because of their abundance in the sea, especially in the net phytoplankton, pelagic diatoms have been regarded as the chief food of plant-feeding (*phytophagous*) fish, copepods, and other animals in the ocean. Recently, many authors have shown that, at least in the warmer waters, the micro-flagellates and nanoplankton generally rival the diatoms in their importance, with the dinoflagellates (excepting the small, naked gymnodiniums), blue-green algae, *Halosphaera*, *Phaeocystis*, and the silicoflagellates of lesser significance.

The diatoms (plates 3 to 5) are usually divided for purposes of classification into two groups, the pennates and the centric diatoms, the former tending to be rod-like or oval in shape, the latter circular. The difficulties of phylogenetic taxonomy have already been mentioned. Pennate diatoms are divided into four groups on the presence or absence of a longitudinal slit in the valve called the *raphe*. Out of this slit, protoplasm is extruded and serves as a kind of pseudopodium for locomotion. Thus, diatoms with a raphe are motile. The four groups are the Araphidineae with no raphe on either valve, the Monoraphidineae with a raphe on one valve only, the Raphidoidineae with only rudimentary raphes, and the Biraphidineae with a raphe on either valve. The Biraphidineae may have the raphe in the central line of the valve, at or near the longitudinal axis or at the margin, and sometimes borne on a *keel*.

Of the Araphidineae, the commoner marine genera are *Thalassiothrix, Asterionella, Fragilaria* (including *Fragilariopsis*), *Synedra, Grammatophora, Licmophora, Climacosphenia,* and *Plagiogramma*; of the Monoraphidineae, *Cocconeis* and *Achnanthes*. It is interesting that the former genus is found at times attached to whales, and must have a very wide salinity and temperature range. The Raphidoidineae (one genus, *Eunotia*) are fresh water forms and only found in the upper parts of estuaries above the tidal range. The Biraphidineae include the important genera *Navicula* and *Nitzschia* as well as less important genera such as *Mastogolia* and *Diploneis*.

The centric diatoms include a number of important species which are characteristic of the phytoplankton. This group may be divided for our convenience into discoid and non-discoid forms. The discoid forms include the genera *Coscinodiscus, Melosira, Planktoniella, Thalassiosira, Schroederella, Skeletonema, Actinocyclus, Cyclotella, Asterolampra, Asteromphalus,* and *Aulacodiscus,* which may not all be true genera since there are possibilities of hybrids. The non-discoid forms include *Biddulphia, Triceratium, Cerataulina, Hemiaulus, Eucampia, Climacodium, Chaetoceros,* and the Solenoids *Bacteriastrum, Rhizosolenia, Leptocylindrus,* and *Corethron*.

It has generally been considered that centric diatoms are usually planktonic, while pennate diatoms are benthic or epontic. Hasle [13] has recently suggested that this is a fallacy and I fully support her view since I abandoned nets in favour of closing samplers for collecting protoplankton. This will become evident when it is considered that *Asterionella japonica, Nitzschia seriata, N. pacifica, N. pungens, Thallassiothrix longissima, T. mediterranea, T. antarctica, T. nitzschioides, Synedra reinboldii, Fragilariopsis antarctica* may each be the dominant species in phytoplankton samples, most of them in oceanic samples, and *Mastogloia rostrata* is typically present in Pacific and Indian Ocean waters. Also, the centric genus *Coscinodiscus,* while frequent in plankton catches, and having planktonic species such as *C. granii, C. concinnus,* and *C. janischii,* occurs mainly in shallow waters such as the Timor and Arafura Seas, or in areas of upwelling, except in boreal regions. Further, *Coscinodiscus* is frequent in marine sediments in water depths to 10,000 m (Wood [14, 15]). *Cyclotella* is a benthic genus adventitious in the plankton, and *Biddulphia, Triceratium, Asteromphalus, Auliscus, Aulacodiscus,* and *Actinoptychus* are frequently benthic or epontic, and there is evidence [15] that *Skeletonema costatum* occurs as spores in the surface sediments, and that these germinate therein before forming plankton blooms. On the other hand, the larger number of species of *Chaetoceros*, *Rhizosolenia*, *Bacteriastrum* and genera such as *Schroederella*, *Lauderia*, *Leptocylindrus*, *Cerataulina*, *Corethron*, *Dactyliosolen*, and *Ditylum* are essentially planktonic, while, among the naviculate diatoms, most of the species of *Navicula*, *Nitzschia*, *Campylodiscus*, *Surirella*, *Mastogloia*, and *Diploneis* are benthic. Attached or epontic forms include *Achnanthes*, *Cocconeis*, *Amphora*, *Licmophora*, *Climacosphenia*, many *Synedra*, *Fragilaria*, and *Grammatophora* species among the pennates and *Melosira*, *Bellerochea*, and some *Biddulphia* and *Triceratium* species among the centric forms.

Pelagic diatoms are frequently characterized by various mechanisms which assist them to remain in the photic zone of the seas by retarding the sinking rate. This is necessary for species which cannot live heterotrophically and it may well be significant that the Lewins [16] have failed to grow planktonic species in culture without light. Such flotation mechanisms (plate 2) are the curved or asymmetrical spines of *Rhizosolenia*, which cause it to remain horizontal and mat together, the ribbon formation of *Climacodium*, *Navicula membranacea*, or *Fragilariopsis antarctica*, chain formation of *Skeletonema costatum*, *Schroederella delicatula*, *Lauderia annulata*, *Thalassiosira rotula*, *T. gravida* and *T. hyalina*, *Streptotheca thamesis*, the hairs of *Chaetoceros*, *Bacteriastrum*, *Nitzschia longissima*, and *Corethron*, spiral formation of *Chaetoceros secundum*, *Asterionella* spp., and *Rhizosolenia stolterforthii*, the spiral arrangement of the setae of *Ch. convolutum*, or the air-spaces of *Planktoniella sol*. These mechanisms are exemplified in plate 2. In estuaries and fresh water, such mechanisms would not appear to be so essential, as most of the environment is within the photic zone; however, the commoner planktonic forms such as *Fragilaria*, *Tabellaria*, *Melosira*, and *Asterionella* occur in chains or ribbons, and there is also a fresh water *Rhizosolenia*, *R. eriensis*, with long asymmetric spines. Perhaps these mechanisms are necessitated by the frequent turbidity of the water. Braarud [17] stresses the important part played by flotation mechanisms in protoplankton ecology and quotes numerous examples. In addition to the mechanisms which I have discussed, he points to the selective permeability of ions resulting in a lowering of sodium, potassium, calcium, and sulphate ions inside the cells of *Ethmodiscus rex*, and assumes that this occurs also in *Halosphaera*. He gives vacuolation as an aid to buoyancy in *Rhizosolenia*, but does not mention the production of oil as a storage product of diatoms, *Chlorella* and other protoplankton members as a factor in increasing buoyancy.

The epontic or epiphytic species are usually attached by gelatinous *stipes* or stalks or by sheaths, some of which are many-branched, e.g. the stipitate *Licmophora, Striatella, Achnanthes, Climacosphenia, Rhabdonema, Terpsinoe,* and the sheathed *Schizonema, Homoeocladia, Berkeleya,* and *Micromega,* which were formerly known as separate genera, but are in fact macroscopic linear or branched colonies of diatoms consisting of single or multiple rows of cells in a pectinoid sheath, often many times the width of the cells. *Schizonema* and *Micromega* consist of colonies of *Navicula,* mainly *N. grevillei, Homoeocladia* of *Nitzschia martiana,* and *Berkeleya* of *Amphipleura* cells. These macroscopic colonies actually form carpets in the intertidal and subtidal zones, or at times small platforms which may have some geological significance in preventing erosion on a small scale. Mud-dwelling forms (plate 5) do not always have a strong pectinoid sheath, but are usually motile, e.g. *Navicula, Hantzschia, Mastogloia, Diploneis, Pleurosigma, Cymbella, Nitzschia, Surirella,* and *Campylodiscus,* and move both horizontally and vertically in the sediments.

The diatoms have a wide physico-chemical range of environment, though not so wide as that of the bacteria of the blue-green algae. They have been recorded as growing at Eh values from $-70$ to $+600$ mV by Baas Becking and Wood [18] and from pH $9 \cdot 2$ to $1 \cdot 6$, this last in a sulphur spring at Rotorua in the New Zealand thermal region. Apart from *Pinnularia,* there is no definite evidence that diatoms can *photoreduce* carbon dioxide (i.e. reduce $CO_2$ in the absence of oxygen using light as the energy source), but other species may well be able to do so. Diatoms have been found apparently living at depths to 10,000 m with corresponding pressures of up to 1,000 atmospheres. Littoral species have been pressurized to 500 atmospheres and grew and reproduced at this pressure (Wood [14]). A diatom, *Nitzschia seriata,* has been cultivated from water taken at 4,000 m, while species of *Coscinodiscus, Navicula,* and *Amphora* all containing chlorophyll have been collected from depths of 900 to 3,000 m under aseptic conditions (Kimball, Corcoran, and Wood [19]). Diatoms vary in their sensitivity to temperature and salinity. Some, such as *Eunotia* and *Neidium* are restricted to fresh and slightly brackish water, many are *euryhaline* (have a wide salinity tolerance), e.g. *Melosira nummuloides* which occurs in water of chlorinity from $2 \cdot 1$ to $19 \cdot 9\%_0$. Most marine species, however, are more stenohaline (i.e. have a lower tolerance); many centric species, e.g. most of the Rhizosolenias and *Chaetoceros* species, do not tolerate brackish or fresh water, though I have found a species of *Chaetoceros* in an underground river in the Jenolan limestone caves, 100 miles from the coast. There are also anomalies, e.g. *Rhopalodia* is characteristically a fresh water diatom in Australia, but is frequent and abundant in the evaporite Laguna Madre of Texas (Wood [15]). In the open ocean, some species of diatoms occur in narrower salinity limits than others, as can be shown by plotting occurrence against salinity. *Chaetoceros aequatoriale* and *Ch. vanheurckii* have the same relative temperature range ($13°-18°C$ and $14°-19°C$ respectively), but the salinity range of the former is $33.4$ to $35.7\%$ and of the latter $31.4$ to $36.3\%$. *Ch. peruvianum* has been reported from the Antarctic to tropical waters by Crosby and Wood [20] and *Rhizosolenia styliformis* and *R. alata* are both euryhaline and eurythermal, being, in fact, cosmopolitan. *R. alata*, however, has forms confined to Antarctic and sub-Antarctic waters, including the *inerme* and *rostrata* forms which may have one valve belonging to the stenothermal form, the other to the eurythermal form *typica* or even *indica*. *Fragilariopsis antarctica* has not been found north of the $13°$ isotherm in the Tasman Sea, and *Rhizosolenia curvata* has an even smaller temperature range (Hart [21]). Stenothermal and stenohaline species may be used as indicators of the biological water mass or ecosystem in which they occur, for which reason they are studied by the planktologist and the oceanographer. The application and limitations of this will be discussed in detail later.

Normally, diatom occurrences are seasonal, having maxima in spring and autumn. In the waters off the east coast of Australia, the peaks and troughs are not so marked as they are in the cool-temperate zone of the Northern Hemisphere or in the Antarctic. Large populations of diatoms occur regularly in the Antarctic and the Arctic and in such areas as the west coast of western Australia, in which area only one species, *Rhizosolenia castracanei*, is represented. In the Antarctic, several species of *Rhizosolenia*, *Coscinodiscus*, or *Chaetoceros* are usually concerned in the maxima, and in the sub-Antarctic waters, the pennate species *Thalassiothrix antarctica*, *Synedra reinboldii*, and *Fragilariopsis antarctica* are the usual dominants. In the estuaries of eastern Australia, we often get maxima of at least two species, e.g. *Rhizosolenia robusta* with *Coscinodiscus granii* or *Asterionella japonica* with *Chaetoceros secundum*; in oceanic–neritic waters one often finds ten or more species of several genera forming a bloom, e.g. many *Chaetoceros* species plus *Climacodium frauenfeldianum*, *Bacteriastrum*, *Streptotheca*, *Lauderia*, *Melosira*, etc., or *Schroederella*, *Nitzschia seriata*, and *Leptocylindrus*. One may also find a succession (frequently overlapping) of species, each persisting for one or two weeks and each reaching the same order of magnitude. The fact that a number of *Chaetoceros* species occurs in the same sample on such occasions appears to cast doubts on the taxonomy of the genus (see Chapter 1). In fresh water, blooms consist of one or two species, e.g. *Asterionella formosa* or *Fragilaria crotonensis* with *Tabellaria fenestrata* in Lake Windermere (Lund [22]).

The relative productivity of tropical and cool waters has been the subject of a great deal of controversy, and the arguments have been based largely on the assumption of the overall importance of diatoms in all waters. Among the diatoms, the number of species recorded from the tropics is greater than that from colder waters, while the tropics rarely show the tremendous blooms that occur in polar waters except on a limited scale as in Lombok Strait, the Arafura, Java and Banda Seas, the Texas Bays, and the Gulf of Mexico. On the other hand, growth and reproduction are more rapid and more continuous in lower latitudes, and the photic zone is deeper and illumination more intense. Sverdrup, Johnson, and Fleming [12] state that the standing population of plankton organisms in the Antarctic is tenfold that of the tropics, but this figure includes both phytoplankton and zooplankton, while ignoring the microplankton. Diatoms preponderate in the protoplankton only in high latitudes, and close inshore in the Pacific and Indian Oceans (Wood [23]). In higher latitudes there is a sediment of diatomaceous earth ringing the poles, but this may be due to diatom frustules from animal faeces, to heterotrophic forms or to diatoms which have sunk to the bottom in shallower waters and thus short-circuited the productivity cycle. Further, most of the species in these sediments do not occur as dominants in the plankton today, and would seem to have historical significance. I have already mentioned the fallacies inherent in the 'rain of diatoms' theory. It seems reasonable to assume that the large deposits of diatomaceous earth represent an ecosystem which no longer exists in the oceans, possibly due to a change in the dominance of other groups such as the nanoplankton or the blue-green algae.

## The Blue-Green Algae

The blue-green algae, also known as the Cyanophyceae or Myxophyceae, have an exceedingly wide range of habitat, occurring in fresh water, sea water, salt lakes and even in salterns; they are found in symbiosis with fungi in lichens and in soils. They may be found in thermal regions at temperatures up to 70°C, and in a pH range from 4 in peat bogs to 9 in salt lakes, e.g. Searles Lake, California. They are often the first colonists of the land at or above the water line in association with *Salicornia, Juncus, Spartina* and other swamp plants, and even in pure white sand as at Port St Joes in Florida or Lake Coila in eastern Australia. They form incrustations on the rocks or form felts or carpets (*tapetic* forms) in shallow water, sometimes in a presumably annual cycle as in the intertidal regions of the South Texas Bays where, particularly in certain areas of the Laguna Madre, they occur in interrupted layers many inches thick. Baas Becking [24] records black 'nigger heads' of Nostocaceae on coral reefs in the Pacific Ocean, and they can precipitate calcium carbonate by raising the pH of water due to photosynthesis. Blue-green algae may grow in full sunlight or in almost complete darkness, and in media with redox potential from — 170 to + 600 mV. In the Jenolan Caves in New South Wales, they grow on moist limestone near incandescent lamps which are illuminated for only about 6 hours a week while tourists are being shown through. In a slough at Port Aransas, Texas, a felt of mixed blue-green algae was formed close to the effluent of a laundromat with a high concentration of detergent. This felt disappeared as the detergent became diluted (Oppenheimer and Wood [25]).

The forms which are most significant in the seas belong to the Hormogonales, mainly the Oscillatoriaceae and the Nostocaceae (fig. 6). Pelagic species belong to the genera *Trichodesmium* (placed in *Oscillatoria* by Geitler [26]), *Pelagothrix*, *Haliarachne*, and *Katagnymene*, but Bernard and Lecal [27] report *Nostoc* from the sub-photic waters of the tropical Atlantic and Indian Oceans and the Mediterranean Sea. We should here

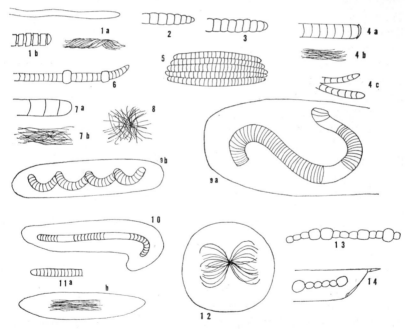

FIG. 6. Planktonic blue-green algae. 1. *Oscillatoria bonnemaisonii*, 2. *O. nigroviridis*, 3. *O. margaritifera*, 4a–c. *O. hildebrandti*, 5. *O. (Trichodesmium) erythraea*, 6. *O. brevis*, 7a–c. *O. thiebautii*, 8. *O. contortum*, 9a, b. *Katagnymene spiralis*, 10. *K. pelagica*, 11. *Pelagothrix clevei*, 12. *Haliarachne lenticularis*, 13. *Anabaena baltica*, 14. *Richelia introcellularis* in *Rhizosolenia*.

differentiate between forms which occasionally appear in the plankton but which normally dwell in other environments, facultative plankters which spend only part of their life in the plankton and euplanktonic forms which are truly planktonic. The only order not found in the plankton is the Chamaesiphonales. Many non-planktonic species of *Oscillatoria, Lyngbya,* etc., have planktonic spores in the fall as a means of dissemination as in the Florida Everglades. Some of the planktonic forms possess gas vacuoles which render them lighter than water, e.g. *Trichodesmium erythraeum,* but others are slightly heavier and slowly sink, depending on upward water movements or wind turbulence to keep them suspended in the photic zone of the water. Other planktonic species, such as *Katagnymene* and *Haliarachne,* have filaments embedded in lumps of pectinoid material, while others form characteristic rafts (*T. erythraeum*) or bundles (*T. thiebautii* and *T. contortum*).

The blue-green algae form an important part of the plankton in the tropics, where they may exceed all other phytoplankters in numbers. *Trichodesmium* is frequently abundant in the Arafura and Coral Seas, the Banda Sea, and the tropical Pacific and Indian Oceans in the equatorial currents and the Gulf of Mexico. It frequently occurs in long windrows, sometimes a few feet, and sometimes miles wide as Baas Becking [24] has vividly described. When present in these quantities, it is inimical to fish, which avoid it, e.g. the 'milk fish', *Chanos chanos,* but the same fish at the larval stage may feed on small blooms of the same seaweed. The case seems similar to that described for the diatom *Rhizosolenia* in the Barents Sea by Manteufel. Baas Becking described these *Trichodesmium* blooms as follows:

> 'The massed algae appear, often as wavy lines, miles in length, stretched perpendicular to the direction of the wind. The color of the rills as observed by the author varies from deep gray to deep orange. The purple patches so often mentioned in the literature were once or twice observed in restricted areas from a low boat. The water bloom must have covered an area of at least 40,000 square kilometers with several thousand tons of living matter.'

I have seen these windrows in the Red Sea (which owes its name to *T. erythraea*), the Arafura Sea, the Indian Ocean between Colombo and Fremantle about 1,000 miles from the nearest shore, in the Java, Banda and Coral Seas, and the Gulf of Mexico. On one occasion a bloom stretched along the Queensland coast for about 1,000 miles from Port Curtis to Cairns, extending from the shore line to the Great Barrier Reef and occupying about 20,000 square miles. From the air it looked like a series of sandbanks, steep on one side and shallow on the other. The bloom, on close inspection, was about $\frac{1}{2}$ m deep, with maximum growth at the surface, and the individual fascicules of the alga stuck to the walls of the plastic and glass vessels, making it impossible to estimate the amount present in a given volume. Such large blooms are frequent in the Coral Sea in the spring. They do not seem to have been considered by those who maintain that the fertility of the boreal regions is greater than that of the tropics, and one well-known phytoplanktologist has even stated that the blue-green algae are unimportant in the phytoplankton.

Baas Becking also records the mass death of corals caused by the decomposition of masses of *Trichodesmium* driven ashore by the wind. This could be a very important geological agent, as the mass killing of corals would seriously affect reef formation, resulting in the lowering of the redox potential, which, in turn, could bring about the translocation of minerals such as magnesium, iron, manganese, nickel, and cobalt. With the production of hydrogen sulphide by sulphate-reducing bacteria in this milieu, a strong mineralization could occur, especially close to areas of vulcanicity.

The only cold-water planktonic blue-green alga is *Trichodesmium rubescens* which gives the red colour seen at times in colder waters. I did not find it in plankton from the Antarctic collected by the B.A.N.Z.A.R.E. Ross Sea, Heard Island, or Macquarie Island expeditions, but found it once in plankton taken south of New Zealand above latitude 57° S.

Sessile blue-green algae occur in many terrestrial, aquatic, and marine environments. They may be found in swiftly flowing streams or in stagnant water, the inhabitants of the former being adapted to withstand mechanical abrasion, e.g. *Nostoc, Rivularia, Tolyptothrix, Phormidium*. Stagnant water forms occur in the ecosystem of the sediments, associated with the sulphur bacteria, photosynthetic bacteria, and protozoa, where they are often subjected to high concentrations of hydrogen sulphide. In the supra-, mid-, and lower-littoral zones, genera such as *Anacystis, Chroococcus, Coccochloris*, members of the Chamaesiphonales, *Phormidium, Symploca, Hydrocoleus, Schizothrix, Calothrix, Rivularia, Brachytrichia*, and *Isactis* form felts on rocks and tufts in rock pools, while others including *Gloeocapsa, Nostoc, Lyngbya*, and *Microcoleus* are common felt-forming (tapetic) species in fresh-water swamps such as the Everglades, brackish and salt mangrove areas, and the *Spartina* association. Geitler considers that they are heterotrophic or at least partially heterotrophic, but Rabinowitch [28] believes, in the light of Gaffron's work, that they are photoautrotrophic in this environment. Because of the ability of the blue-green algae to adapt pigment colour to light intensity, and thus filter the light, they can grow in intense light or in very faint illumination. It may be that some of the blue-green algae of the sediments are gradient forms, as they frequently occur above a highly reduced sediment (Eh − 200 mV or lower), and when forming felts on rocks frequently have hydrotroilite (FeSH(OH)) between them and the rock. *Oscillatoria, Lyngbya,* and *Gloeocapsa* have been observed growing in this manner, and have been grown in culture with low Eh values. The felts at Port Aransas already mentioned were immediately overlying a heavy growth of purple sulphur bacteria about 5 mm thick. Schuster [29] recorded living blue-green algae in tambaks (fish ponds in mangrove muds) in the muds in Java to a depth of 12 inches. The development of blue-green algae in tambaks depends on the parent rock; volcanic ash yields a much larger crop than gravel or coarse marl, though the heavy periphyton of the Florida Everglades occurs over a marl substrate. In the tambak environment, *Phormidium* forms a skin over the surface of the mud, and *Oscillatoria, Microcoleus,* and *Lyngbya* dominate the biocoenosis of the ponds, the planktonic hormogonia of these forms being of importance in the food chain. These blue-green algae are the most important element in the tambaks as they give greater continuity of production than the diatoms and green algae which occur in bursts. It is probable, too, that the long-continued productivity of tambaks without fertilization is due to the blue-greens, some of which fix nitrogen, and to their metabiotic association with bacteria which dissolve calcium and ferric phosphates at pH values up to 8·5. Some tambaks have been actively producing fish for eighty human generations.

Various members of the blue-green algae such as *Phormidium, Gloeocapsa, Lyngbya, Microcoleus,* and *Nostoc commune* act as shore-binders forming felts as mentioned above. Such felts help to stabilize the shore and also decompose to form humus so that the organic content of the substrate is gradually built up to the point where other plants such as *Salicornia* or *Spartina* can enter the association. Rocky shore lines, especially in estuaries, have blue-green components which form a closed association or a definite zone, e.g. a *Tolyptothrix* zone with a *Rivularia* zone extending below low water and below this a *Schizothrix* zone. Such species often serve as food for fish and zooplankton.

Dyer and Gafford [30] record the thermophilic *Synechococcus lividus* as having a generation time of less than 3 hours. If this rate pertains among other members of this group, it would account for the rapid incrustations that may be observed and for the amazing bursts of *Trichodesmium.*

**The Dinoflagellates** (plates 6 and 7)
Dinoflagellates occur both in fresh and salt water, the former being restricted almost entirely to the naked forms, some *Peridinium* species and

*Ceratium hirundinella*. They are not as tolerant of salinity and temperature changes and ranges as the other groups I have mentioned. They may be holozoic or holophytic or may adopt both these modes of nutrition. The naked forms (Gymnodiniaceae) and some of the armoured forms, e.g. the Prorocentraceae and Peridineaceae, are probably mainly holophytic or facultatively heterotrophic or phagotrophic, but many of the Dinophyseae, Ceratia, Heterodinia, and Oxytoxums are holozoic. On the whole, the oceanic and planktonic dinoflagellates tend to be holozoic, and the neritic forms holophytic or facultatively so, although there are numerous exceptions to such a wide generalization. Bernard [31] has recorded *Exuviaella* as an important component of mid-water plankton in the Atlantic and Indian Oceans and the Mediterranean Sea. Although normally a photosynthetic genus, it may, in this instance, be regarded as heterotrophic or phagotrophic.

Difficulties in dinoflagellate taxonomy have already been discussed in Chapter 1. The Prorocentraceae, with the frequent estuarine–neritic (sometimes sub-photic and oceanic) genera *Exuviaella* and *Prorocentrum*, are readily separated from the rest of the dinoflagellates by their polar flagella. Their bilateral arrangement is similar to that of the Dinophyseae which have some of the most beautiful and most bizarre forms to be found in the plankton, including the rod-like *Amphisolenia*, the tricornuate *Triposolenia*, the goose-stepping *Dinophysis miles*, and the highly ornate and complicated *Histioneis*, the most beautiful unicellular organism to be found in the plankton. The Peridineaceae have strong, cellulosic walls arranged in a series of plates which are used in diagnosis. They tend to be estuarine or neritic, though there are oceanic species. The genus *Heterodinium*, which is similar to *Peridinium* in general shape and in the possession of a strongly armoured cellulosic wall, is essentially oceanic, and most samples collected do not contain chlorophyll. They are characteristic of deeper waters, and their presence at or near the surface is a useful indication of convergence or limited upwelling of tropical water. *Ceratium* with its customary three horns, one projecting forward, the other two normally backward near the base, but turning forward or linear with one of them reduced or absent, is characteristic of the oceans, and provides some of the most useful indicator species. There are, however, some species of *Ceratium* which occur in the estuaries, such as *C. buceros*, *C. furca*, and at times, *C. symmetricum* and *C. fusus*. The top- or spindle-shaped *Oxytoxum* is often relatively abundant in warmer waters, though the smaller forms of this genus are often missed in plankton taken in nets. The reader is referred to Schiller [32] or to Wood [11, 33, 34] for further details in the taxonomy of this interesting group of micro-organisms.

In colder waters, diatoms are usually, if not always, more important than the dinoflagellates, but, in the tropics and sub-tropics, dinoflagellates, especially the genera *Peridinium, Ceratium, Prorocentrum, Goniaulax, Exuviaella, Oxytoxum,* and *Gymnodinium* normally outnumber the diatoms in the plankton of oceanic waters. However, by and large, the dinoflagellates do not represent the large source of regenerated phosphate that the diatoms or tropical Cyanophyceae do. Pavillard's [35] statement that *Prorocentrum micans* as an occasional 'red tide' organism, *Ceratium tripos, C. furca, C. fusus, Peridinium divergens, P. depressum, Goniaulax polyedra, Dinophysis caudata* are the only species capable of reaching sufficient numbers to be important as primary food is possibly applicable to the Mediterranean and the North Atlantic, but not to the waters with which I have been acquainted. Frequently, in tropical waters of the Pacific and East Indian Oceans, *Gymnodinium simplex, G. marinum* and other gymnodiniums may and frequently do dominate, and I have reason to believe that this is also true of the tropical and sub-tropical Atlantic. At times, such *Ceratium* species as *C. massiliense, C. extensum* and some *Gyrodinium* species are sufficiently numerous to be significant in the biomass; in the estuaries, *Peridinium ovatum, Diplopsalis lenticula, Ceratium buceros, Goniaulax digitale, G. polygramma, Gymnodinium* spp. and, on rare occasions, *Exuviaella marina* must be added. Authors have suggested that possibly significant numbers of minute peridineans are missed in net samples, but I have found that it is mainly the naked dinoflagellates which pass through the nets, and these may form a large part of the nanoplankton. Whether the ceratia are used as food by many organisms is doubtful, as I have not seen them so used in hundreds of live samples which I have studied, but the peridiniums are so used by the tintinnids, salps, and even by larger peridineans, as can readily be seen in plankton samples from the south-west Pacific and eastern Indian Oceans. Some *Goniaulax, Pyrodinium,* and *Gymnodinium* species on the other hand are known to produce definite toxins which can and do poison fish and molluscs, and may by their rapid reproduction deoxygenate the water to such an extent as to asphyxiate other organisms causing mass death of fish and pollution. This will be discussed in more detail in connexion with the phenomenon of 'red tides'. Many species of dinoflagellates are luminescent (Sweeney [36]).

**Flagellates (other than Dinoflagellates) (fig. 5)**
These may be divided according to size into micro- and macro-flagellates. The former, ranging in size from 1 μ upwards, are the chlorophyll-bearing counterparts of the bacteria with regard to size. In shallower waters they are confined to the water and the surface of the sediments, in the ocean,

chiefly to the photic zone, except for the coccolithophores. At times, and in certain places, they are very numerous, and may form a large part of the biomass in aquatic, marine, and estuarine environments. Miller, Moore, and Kvammen [37] found by chlorophyll determinations that they are up to 1,000 times as numerous as the net phytoplankton off Miami, and that 90% of net-passing phytoplankton also passed through a No. 1 Whatman filter, but was retained by a Whatman No. 54. Wood and Davis [38] found that nanoplankton (or microplankton) may be up to 10,000 times as numerous as the net phytoplankton (over 30 µ in diameter) and that the chlorophyll of the former may be 3,000 times as high. The ratio varies, however, the generation times of the smaller elements being much shorter than that of the larger (Wood [109]), while the logarithmic growth phase of the one is not always coincident with that of the other. Wood [23] recorded a bloom consisting almost entirely of microplankton (some $5 \times 10^{7-8}$ cells per litre), in the Coral Sea. These small phytoplankters are also very numerous in the turbulent intertidal zone of the oyster grounds of Botany Bay, in parts of Jervis Bay, Lake Macquarie, and other estuaries of the east Australian coast, and in these estuaries they sometimes turn the water bright green. They occur in fresh water and brackish environments as well as in the marine environment. Knight-Jones [39], Knight-Jones and Walne [40] found that minute flagellates, particularly that known as *Chromulina pusilla* Butcher and now designated *Micromonas pusilla* by Manton and Parke [41], is extremely common in British waters, and endeavoured to estimate their numbers by dilution methods. Scagel and Stein [42] have recently classified some of these organisms from British Columbia. It is probable that species of these microflagellates are widely distributed through the oceans, and further studies of their taxonomy and distribution are urgently needed. Unfortunately, the organisms are delicate, so fresh material must be studied, and this presents problems in oceanic surveys; frequently the most important microbe fails to grow in cultures while the lesser ones grow in profusion. Ryther [43] studied the ecology and succession of some microplankton in estuaries in the vicinity of New York, and showed a relation between succession and nutrition.

Wood [44] has recorded that colourless flagellates, which may be identified under fluorescence by staining with acridine orange, particularly those 1 to 5 µ in diameter may at times be far more numerous than the pigmented ones in the open ocean. Imai and Hatenaka [45] have shown that a species of *Monas* (a colourless flagellate about 10 µ in diameter) serves as food for the larvae of *Ostrea gigas* in Japan, and is associated with the death and decomposition of *Zostera* at Mangoku-ura (Watanoha) and in Matzushima Bay. From Manteufel [46] one might conclude that small colourless flagellates feeding on plankton blooms of the diatom *Rhizoso-lenia* form the food of copepods such as *Calanus*, though this has yet to be conclusively proved (see also Yanovsky in Chapter 4). One of the difficulties in the study of these organisms in the food chain is their fragility; they are rapidly destroyed by digestive juices so it is difficult to demonstrate them in stomach contents.

The larger flagellates (and these, except for some Euglenids, are still smaller than the average diatom or dinoflagellate – i.e. are not normally trapped by nets) are very widely distributed and may be very numerous.*

## The Classification of the Flagellates

The following classification is essentially a working one and will I believe be sufficient for ecological purposes where the identity of an organism is more important than its phylogenetic relationships with other species or groups.

### Class CHLOROPHYCEAE

### Order CHLOROCOCCALES

These, although not flagellates, are included here as they occur in the same communities and ecosystems as the other members of the nanoplankton.

The most important member of this family is the genus *Chlorella*, of which several marine species are known (Jenkins [47]). Two *Chlorella* species have been cultured from plankton of the continental shelf of eastern Australia.

A member of the Oocystaceae, *Palmellococcus marinus*, is known from rock pools in various parts of the world, and I have cultured it from marine environments of eastern Australia.

### Order PHYTOMONADIDAE (VOLVOCALES)

The Volvocales are included by protozoologists among the Phytomona-didae.

The genera *Chlamydomonas*, *Carteria*, *Platymonas*, and *Sphaerella* have been recorded from marine sources by Lemmermann [48] and others. Margalef [49] records the following marine *Platymonas* species: *P. bolsiana* Marg., *P. fontata* Marg., *P. contracta* Carter (= *P. subcordiformis* Skuja), *P. subcordiformis* Hazen (non *Carteria subcordiformis* Wille), *P. sulcifera* Kylin, *P. gracilis* Kylin, *Aulacochlamys roskoffensis* (= *P. roskoffensis* Dang.). Scagel and Stein [42] have described new species tentatively assigned to this group, but possibly belonging to the Xanthomonads.

* The classification of the flagellates has recently been revised by Drs Mary Parke and Peter Dixon (*J. Mar. Biol. Ass. U.K.*44, 499–542). The reader is referred to this paper as authoritative for the new taxonomic groupings. These authors have also considerably increased the number of records of marine flagellates.

Family POLYBLEPHARIDAE (POLYBLEPARIDACEAE)
The genus *Dunaliella*, especially *D. euchlora*, is quite common in the marine environment, and has been cultured from both hemispheres. *Pyramimonas* occurs in marine-dominated estuaries such as Port Erin (Parke [50]) and Port Hacking, and is probably widespread.

The spherical planktonic form *Halosphaera*, which is common in the Atlantic and less so in the cooler waters of the Pacific and Indian Oceans, has spores which Parke and Manton [60] ascribe to the genus *Pyramimonas*.

The following species have been described from marine environments: *P. adriaticus* Schiller, *P. grosii* Parke, *P. oltmannsi* Schiller, and *P. impressus* Schiller.

Family POLYTOMIDAE
Members of the colourless genus *Polytoma* have been seen in phytoplankton collections from the Australian continental shelf.

Class XANTHOMONADINEAE (HETEROKONTAE)
Order HETEROCHLORINEAE
Marine genera include *Heterochloria*, *Beckingia*, *Phacomonas*, *Bothrochloris*. Deflandre [51] mentions several species which have been assigned to this family erroneously, *Chloramoeba marina* Schiller, *Schillerochloris* Ruinen, and *Chlorochromomonas* Lewis. Scagel and Stein described two new Xanthomonads from British Columbia.

Order RHIZOCHLORINEAE (RHIZOCHLORALES)
Family RHIZOCHLORIDAE
Marine genera include *Rhizochloris* with several species from marine environments.

Order (EUGLENINEAE) EUGLENALES
Pringsheim [52] in an exhaustive and illuminating discussion on the taxonomic problems in the Euglenineae points out the difficulty of phylogenetic classification of these organisms. He points out that, for practical purposes, the green species may be separated as Euglenaceae from the saprobic Astaceae and the zootrophic (holozoic) Peranemaceae, but that these divisions do not appear to coincide with the true taxonomic groupings. He shows that similar problems exist in the Chrysophyceae at least and probably in the other flagellate groups. The relationship between colourless and pigmented forms is complicated by the fact that pigmented forms may have colourless variants, some of which breed true, while some coloured and colourless species are morphologically closer than some

E

coloured species belonging to the same taxonomic group. The classification of Hollande [53] is adopted here.

Family EUGLENAEAE (EUGLENIDAE)
*Eutreptia* and *Euglena* are common in the estuarine environment, and the former particularly is quite frequent though not numerous in protoplankton samples from oceanic stations. A primitive Euglenoid, *Protoeuglena noctilucae*, is recorded as a symbiont in *Noctiluca* by Subrahmanyan [54]. The colourless genus *Astasia* occurs in estuarine muds, including those with a low redox potential and free hydrogen sulphide.

Class (CRYPTOMONADIDAE) CRYPTOPHYCEAE
*Hemiselmis rufescens* is recorded from marine environments by Parke [50] and Jenkins [47]. Many zooxanthellae (algae symbiotic with corals and other marine animals) are believed to belong to this group, most of them to the genus *Rhodomonas*.

Class SILICOFLAGELLINEAE
Family DICTYOCHIDAE
These organisms are supported by a siliceous skeleton consisting of one to several rings or whorls and spines. Deflandre [55] recognizes only one living genus *Dictyocha*, but Lemmermann [48] names *Mesochena*, *Dictyocha*, and *Distephanus*, the names being based on the complexity of the skeletal structure.

Class COCCOLITHOPHORINEAE
Family (SYRACOSPHAERIDAE) SYRACOSPHAERACEAE
Deflandre [56] lists the following genera from marine sources:
   *Calyptrosphaera*, *Sphaerocalyptra*, *Acanthoica*, *Anacanthoica*, *Pontosphaera*, *Lohmannosphaera*, *Scyphosphaera*, *Thaosphaera*, *Syracosphaera*, *Syracolithus*, *Algirosphaera*, *Clavosphaera*, *Rhabdosphaera*, *Anthosphaera*, *Deutschlandia*, *Michaelsarsia*, *Ophiaster*, *Halopappus*, *Calcioconus*, *Thalassopappus*, *Zygosphaera*, *Najadea*, *Corisphaera*, *Homozygosphaera*, *Helladosphaera*, *Periphyllophora*, and Gaarder and Ramsfjell [57] add the genus *Calciopappus*.

Family (COCCOLITHIDAE) COCCOLITHACEAE
Marine genera of this family include:
   *Coccolithus*, *Coccolithophora*, *Umbilicosphaera* (*Neosphaera*), *Gephyrocapsa*, *Tergestiella*, *Rhabdosphaera*, *Discosphaera*.

Family CALCIOSOLENIDAE
Marine genera include *Calciosolenia*, *Acanthosolenia*, and *Anoplosolenia*.

Class (CHRYSOMONADINEAE) CHRYSOMONADACEAE
Genera recorded from marine environments are *Ochromonas*, *Monas* (colourless), *Phaeocystis*, *Dinobryon* (mainly fresh water and estuarine), *Chrysochromulina*, *Chromulina*, *Chrysamoeba*, *Isochrysis*, and *Dicrateria*.

Class ZOOFLAGELLATA
Marine species of this order include *Bodo marina* Braarud, *Rhynchomonas nasuta* (Stokes) Klebs, *R. mutabilis* Griesm., and *Cruzella* sp.

Order TRICHOMONADINA
*Tramastix marina* Saville Kent.

*The Ecology of the Flagellates*
The flagellates are extremely versatile in their nutrition as Pringsheim points out:

> 'In the Euglenidae, Chrysophyceae, Chloromonadineae and Dinophysidae, there are to be found all types of nutrition which exist among the non-bacterial lower organisms; photoautotrophy (holophytism), mixotrophy, saprotrophy, zootrophy (holozoism) and parasitism; the last three are often associated with the absence of chlorophyll. Such colorless organisms require food either in the form of dissolved substances (saprotrophy) or as food particles (zootrophy). Pigmented euglenoids, cryptomonads and chloromonads do not ingest food particles, though many pigmented chrysophycean and dinophycean members do so.'

To what extent saprotrophy and phagotrophy supplement photosynthesis in this group we do not know, but the presence of flagellates, especially coloured flagellates, in the aphotic zone suggest that alternate modes of nutrition may be important in this group. The photosynthesis of the group is discussed by Hutner and Provasoli [58]. It is normally aerobic with evolution of oxygen, but a number of species such as *Chalamydomonas moewusii* can photoreduce carbon dioxide. In their saprotrophic (heterotrophic) nutrition, they can utilize acetic, pyruvic, and lactic acids and acetates, but not glucose and other sugars, and are very tolerant of fatty acids even at pH 2·2 and grow in their presence at 4·5. They require nitrates in the light and ammonia or amino-acids in the dark as sources of nitrogen, though there are some exceptions to this rule. Many of this group do not require accessory growth factors, and the green forms synthesize aneurin; *Chlamydomonas chlamydogama* requires cobaltamine, histidine, and aspartic acid, and the truly colourless forms require thiazol and pyrimidine.

The *Volvocales* or *Phytomonads* (to give them their botanical and zoological names) are biologically the highest development of the flagellates. They may be unicellular as in *Chlamydomonas* or multicellular as in *Volvox*, with some segregation of cellular function. The individuals are biflagellate, reproduction is by longitudinal fission (asexual) or sexual with equal or unequal gametes. The life history, like the morphology, grades from simple, unicellular, isogamous forms to multicellular, oogamous forms. This group is largely confined to fresh water, except for the important genera *Dunaliella* of which *D. marina* is frequent in estuarine and neritic environments, and *D. salina* in salterns and salt lakes, *Pyramimonas* and *Platymonas* which are common in estuarine, and occasionally, in oceanic plankton. Among the colourless species, *Polytoma* has been collected from the Australian continental shelf.

The *Xanthomonads* with two unequal flagella or a single flagellum are often undistinguishable from the flagellate zoospores of the Heterokontae. Their cytology and biology are little known. They occur in the microplankton of fresh, brackish, and sea water, but we do not know their relative importance in the oceans, and more studies of this group are badly needed.

The *Euglenidae* divide by longitudinal fission, and are ecologically more restricted to localities with a high content of organic matter, occurring mainly in sediments, and in heavily polluted water. The cytology and biology of this group have been extensively studied by Pringsheim [52].

The *Cryptophyceae* or *Cryptomonads* are morphologically well-defined, and have two unequal flagella; reproduction is by longitudinal fission; autotrophic and heterotrophic forms occur. The pigmented forms occur in the plankton of lakes, rivers, estuaries, and the ocean, but the non-pigmented ones are usually found in polluted waters, or waters with a high organic content. Parasitic fungi, presumably Chytrids, are frequently found attacking Cryptomonads. As with the other microplanktonic forms the importance of these organisms is inadequately known.

The *Silicoflagellates* are marine and, according to Deflandre [55], are apparently on the way to extinction, as they have steadily declined in importance through recent geological time. They have yellowish-brown or greenish-brown chromatophores, and may be related to the Chrysomonads. Only vegetative reproduction is known. They appear to serve as food for echinoderm larvae, although their numbers in the plankton are never very great; 50·4 cells per litre is mentioned by Deflandre, though I have not seen so many in Australian waters. They are recorded from the North Sea and other cooler waters in the Northern Hemisphere and I have found them in the warm waters of the Coral, Tasman, and Timor Seas, though less frequently than in the waters south of the sub-tropical convergence.

Coccolithophores or Coccolithophorids are small (5 to 20 μ) biflagellate organisms with an external skeleton of calcareous rings, discs, or spines (called coccoliths) usually embedded in a thick, gelatinous sheath. They are chiefly marine, though some have become adapted to fresh water. Reproduction is by longitudinal fission though schizogony may occur, and some forms, e.g. Coccolithus fragilis, may have a 'palmella' stage. Endogenous cysts are recorded for a number of species. The coccolithophores contain chlorophyll and are potentially autotrophic. They have been recorded to a depth of 4,000 m by Bernard [59], and at such depths frequently retained their pigments though living in the aphotic zone. They may also attach to the carapaces of decomposing copepods and to diatoms, though many are free. They occur in numbers up to $30 \times 10^6$ cells per litre in warm, tropical waters according to Deflandre [56]. Coccolithophores are important members of the protoplankton in the tropical Atlantic and Indian Oceans, and in the tropical Pacific except in the Coral Sea region. In fresh water, coccolithophores are found in eutrophic waters. Detailed study of this group is being currently carried out at Oslo by Braarud and his colleagues.

The Chrysomonads include flagellate and rhizopod-like forms, with or without a cellulose wall, or more rarely a siliceous sheath. They may be free-swimming, sedentary, or colonial, photosynthetic with a yellowish-brown or yellowish-green pigment, e.g. Chrysochromulina, or non-pigmented; they may be autotrophic, heterotrophic, or phagotrophic. Chrysomonads have been recorded from the coldest waters to the tropics, may form slimes on rocks, or an important part of the plankton in fresh, brackish, or salt water. It is significant that autotrophic nutrition is at times accessory, pigments being developed in inverse proportion to the organic nutrients present. They are frequently abundant in oceanic protoplankton, and may be dominant; they have been cultured from depths to 4,000 m in the tropical Atlantic by Kimball and Corcoran using erdschreiber medium. They are, no doubt, an important food for planktonic larvae, as Parke has found three genera Chromulina, Isochrysis, and Dicrateria to serve as food for Ostrea edulis. Some excellent studies on the taxonomy of marine Chrysomonads, especially Chrysochromulina, have been made by Parke and her colleagues at Plymouth [60], while McLaughlin [61] has made very interesting nutritional studies of *Prymnesium parvum*, *Isochrysis galbana*, and *Monochrysis lutheri*.

*Zooxanthellae.* The Zooxanthellae are a group of photosynthetic flagellates, not confined to one group, which live in symbiosis with a large number of protozoa and invertebrates and appear to provide their hosts with large amounts of extracellular photosynthate. They have been recorded in association with foraminifera, radiolaria, ciliates (including tintinnids), sponges, coelenterates, turbellarians, nudibranchs and possibly bryozoa, echinoderms, and tunicates. The algal components of some of these have been ascribed to the cryptomonads. Nigrelli, McLaughlin, and Jakowska [62] found that the histozoic algae in fish belong to the Chlorococcales or to *Stigocloneum*. Fauré Frémiet [63] recorded a chlorophyte living as a symbiont in the ciliate *Condylosoma tenuis*, and Subrahmanyan [54] found that a euglenid is responsible for the green coloration of *Noctiluca* in the sea off Calicut during blooms of that organism. A significant advance in the study of zooxanthellae was made by Zahl and McLaughlin [64], and McLaughlin and Zahl [65, 66], when they succeeded in cultivating the algae of the zooxanthellae from various hosts. These produced motile swarmers which are unequivocally dinoflagellate in character (*Gymnodinium* or *Exuviaella*), and the authors believe that they are the means of dispersing the algae which form the vegetative zooxanthella cells, which later divide by fission. The authors also suggest that the susceptibility to infection is related to a paucity of growth factors as well as of nitrates and phosphates and that the zooxanthellae of corals may play a dominant part in the size, form, and character of the calcareous skeletons. It is possible that the raising of the pH, thereby increasing the precipitation rate of calcium carbonate, is as important as the production of oxygen by the algal cells of the zooxanthellae.

## The Ciliates

Apart from the pathogenic forms, there is a number of genera of ciliates in the sea and in fresh water, especially just above the sediments. As ciliates have no chlorophyll, they are confined to holozoic nutrition, and require other organisms or organic material as food, except perhaps for those just referred to as algal symbionts, though it is more probable that these assimilate accessory factors from the algae, because they seek particulate food as their colourless counterparts do.

### Planktonic Ciliates

The largest group of ciliates associated with the plankton is the Tintinnoidea, which occur, sometimes in abundance, in all oceans from the equator to the polar ice. The ciliates are to be found in oceanic, neritic, and estuarine environments, in rivers and fresh water lakes, and feed on diatoms, dinoflagellates and presumably bacteria, while they are in turn consumed by ascidians and other members of the zooplankton. They feed on the edge of plankton swarms and on the dead and dying plant forms, being a link in the oceanic food chain. Although rarely abundant in oceanic plankton, they are rarely absent from plankton samples, and are a constant source of trouble in isolating phytoplankton, as they often breed rapidly in primary plankton cultures.

The Tintinnoidea are characterized by being encased in a sheath or lorica, the front end of which is open, and out of which the cilia are extruded. Because of the mode of preservation of plankton, the animals were either totally retracted or absent from the lorica when the material was examined by the systematist, so the taxonomy is based on the shape and material of the lorica. Kofoid and Campbell [67] stated their belief that the lorica adequately reflected the biology and physiology of the organisms, but theirs was a strictly *ad hoc* argument. However, the lorica does give a classification which allows the separation of species and groups which are characteristic of certain water types and may therefore be used as indicators. The study of this group has been restricted by the fact that they do not contain chlorophyll and are therefore not concerned with the primary productivity of water, though they may be important at the next trophic level. The structure, proportions, and shape, and presence or absence of adhering particles such as sand grains, coccoliths or other material are used as diagnostic features. Kofoid and Campbell, in their classic monograph, described 51 genera and include all known species which they believed to be valid at that date (1929). The ciliates other than the tintinnids which occur in the plankton have been little studied, but they are usually present, and become very numerous if the sample is left for a day or so without any preservative, an indication of their potential role in the destruction of oceanic plankton swarms or blooms.

*Ciliates Associated with Sediments*
Ciliates are usually abundant in sediments, especially in estuarine sediments. There we may separate two biocoenoses, though the ciliates move freely from one to the other.

1. Among sedentary plants and animals, e.g. *Thalassia, Zostera, Posidonia* and their epiphytes, or among the littoral fauna and that associated with ship fouling.

2. With the sediments, where some species graze on the surface plants, micro-organisms including bacteria, while others, e.g. *Euplotes*, live in an

anaerobic environment, feeding on bacteria and colourless flagellates. I have grown *Euplotes* on synthetic cultures of *Desulphovibrio* at a redox potential of − 270 mV in a medium with no organic constituents other than the bacteria and their products of metabolism. The ecological importance of the ciliates in these environments is still to be studied in detail. Ciliates are also important in clearing polluted waters as has been shown by Purdy and Butterfield [68], who found that *Colpidium* and *Paramecium* devoured polluting bacteria, but tended to die out on a strictly bacterial diet. However, in the presence of natural plankton, the bacteria were soon reduced to a very low figure which was maintained. This is obviously a case of metabiosis in which there are other organisms contributing to the balance.

## The Sarcodina

The two important groups in this class are the Foraminifera and the Radiolaria, the former having calcareous, the latter siliceous tests or skeletons. These organisms occur in the plankton where they are very numerous at times. In shallow waters, the tests sink to the bottom, forming oozes, often composed of one genus or species, e.g. *Globigerina* ooze. The extent to which the ocean floor is covered with foraminiferal oozes may be gauged by a glance at navigational charts where they are distinguished by the letters gl. oz. These oozes consolidate to form limestones, cherts, or jaspers, so that the rhizopod section of the Sarcodina are of great geological significance. Naked sarcodina are also to be found in the plankton, and are at times quite numerous. Planktonic foraminifera are only now receiving the attention they deserve. Bé [69] has made some observations on the horizontal distribution in the Atlantic. He concluded that there are more species to be found in the Gulf Stream than in the slope water to the north or in the Sargasso Sea, and divided them into cold-tolerant and warm-tolerant species. In plankton samples from the Coral and Tasman Seas, in the south-west Pacific, foraminifera are usually present but sparsely distributed. However, on occasion, they do occur in rich concentrations in which they are far more numerous than the phytoplankton. They are also quite frequently attached to algae including the kelps. The vast concentrations of foraminifera and radiolaria in sediments and sedimentary rocks would not seem to be reproducible at the present time. The nutrition of these organisms is holozoic, and they ingest particulate matter including diatoms. I have found apparently living foraminifera in some sediments taken during the *Galathea* expedition from a depth of 7,400 m in the Weber Deep, suggesting that they may be autochthonous on the surface of even the deepest sediments.

## Green, Brown, and Red Microscopic Algae

The *Chlorophyceae, Phaeophyceae,* and *Rhodophyceae* (to use the botanical terms for these organisms), other than the unicellular members already discussed, are unimportant in the protoplankton, but are often of significance in the plant biomass of fresh water and estuaries, as well as of atolls and foreshores. The Corallines serve as food for parrot fish on coral reefs, as one can find evidence of grazing of the algae themselves and fragments of the algae can be found in the gut of fish which have a stomach mill for grinding them. The simple filamentous algae such as *Chaetomorpha, Cladophora,* and *Vaucheria* occur in fresh and brackish water, and these genera, as well as the brown *Ectocarpus* and the red *Polysiphonia, Ceramium,* and *Antithamnion* are important epontic forms on rocks and sea-grasses in estuaries and on the coast. They supply a large quantity of carbohydrate and fatty food for crustaceans and fish, and so are greatly involved in the productivity of lakes and ponds as well as coastal lagoons and estuaries. *Chaetomorpha* and *Cladophora* proliferate rapidly in the spring and serve as an important food for the mullets in the rivers, before these fish move out into the estuaries, and before the protoplankton blooms occur.

## Fungi

Fungi have been shown to be important in the decomposition of organic matter in the bottom of fresh water lakes and rivers, and Weston [70] believes that they are as important as the bacteria in these environments. Their importance in the sea is only now becoming evident. They are, in the opinion of Vishniac [71], likely to occur in the same aerobic communities as the bacteria. She points out that marine fungi are strongly aerobic saprophytes, are associated with plankton blooms and with algal and animal species, and that their importance has not been adequately considered. Some fungi can also live and reproduce under microaerophilic conditions. They are independent of light, can grow in a pH range from 3·2 to 9·6 and under artificial conditions at a negative pH. Most of them require organic nitrogen and ammonia and cannot use nitrates. They obtain their sulphur from cysteine and other organic sulphur compounds, though *Leptomitus* and *Achyla* can reduce sulphates. Adair and Vishniac [72] found an obligately marine fungus which required cyanocobaltamine, and they have used this strain for assays of this vitamin in marine environments. Ritchie [73, 74] studied the effect of temperature on the salinity requirements of marine fungi, and Vishniac [75] also studied the salt requirements. There is also a number of parasitic genera of fungi in aquatic environments, e.g. *Saprolegnia, Achyla,* and the Chytridiales, the first two being parasitic on animals, the last on algae and grasses. The fungal parasites will be considered later. Many forms, especially of the Chytridiales and the Pyrenomycetes, are adapted to an aquatic environment.

Earlier workers such as Sparrow [76] found only species of terrestrial origin in marine environments, but later work has shown that there is a whole fungal flora adapted to life in the sea in addition to that derived from terrestrial sources. Moore and Meyers [77] have suggested that marine fungi be placed in a separate group which they call Thalassiomycetes (meaning 'sea fungi'), but this does not seem to be warranted. One will probably find that, as with the bacteria, some forms are restricted to marine habitats, others prefer such habitats, while still others can live in salt or fresh water or even terrestrial environments. Johnson and Sparrow [78] give an admittedly arbitrary definition of marine fungi as those which can complete their development and reproduce if exposed at some period of their growth to a salinity of $30\%_0$ while immersed intermittently or continuously. They have found no morphological or physiological adaptation to existence in salt water, although they believe that some forms are exclusively found in a salt water environment. So far, little work has been done to determine the ionic requirements of fungi isolated from the sea, and it is most probable that they will be found to conform with the bacteria in having an ionic balance which governs their distribution rather than a tolerance for a particular ion such as sodium or chloride.

There is doubt too as to whether the fungi are important denizens of the marine ecosystem. This is largely due to a strange lack of interest in marine mycology *per se*, and is a tacit condemnation of *ad hoc* research as a means of advancing knowledge. Most marine mycological studies have been made in connexion with the destruction of wooden structures and cordage in the sea, with a view to the preservation of such material. As a result of this, we have descriptions of estuarine, wood-destroying (lignicolous) fungi from India (Becker and Kohlmeyer [79]), Germany (Höhnk [80]), North America (Meyers [81, 82], Barghoorn and Linder [83], Meyers and Reynolds [84], Kohlmeyer [85, 86], Johnson [87, 88]) and Australia (Cribb and Cribb [89]). These economic considerations have diverted attention from a systematic attempt to study the importance of fungi in the oceans and in the sediments. The few samples that have been taken from the continental shelf and from oceanic cores have contained saprophytic fungi, and I have by no means infrequently found fungal spores in protoplankton samples taken with van Dorn samplers, when I examined the material within minutes of capture. It is my belief that these organisms do play a relatively important part in the reduction and transformation of organic material in the oceans and sediments, and that a study of the true role of fungi in the oceans is long overdue. The parasitic fungi are known to be important in fresh water environments, especially among the algae, including diatoms. Their role in the ocean is not nearly so well known, but their occurrence will be discussed in a later section.

An interesting problem is the relation between fungal infestation of timber and marine borer attack. Meyers and Reynolds [90], Becker, Kampf, and Kohlmeyer [91], Schafer and Lane [92], Kohlmeyer et al. [93] and Kampf et al. [94] believe that fungi assist the attack of wood by gribbles (Limnoria) and marine borer (Teredo), Kohlmeyer et al. [93] finding that gribbles obtain nutrients from the fungi. Ray and Stuntz [95], on the other hand, did not find a consistent connexion between fungal attack and the occurrence of Limnoria. They did find, however, that bacteria, some undoubtedly cellulolytic, are nearly always present on the wood surface. This question of the possible symbiosis of bacteria, fungi, and marine borers is therefore still in doubt, though it has important ecological as well as economic implications.

A bibliography of marine fungi was published by Johnson and Meyers [96] and a more complete one is to be found in the recent monograph on marine fungi by Johnson and Sparrow [78].

The groups of fungi recorded as having marine representatives are the Labyrinthulae, Phycomycetes, Deuteromycetes (fungi imperfecti), and Ascomycetes with one representative of the Basidiomycetes, a smut Melanotaenium ruppiae on the sea-grass Ruppia maritima. It is perhaps significant that the only Basidiomycete to be found in the marine environment is associated with a phanerogam and moreover one which prefers a fresh water to a marine habitat.

We may sum up our knowledge of marine fungi by stating that there is considerable information regarding the species concerned with the deterioration of man-made structures in the sea, and those which are parasites in marine, particularly estuarine, plants and animals, but practically nothing is known of any distinctive physiology that may separate marine from fresh water and terrestrial fungi or of the true distribution and importance of fungi in the sea or as part of the trophic chains in marine ecosystems.

### Yeasts in the Sea

Studies of marine yeasts are limited, and the true function of these microbes is not yet known. Earlier workers recorded yeasts associated with fish spoilage, sea water, and sediments (e.g. Wood [4]). Systematic studies have been made for the Black Sea by Kriss, Rukina, and Tiknonenko [97], and Novoshilova [98], for the Sea of Okhotsk and the Pacific Ocean by

Novoshilova [98], for India by Bhat *et al.* [99], for Biscayne Bay, Florida by Fell [100], and for the Atlantic and Pacific Oceans off the American coast by Fell and van Uden [101]. van Uden and Castelo Branco [102] described two yeasts which were parasitic on *Daphnia major* in culture; Kriss and his co-workers (see Kriss [103]) have depicted a number of forms which had attached to slides submerged in several oceans and which appeared morphologically to be yeasts. Novoshilova studied some 525 strains in her investigations and found that some were obviously of terrestrial origin, but others seemed to have developed an essentially marine character, i.e. they seemed restricted to marine habitats and to salinities around 30‰. The ability of some yeasts to live anaerobically could allow them to extend their regime into the sediments.

Fell and van Uden state that normally sea water will contain tens or hundreds of cells per litre, but close to sea-grass and algal beds and to plankton swarms, though not as a rule in contact with the last (probably due to antibiotics), the counts are far higher. In such cases, the yeasts could well be important saprophytic agents in the decomposition of dying or dead organic matter in the seas. These authors conclude that they could not designate a true marine yeast flora, and that most, if not all, were transients in the marine environment.

## Marine Viruses

Viruses have been reported in the sea by few authors. Earlier studies were confined to phages for the Enterobacteriaceae, which were found with their hosts in polluted water. These, however, must be considered as transients in the marine environment, and of minimal importance to marine ecology as a whole. Lewin [104] has shown the existence of a marine plant virus, and Ordal and his colleagues describe a virus attacking *Chondrococcus*, but no systematic study of the occurrence of plant and animal viruses in the marine environment has yet been made. Bacteriophages have been collected from water beyond the littoral zone by Kriss and Rukina [105], and by Spencer [106–108], who report that these phages are active against marine strains of bacteria. Spencer maintains that his phages have characteristics which distinguish them from terrestrial phages. They were inactivated in an hour at 55°C, whereas terrestrial phages are not appreciably inactivated in an hour at 60°C, the effect of monovalent and divalent cations for inactivation and for lysis of the host cells were different, and so were temperature and salinity effects. In all cases the marine-isolated phages were conditioned to a higher salt tolerance, higher divalent cation ratios, and lower temperature than their terrestrial counterparts.

# REFERENCES

[1] ZOBELL, C. E. (1946), *Marine Microbiology*, Chronica Botanica Press, Waltham, Mass., 240 pp.
[2] WILSON, D. P. (1955), 'The role of micro-organisms in the settlement of *Ophelia bicornis*, Savigny', *J. Mar. Biol. Ass. U.K.*, **34**, 531–43.
[3] WOOD, E. J. F. (1950), 'The role of bacteria in the early stages of fouling', *Aust. J. Mar. Freshw. Res.*, **1**, 85–91.
[4] WOOD, E. J. F. (1953), 'Heterotrophic bacteria in marine environments of Eastern Australia', *Aust. J. Mar. Freshw. Res.*, **4**, 160–200.
[5] HENRICI, A. T. (1939), 'Distribution of bacteria in lakes', *Problems in Lake Biology*, *Amer. Ass. Adv. Sci.*, **10**, 39–64.
[6] VENKATARAMAN, R. and SREENIVASAN, A. (1954), 'Bacteria of offshore water of the west coast', *Proc. Ind. Acad. Sci.*, **40B**, 161–66.
[7] WOOD, E. J. F. (1946), 'The isolation of *Sarcina ureae* (Beikerinck) Lohnis from sea water', *J. Bact.*, **51**, 287–89.
[8] FISCHER, B. (1894), 'Die Bakterien des Meeres nach den Untersuchungen der Planktonexpedition unter gleichseitiger Berücksichtigung einiger alterer und neuer Untersuchungen', *Z. Bakt.*, I, **15**, 657–66.
[9] RUSSELL, H. L. (1891), 'Untersuchungen über in Golf von Neapel lebende Bakterien', *Z. Hyg. Infektionkr.*, **2**, 165–206.
[10] GRAY, P. H. H. and THORNTON, E. G. (1928), 'Soil bacteria that decompose aromatic compounds', *Z. Bakt.*, I, **73**, 74–95.
[11] WOOD, E. J. F. (1954), 'Dinoflagellates of the Australian region', *Aust. J. Mar. Freshw. Res.*, **5**, 171–351.
[12] SVERDRUP, H. U., JOHNSON, M. W., and FLEMING, R. H. (1949), *The Oceans*, Prentice Hall, New York, 1,087 pp.
[13] HASLE, GRETHE R. (1960), 'Phytoplankton and ciliate species from the tropical Pacific', *Skr. Norske Vidensk-Akad. I. Mat. Nat. Kl.*, **2**, 1–50.
[14] WOOD, E. J. F. (1956), 'Diatoms in the ocean deeps', *Pac. Sci.*, **10**, 377–81.
[15] WOOD, E. J. F. (1963), 'A study of the diatom flora of fresh sediments of the South Texas Bays and adjacent waters', *Inst. Mar. Sci. Publ.* **9**, 237–310.
[16] LEWIN, JOYCE C. and LEWIN, R. A. (1960), 'Autotrophy and heterotrophy in marine littoral diatoms', *Can. J. Microbiol.*, **6**, 127–34.
[17] BRAARUD, T. (1962), 'Species distribution in marine phytoplankton', *J. Oceanog. Soc. Jap.*, **20** (anniv. vol.), 628–49.
[18] BAAS BECKING, L. G. M. and WOOD, E. J. F. (1955), 'Biological processes in the estuarine environment, I, II', *Kon. Ned. Akad. Weten. Proc.*, **B58**, 160–81.
[19] KIMBALL, J. F. JR., CORCORAN, E. F., and WOOD, E. J. F. (1963), 'Chlorophyll-containing micro-organisms in the aphotic zone of the oceans', *Bull. Mar. Sci. Gulf Caribb.*
[20] CROSBY, L. H. and WOOD, E. J. F. (1958), 'Studies on Australian and New Zealand diatoms, I', *Trans. Roy. Soc. N.Z.*, **85**, 482–530.
[21] HART, T. (1937), '*Rhizosolenia curvata* Zacharias, an indicator species in the Southern Ocean', *Discovery Repts.*, **16**, 2, 415–46.

[22] LUND, J. W. G. (1950), 'Studies on *Asterionella formosa* Haas; nutrient depletion and the spring maximum', *J. Ecol.*, **38**, 1–35.

[23] WOOD, E. J. F. (1963), 'Relative importance of groups of protozoa and algae in marine environments of the south-west Pacific and east Indian Oceans', *Symp. Mar. Microbiol.*, Ch. 24, C. H. Oppenheimer, ed. Thomas, Springfield, Ill.

[24] BAAS BECKING, L. G. M. (1951), 'Notes on some Cyanophyceae of the Pacific region', *Kon. Ned. Akad. Weten. Proc.*, **54C**, 3.

[25] OPPENHEIMER, C. H. and WOOD, E. J. F. (1962), 'Note on the effect of contamination on a marine slough and the vertical distribution of marine plants in the sediment', *Z. allg. Mikrobiol.*, **2**, 45–7.

[26] GEITLER, L. (1932), 'Cyanophyceae in Rabenhorsts *Kryptogamenflora der Deutschland, Österreich und der Schweiz*', **XIV**, 1,196 pp.

[27] BERNARD, F. and LECAL, J. (1960), 'Plancton unicellulaire recolté dans l'ocean Indien par le *Charcot* (1950) et le *Norsel* (1955–6)', *Bull. Inst. Oceanog.*, Monaco, 1, 166, 1–59.

[28] RABINOWITCH, E. I. (1945), *Photosynthesis*. Interscience Publications, New York.

[29] SCHUSTER, W. H. (1949), 'Die Viscultur in der Kustvijvers op Java', Dept. Landbw. en Viss. Publ. 2.

[30] DYER, D. L. and GAFFORD, R. D. (1961), 'Some characteristics of a thermophilic blue-green alga', *Science*, **134**, 616–17.

[31] BERNARD, F. (1963), 'Density of flagellates and myxophyceae in the heterotrophic layers related to environment', *Symp. Mar. Microbiol.*, Ch. 22, C. H. Oppenheimer, ed. Thomas, Springfield, Ill.

[32] SCHILLER, J. (1933, 1937), 'Dinoflagellatae in Rabenhorsts *Kryptogamenflora der Deutschland, Österreich und der Schweiz*', **I**, 1–617, **II**, 1–590.

[33] WOOD, E. J. F. (1963), 'Dinoflagellates in the Australian region, II', *Div. Fish. Oceanog. C.S.I.R.O. Tech. Paper*, 14, 55 pp.

[34] WOOD, E. J. F. (1963), 'Dinoflagellates in the Australian region, III', ibid., 17, 20 pp.

[35] PAVILLARD, J. (1935), 'Peridinéens et diatomées pélagiques cueillis par Alain Gerbault entre les Marquésas et les Ilês Galapagos', *Bull. Inst. Oceanog.* Monaco, **669.**,

[36] SWEENEY, B. M. (1963), 'Luminescent dinoflagellates', *Biol. Bull.*, **125**, 277–81.

[37] MILLER, S. M., MOORE, H. B., and KVAMMEN, K. R. (1953), 'Plankton of the Florida current', *Bull. Mar. Sci. Gulf. Caribb.*, **2**, 465.

[38] WOOD, E. J. F. and DAVIS, P. S. (1956), 'Importance of smaller phytoplankton elements', *Nature*, **177**, 438.

[39] KNIGHT-JONES, E. W. (1951), 'Preliminary studies of nanoplankton systematics and abundance by a quantitative culture method', *J. Cons. Int. Expl. Mer*, **17**, 140–55.

[40] KNIGHT-JONES, E. W. and WALNE, P. R. (1951), 'Chromulina pusilla Butcher, a dominant member of the ultraplankton', *Nature*, **167**, 445.

[41] MANTON, I. and PARKE, M. (1960), 'Further observations of small green flagellates with special reference to possible relations of *Chromulina pusilla* Butcher', *J. Mar. Biol. Ass. U.K.*, **39**, 275–98.

[42] SCAGEL, R. F. and STEIN, JANET R. (1961), 'Marine nanoplankton from a British Columbia fjord', *Can. J. Bot.*, **39**, 1205–13.

[43] RYTHER, J. H. (1954), 'The ecology of phytoplankton blooms in Moriches Bay and Great South Bay, Long Island, N.Y.', *Biol. Bull.*, **106**, 198–209.

[44] WOOD, E. J. F. (1962), 'A method for phytoplankton study', *Limnol. Oceanog.*, **7**, 32–35.

[45] IMAI, T. and HATANAKA, M. (1949), 'On the artificial propagation of the Japanese oyster *Ostrea gigas* fed by non-coloured naked flagellates', *Bull. Inst. Agr. Soc. Tohoku Univ.*, **1**, 1, 33.

[46] MANTEUFEL, B. P. (1941), 'Plankton and herring in the Barents Sea', Trans. Knipovich, *Polar Sci. Inst. Sea fish. Oceanog.*, **7** (Russian).

[47] JENKINS, PAMELA G. (1955), 'Seasonal changes in the photoplankton as indicated by spectrometric chlorophyll estimations, 1952–53', Pap. Mar. Biol. Oceanog. 58–67, *Deep Sea Res.* **3**, supp.

[48] LEMMERMANN, E. (1908), 'Flagellatae, Chlorophyceae, Coccosphaerales und Silicoflagellatae. Nordisches Plankton', *Bot. Teil.* **21**.

[49] MARGALEF, R. (1946), 'Contribucion al conocimiento del genero *Platymonas* (Volvocales)', *Collect. Bot.*, **1**, 1, 8, 2.

[50] PARKE, MARY (1949), 'Studies on marine flagellates, I', *J. Mar. Biol. Ass. U.K.*, **28**, 255–86.

[51] DEFLANDRE, G. (1952), 'Classe de Zanthomonadines', *Traite de Zoologie*, P. Grassé, ed. **I**, 212–26.

[52] PRINGSHEIM, E. G. (1948), 'Taxonomic problems in the Euglenidae', *Biol. Rev.*, **23**, 46–61.

[53] HOLLANDE, A. (1952), 'Classe des Eugleniens', *Traite de Zoologie*, P. Grassé, ed. **I**, 237–55.

[54] SUBRAHMANYAN, R. (1954), 'A new member of the Euglenidae, *Protoeuglena noctilucae* gen. et sp. n. occurring in *Noctiluca miliaris* Suriray causing green discoloration of the sea off Calicut', *Proc. Ind. Acad. Sci.*, **39**, 118.

[55] DEFLANDRE, G. (1952), 'Classe des Silicoflagellides,' *Traite de Zoologie*, P. Grassé, ed. **I**, 425–38.

[56] DEFLANDRE, G. (1952), 'Classe des Coccolithophorides', *Traite de Zoologie*, P. Grassé, ed. **I**, 439–70.

[57] GAARDER, K. R. and RAMSFJELL, E. (1954), 'A new coccolithophorid from northern waters, *Calciopappus caudatus* n. gen., n. sp.', *Nytt Mag. Bot.*, **2**, 155–56.

[58] HUTNER, S. H. and PROVASOLI, L. (1951), 'The Phytoflagellates', *Biochemistry and Physiology of the Protozoa*, A. Lwoff ed. Academic Press, New York.

[59] BERNARD, F. (1948), 'Réchérches sur le cycle de *Coccolithus fragilis* Lohm. flagellé dominant des mers chaudes', *J. Cons. Int. Expl. Mer*, **15**, 177–88.

[60] PARKE, M., MANTON, I., and CLARKE, B. (1955–1959), 'Studies on marine flagellates', *J. Mar. Biol. Ass. U.K.*, **34**, 579–609; **35**, 387–414; **37**, 209–28; **38**, 169–88.

[61] MCLAUGHLIN, J. J. A. (1958), 'Euryhaline chrysomonads; nutrition

and toxigenesis in *Prymnesium parvum* with notes on *Isochrysis galbana*, and *Monochrysis lutheri*', *J. Protozool.*, **5**, 75–81.

[62] NIGRELLI, R. F., MCLAUGHLIN, J. J. A., and JAKOWSKA, S. (1958), 'Histozoic algal growth in fish', *Copeia*, **4**, 331–33.

[63] FAURÉ FRÉMIET, E. (1958), 'Le cilié *Condylosoma tenuis* n. sp. et son algue symbionte', *Hydrobiol.*, **10**, 43–48.

[64] ZAHL, P. A. and MCLAUGHLIN, J. J. A. (1957), 'Isolation and culture of Zooxanthellae', *Nature*, **180**, 199–200.

[65] MCLAUGHLIN, J. J. A. and ZAHL, P. A. (1957), 'Studies in marine biology, II. *In vitro* culture of Zooxanthellae', *Proc. Soc. Exp. Biol. Med.*, **95**, 115–20.

[66] MCLAUGHLIN, J. J. A. and ZAHL, P. A. (1959), 'Axenic zooxanthellae from various invertebrate hosts', *Ann. N.Y. Acad. Sci.*, **77**, 55–72.

[67] KOFOID, C. A. and CAMPBELL, A. (1939), 'The Ciliata; the Tintinnoidea', *Bull. Mus. Comp. Zool. Harv.*, **84**, 473.

[68] PURDY, W. C. and BUTTERFIELD, T. C. (1918), 'The effect of plankton on the bacterial death rates', *Amer. J. Publ. Health*, **8**, 499–505.

[69] BÉ, A. W. H. (1959), 'Ecology of recent planktonic foraminifera', *Micropaleont.*, **5**, 77–100.

[70] WESTON, W. H. (1941), 'The role of aquatic fungi in hydrobiology', *Symp. on Hydrobiology*, Univ. Wisconsin Press, 129–51.

[71] VISHNIAC, HELEN S. (1956), 'On the ecology of the lower marine fungi', *Biol. Bull.*, **111**, 410–14.

[72] ADAIR, ELIZABETH J. and VISHNIAC, HELEN S. (1958), 'Marine fungus requiring vitamin B$_{12}$,' *Science*, **127**, 147–48.

[73] RITCHIE, D. (1959), 'The effect of salinity and temperature on marine and other fungi from various climates', *Bull. Torrey Bot. Club*, **86**, 367–73.

[74] RITCHIE, D. (1957), 'Salinity optima for marine fungi affected by temperature', *Amer. J. Bot.*, **44**, 780–81.

[75] VISHNIAC, HELEN S. (1960), 'Salt requirements of marine phycomycetes', *Limnol. Oceanog.*, **5**, 362–65.

[76] SPARROW, F. K. (1934), 'Observations on marine phycomycetes collected in Denmark', *Dansk Bot. Ark.*, **8**, 1.

[77] MOORE, R. T. and MEYERS, S. P. (1959), 'Thalassiomycetes I', *Mycologia*, **51**, 871–76.

[78] JOHNSON, T. W. and SPARROW, F. K. JR. (1961), *Fungi in Oceans and Estuaries*, J. Carmer, Weinheim, 668 pp.

[79] BECKER, G. and KOHLMEYER, J. (1956), 'Deterioration of wood by marine fungi in India and its special significance for fishing crafts', *J. Timber Dryers Pres. Ass. India*, **4**, 1–10.

[80] HÖHNK, W. (1955), Studien über Brack- und Seewassermikrobiologie, IV', *Ver. Meeresf. Bremerhaven*, **3**, 199–227.

[81] MEYERS, S. P. (1953), 'Marine fungi in Biscayne Bay, Florida', *Bull. Mar. Sci. Gulf Caribb.*, **2**, 599–601.

[82] MEYERS, S. P. (1954), 'Marine fungi in Biscayne Bay, Florida, II', *Bull. Mar. Sci. Gulf Caribb.*, **3**, 307–27.

[83] BARGHOORN, E. S. and LINDER, D. H. (1944), 'Marine fungi; their taxonomy and biology', *Farlowia*, **1**, 395.

THE MICRO-ORGANISMS · 69

[84] MEYERS, S. P. and REYNOLDS, E. S. (1961), 'Occurrence of lignicolous fungi in Northern Atlantic and Pacific marine localities', *Can. J. Bot.*, 38, 217–26.
[85] KOHLMEYER, J. (1958), 'Holzzerstörende Pilze im Meereswasser', *Holz als roh- und Werkstoff*, 16, 215–20.
[86] KOHLMEYER, J. (1960), 'Wood-inhabiting marine fungi from the Pacific North-west and California', *Nova Hedwigia*, 2, 293–343.
[87] JOHNSON, T. W. (1956), 'Marine fungi; *Leptosphaera* and *Pleospora*', *Mycologia*, 48, 495–505.
[88] JOHNSON, T. W. (1956), 'Marine fungi, II. Ascomycetes and Deuteromycetes from submerged wood', *Mycologia*, 48, 841–51.
[89] CRIBB, A. B. and CRIBB, JOAN W. (1955), 'Marine fungi from Queensland', *Univ. Qld. Bot. Dept. Pap.* 3, 10.
[90] MEYERS, S. P. and REYNOLDS, E. S. (1957), 'Incidence of marine fungi in relation to marine borer attack', *Science*, 126, 969.
[91] BECKER, G., KAMP, W. D., and KOHLMEYER, J. (1957), 'Zür Ernährung der Holzböhrasseln der Gattung *Limnoria*', *Naturwiss.*, 17, 474–84.
[92] SCHAFER, R. D. and LANE, C. E. (1957), 'Some preliminary observations bearing on the nutrition of *Limnoria*', *Bull. Mar. Sci. Gulf Caribb.*, 7, 289–96.
[93] KOHLMEYER, J., BECKER, G., and KAMPF, W. D. (1959), 'Versuche zür Kenntnis der Ernährung der Holzböhrassel *Limnoria tripunctata* und ihre Beziehung zur holzzerstörenden Pilzen', *Z. ang. Zool.*, 46, 457–89.
[94] KAMPF, W. D., BECKER, G., and KOHLMEYER, J. (1959), 'Versuche über das Auffinden und den Befall von Holz durch Larven und der Bohrmuschel *Teredo pedicillata*', *Z. ang. Zool.*, 46, 257–83.
[95] RAY DIXY L., and STUNTZ, D. E. (1959), 'Marine fungi and *Limnoria*', *Science*, 130, 46–47.
[96] JOHNSON, T. W. and MEYERS, S. P. (1957), 'Literature on halophilous and halolimnic fungi', *Bull. Mar. Sci. Gulf Caribb.*, 7, 330–59.
[97] KRISS, A. E., RUKINA, E. A., and TIKNONENKO, A. S. (1952), 'Distribution of yeast organisms in the sea', *Zur. Obschei Biol.*, 13, 232–42.
[98] NOVOSHILOVA, M. I. (1955), 'The quantitative characteristics, species composition and distribution of yeast-like organisms in the Black Sea and the Sea of Okhotsk and the Pacific Ocean', *Trudy Inst. Mikrobiol.*, 4, 155–95.
[99] BHAT, J. V., NAFISA, K., and MODY, B. (1955), 'Some aspects of the nutrition of marine yeasts and their growth', *J. Sci. Ind. Res. India*, 14C, 24.
[100] FELL, J. W., AHERN, D. G., MEYERS, S. P., and ROTH, F. J. (1960), 'Isolation of yeasts from Biscayne Bay, Florida, and adjacent benthic areas', *Limnol. Oceanog.*, 5, 366–71.
[101] FELL, J. W. and VAN UDEN, N. (1963), 'Yeasts in marine environments', *Symp. Mar. Microbiol.*, Ch. 32, C. H. Oppenheimer, ed. Thomas, Springfield, Ill.
[102] VAN UDEN, N. and CASTELO BRANCO, R. (1961), '*Metschnikowiella zobellii* sp. nov. and *M. krissii* sp. nov. two yeasts from the Pacific Ocean pathogenic to *Daphnia major*', *J. Gen. Microbiol.*, 26, 141–48.
F

[103] KRISS, A. E. (1959), *Morskaya Mikrobiologiya*, Akad. Nauk S.S.S.R., 455 pp.

[104] LEWIN, R. L. (1961), 'A marine virus parasitic on algae', *Abs. Mar. Microbiol. Symp.*, Chicago.

[105] KRISS, A. E. and RUKINA, E. A. (1947), 'Bacteriophage in the sea', *Rept. U.S.S.R. Akad. Sci.*, **57**, 833–36.

[106] SPENCER, R. (1955), 'A marine bacteriophage,' *Nature*, **175**, 160–61.

[107] SPENCER, R. (1960), 'Indigenous marine bacteriophages', *J. Bact.*, **79**, 614.

[108] SPENCER, R. (1963), 'Bacterial viruses in the sea', *Symp. Mar. Microbiol.*, Ch. 34, C. H. Oppenheimer, ed. Thomas, Springfield, Ill.

[109] WOOD, E. J. F. (1964), 'Studies in the microbial ecology of the Australasian region', *Nova Hedwigia*, **8**, 1–2, 1–54.

# CHAPTER 4

# Aspects of Productivity

## Photosynthesis

In the water as on the land, life is ultimately dependent on the energy contributed by the sun's rays. Plants are capable of using certain wavelengths of these rays and transforming them into chemical energy, part of which is used in the life-processes, and part stored as combustible material such as sugars, starches, and fats. Photosynthesis in the sea is important in the water-grasses (aquatic angiosperms closely related to the terrestrial grasses), macroscopic algae, protoplankton (including microscopic algae and pigmented protozoa), epontic and benthic plants and the purple and green bacteria. The first two groups, being macroscopic, do not concern us except in their effect on the aqueous environment, and the interaction between them and the micro-organisms. The protoplankton and photosynthetic bacteria are of the greatest interest, and present nutritional problems which do not seem to have been adequately considered. Both the green and purple sulphur bacteria utilize the radiant energy of light to oxidize reduced sulphur compounds such as hydrogen sulphide, thiosulphate, and tetrathionate to sulphur or sulphate, and molecular hydrogen to water (Larsen [1]). The green bacteria are phototrophs and obligate anaerobes, but Stanier [2] has recently shown that *Chlorobium limicola* which belongs to this group can utilize organic substances as well as, or instead of, $CO_2$. However, they seem normally to live as autotrophs and to use hydrogen sulphide, probably in the form of $SH^-$ as electron donor, according to the overall equations given by Larsen:

$$CO_2 + 2H_2S \xrightarrow{\text{light}} CH_2O + 2S + H_2O$$

$$3CO_2 + 2S + 5H_2 \xrightarrow{\text{light}} 3(CH_2O) + 2H_2SO_4$$

Although the green pigment, variously called *bacterioviridin, chlorobium-chlorophyll*, etc., is chemically related to the plant chlorophylls, the thermodynamic efficiency of anaerobic bacterial photo-reduction using $H_2$ or $H_2S$ as hydrogen donor is higher than that of the green plants if $H_2O$ is the hydrogen donor, as $H_2O$ requires 115,000 cal. per mole of $CO_2$

71

reduced, $H_2S$ only 15,000 cal. per mole. The purple sulphur bacteria do not grow at the lowest redox potentials in which the green bacteria occur (see fig. 2) and their range extends well into the region of the aerobic photosynthesis of the algae. Their metabolism is essentially the same as that of the green bacteria, though their quantum efficiency is probably lower.

The overall photosynthesis equation has been written by van Niel [3, 4]

$$CO_2 + 2H_2A \xrightarrow{\text{light}} (CH_2O) + H_2O + 2A$$

where A may be O in plant photosynthesis or S or a reduced sulphur compound, e.g. thiosulphate. Stanier [2] has developed a concept to cover both bacterial and plant photosynthesis in the light of our present knowledge. He points out that the common event is the photo-excitation of chlorophyll with the expulsion of electrons, and that the result is the generation of ATP. From here there is a difference in the use of the ATP, either in the synthesis of organic constituents from $CO_2$ or from organic substrates. He believes that many photosynthetic organisms may be able to use organic substrates as can *Chlorobium* so that the use of $CO_2$ as the sole source of carbon is not fundamental to any photosynthetic process. Photosynthesis is unique only in the way ATP is formed. There is increasing evidence (see Chapter 3) that many of the photosynthetic members of the protoplankton, epontic, and tapetic communities may substitute $H_2S$, $H_2$ and other reduced compounds for $H_2O$ as hydrogen donor, thus indulging in both 'bacterial' and 'plant' types of photosynthesis, and extending their regime into anaerobic substrates. So far, photoreduction has been recorded for *Pinnularia, Oscillatoria, Synechococcus, Scenedesmus, Chlamydomonas,* and *Chroococcus.* I have grown oceanic phytoplankton (including the diatoms *Schroederella, Thalassiosira* spp., *Chaetoceros, Nitzschia, Streptotheca,* and *Grammatophora*) as well as the blue-green *Gloeocapsa* in Allen and Nelson's sea water (see Chapter 8) with 0·1% $Na_2S$ for 28 days. The original pH was 7·8, Eh − 140 mV, the final pH 8·0 and Eh + 230 mV, i.e. within the milieu of the purple sulphur bacteria. At the end of the experiment, all species were actively reproducing and chains of up to 40 cells were common, while the controls without sulphide (pH 8·0, Eh + 300 mV) showed only degenerating forms. It may well be that tapetic forms and many dominant species in the protoplankton gain their ascendancy by their ability to photoreduce. It will be seen in fig. 2 that the lower part of the boundary of photosynthesis has the same ph/Eh range as the purple and green sulphur bacteria, and this appears to have great ecological significance among the photosynthetic micro-organisms.

Photosynthesis in the water may be limited by the availability of carbon dioxide, by light intensity, or indirectly by factors limiting plant growth and reproduction. Because of the high solubility of carbon dioxide in water, this substance is rarely a limiting factor, except in conditions of pH mentioned in Chapter 3.

*Light*

Light intensity, however, is frequently limiting. Ryther [5] has shown that in cultures light intensities (8,000 to 10,000 foot-candles), comparable with full noon sunlight at the surface of the water, reduces the photosynthetic activity of diatoms and chlorophyta to 5 to 10%, and of dinoflagellates to 20 to 30% of the saturation intensity for these organisms. Cultures of the phytomonad *Dunaliella* grown at a light intensity of 350 foot-candles contained 4·3 times as much chlorophyll and the photosynthetic rate was 3 to 4 times that at light saturation. This explains why photosynthesis is often a maximum some distance below the surface of the water when the light intensity is high, as in the tropics. Sargent [6] showed that *Chlorella* grown in bright light has a higher maximum rate of photosynthesis than when grown in dim light, and that plants growing actively have a higher photosynthetic capacity, while, if growth is retarded by another factor, the photosynthetic rate is reduced. If grown in very bright light, the chlorophyll content is lower, but the rate of formation of chlorophyll is higher. In natural populations of protoplankton in the Sargasso Sea, Ryther and Menzel [7] found that protoplankton reacted differently to light in winter and in summer. In winter, protoplankton was fully light-saturated at 5,000 foot-candles from surface to 1% light-level, which is usually regarded as the effective limit of photosynthesis. In summer, the protoplankton from the 1% light-level behaved like shade plants and was light-saturated at less than 1,000 foot-candles. Kok [8] and Rodhe [9] have noted an increased efficiency of photosynthesis at low light intensities. Burke, Prager, and McLaughlin [10] have found that the dominant species in mixed dinoflagellate cultures could be selected by altering the light intensity, and this may be an important factor in protoplankton succession. Light intensity will also play a part in determining the depth at which different protoplankters occur. On one occasion I found that a high extinction coefficient of light at 4 m was due to a large bloom of *Prorocentrum micans,* while the main population of mixed species occurred between 75 m and 100 m. There was very little protoplankton between 0 m and 2 m and below 5 m. Such a distribution strongly suggests differences in light saturation for the different species, as a controlling factor in the horizontal distribution of protoplankton.

Light is quickly absorbed by the water, and little penetrates beyond about 450 m even in the tropics. It is further reduced by turbulence and turbidity, but is reflected by the numerous particles that are dispersed in the water. Different parts of the spectrum are differentially absorbed, the red end having greatest penetration. It is usually assumed that the depth at which illumination is 1% of that at the surface is the effective limit for active photosynthesis. *Compensation depth* is the depth at which photosynthesis is balanced by respiration, i.e. the depth at which plants can economically live. It will be realized from what has been said that the depth at which a given species photosynthesizes most actively will vary considerably with local conditions, and that different species will have different rates under identical conditions. As the respiration rate will depend on the physiological state of the cell, it will cause a corresponding variation in the compensation depth of the organism. Thus, the compensation depth may be expected to vary considerably from species to species, and also according to the physiological state of the organisms – rapidly growing, resting, or dying. Ketchum [11] pointed out that the compensation depth can vary with temperature, due to a differential effect of this factor on photosynthesis and respiration, and that different species have different compensation depths under the same conditions of nutrition. He also gives a useful table of compensation depths recorded for a number of localities at different seasons.

Table I

*Compensation depths in the ocean in various locations (after Ketchum, 1951)*

| Location | Month | Comparative depth in metres | Reference |
|---|---|---|---|
| Sargasso Sea | August | more than 100 | Clarke, 1936 |
| George's Bank | June maximum | 59 | Clarke, 1946 |
| English Channel | July | 45 | Jenkin, 1937 |
| Gulf of Maine | June | 24–30 | Clarke and Oster, 1934 |
| Loch Striven | Summer | 20–30 | Marshall and Orr, 1928 |
| Passamaquoddy B. | Summer | 17 | Gran and Braarud, 1935 |
| Puget Sound | Summer | 10–18 | Gran and Thompson, 1930 |
| Oslo Fjord | March | 10 | Gaarder and Gran, 1927 |
| George's Bank | April minimum | 9 | Clarke, 1946 |
| Woods Hole Harb. | August | 7 | Clarke and Oster, 1934 |
| Loch Striven | March | 5 | Marshall and Orr, 1928 |
| Helsingør Sod. | Annual range | 4·5–7 | Steemann Nielsen, 1937 |

Ryther [5] gives a mean value for the *compensation point*, i.e. the light intensity at which photosynthesis and respiration balance, as from 50 to 100 foot-candles, but this could be very different in tropical and Antarctic waters with different protoplankton communities.

Photosynthetic activity in the sea is an extremely complex phenomenon, and its measurement fraught with great difficulty, because of the diversity of the organisms concerned, and of their biological processes, that affect it directly and indirectly. At the present time, our knowledge of the subject is inadequate.

## Marine Trophic Systems

The gain in energy obtained by photosynthesis and by other autotrophic processes has been called productivity though this term has been applied by various authors in different ways (see Ketchum [11]). The non-photosynthetic autotrophs obtain their energy by chemical processes (*chemoautotrophy*) and add nothing to the total energy of our earth. If it were not for the gains from the use of solar energy the biological systems of this planet would ultimately run down, so that the photosynthetic systems have a special importance, and studies of productivity are usually applied to these systems. It is as well, however, not to lose sight of the chemo-autotrophic micro-organisms, as they do represent a considerable transfer of inorganic energy to biological systems, i.e. energy stored in the earth, since the reactions involved are exothermic (exergonic), and the free energy of the reactants is used by the micro-organisms.

The energy stored by the plants passes somewhat inefficiently to herbivorous animals, and thence to the carnivores. On land, the food chains are usually very short; plants are eaten by herbivores such as sheep and cattle, and these are eaten by carnivores, man being part herbivore and part carnivore. However, man rarely preys on the carnivores though he does his best to keep them in check. The process is completed by the micro-organisms which reduce both herbivore and carnivore to simple substances which the plants can use (fig. 7).

In aqueous environments there is a great deal more competition and a somewhat different biological arrangement. Except for the algae and water-grasses, which are limited to shallow waters and are not extensively grazed, the water plants which form the bulk of the photosynthetic material are minute, consisting, as has been shown, of diatoms, flagellates, and unicellular algae. These form the first link in the food chain. The second link is provided by the herbivores, and these are more diverse than on land. There are many herbivorous protozoa, coelenterates, and crustaceans (including copepods, euphausids, and amphipods), there are the tunicates and sagittids, as well as the phytophagous fishes such as the carps, the mullets, the milk-fish, *Chanos*, and *Tilapia* in the estuaries, and the pilchards and other Clupeoids in the oceans, as well as the young of many fishes which are carnivorous in later life. It is interesting that many fishes usually

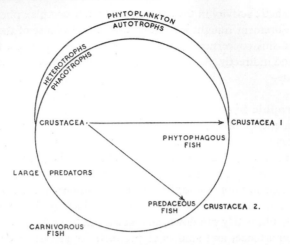

FIG. 7. The cycle of life in the sea, showing the autotrophs imposed on the system and the frequent length of the food chain.

regarded as carnivorous feed on algae at times. Frequently, carnivorous crustaceans prey on other species of the same group or other groups, fish prey on crustaceans and larger fish on the smaller ones, so that we have a food chain which is, on the average, much longer than that occurring on land. Each link in the food chain means from a tenfold to a hundredfold loss of efficiency and thus of solar energy. On the other hand, the turnover in the water is much more rapid than on land, as every cell of the phytoplankton can photosynthesize, and the individual organisms are short-lived. The cycle of life in the water is represented in fig. 7. The larger portion of animals and heterotrophic plants in the water form the lower circle in which the energy level is constantly decreasing. This means that there is a continuous cycle below and to an extent in the photic zone (i.e. the zone above the compensation depth). The energy lost by the cycle is continuously being replaced by that collected by the autotrophic organisms within the photic zone, and perhaps to a limited extent by the chemo-autotrophs, especially in the sediments. This pattern of events agrees with the well-known fact that a protoplankton bloom may have an effect on animal life at a distance from the bloom itself and at a later time. It affects the arguments about the relative abundance of marine life in warm and cold waters, and suggests a reason why the total production estimated from fish-market statistics is higher than that estimated from protoplankton production studies. If this conception is correct, the energy uptake is to be regarded as the hand that turns the wheel of marine life rather than as a portion of the wheel itself. Emery, Orr, and Rittenberg [12] have shown that fixed nitrogen, phosphorus, and silica are present in the oceans in great excess of their annual use; but that this annual use is far greater than the annual contribution from the land. Therefore, most of the nitrogen and phosphorus must be regenerated in the photic zone or in waters from which it can reach the photic zone by upwelling. This appears to give quantitative confirmation of the view I have just expressed. Although the energy required for life in the water must come ultimately from autotrophic organisms (unless the photocatalytic synthesis of organic matter is still possible) the total energy of the aquatic system must represent a summation in time. Bursts of productivity in past centuries could account for the animal populations of today. Against this, Emery, Orr, and Rittenberg [12] conclude that steady-state conditions exist because of the brevity of the renewal times of silica, nitrogen, and phosphorus and the character of the geological record which suggest that the total life in the ocean has been more or less constant over long periods.

**Heterotrophic Growth of Chlorophyll-containing Organisms**
One factor which has not been adequately considered until recently is the possible heterotrophic growth of chlorophyll-containing organisms. Lewin [13, 14] and Lewin and Lewin [15] have shown that a number of pennate diatoms and some centric ones can live entirely heterotrophically. Steemann Nielsen has suggested (verbal communication) that some Arctic red algae may also be able to lead a heterotrophic existence. The evidence given by Bernard [16, 17, 18], Bernard and Lecal [19] and Kimball, Corcoran, and Wood [20] and mentioned in the previous chapter, shows that heterotrophy (or phagotrophy) must be normal in a number of protoplankton groups. It is probable that the larger flagellates, particularly the dinoflagellates, rely on phagotrophic rather than heterotrophic growth. The genera *Heterodinium*, *Triposolenia* and certain species of *Ceratium* such as *C. teres* do not possess chlorophyll and their normal habitat is below the photic zone (Kofoid and Adamson [21], Steemann Nielsen [22]). Hutner and Provasoli [23] were unable to demonstrate heterotrophy in dinoflagellates, chrysomonads, cryptomonads, and coccolithophores which they have studied, though these organisms were active phagotrophs. Cultures of diatoms graciously supplied to the author by Dr Joyce Lewin retained their chlorophyll when grown in the dark for 11 days at various pressures to 500 m (Wood [24]), and chlorophyll-bearing diatoms have been frequently found below the euphotic zone on the continental shelf and in the oceans so the presence of chlorophyll does not necessarily mean active photosynthesis. Bursa [25] and Bunt and Wood [26] have found diatoms

attached to the under-side of ice floes and winter ice in the Arctic and Antarctic with minimal or sub-minimal light values. One naturally assumes that these organisms, when they occur in the dark, are living heterotrophically or phagotrophically. However, the possession of chlorophyll or the ability to form it when exposed to light has no survival value unless the pigment has some use in the environment. Other possibilities should be excluded before the obvious is assumed to be true. We cannot base conclusions regarding heterotrophic growth in this region on the amount of dissolved or particulate organic matter in the water because we can only sample the residuum of that which is consumed by the organisms. The relation between potential and actual photosynthesis of myxotrophic populations is an essential factor in any productivity equation; to evaluate this factor, we must know whether active phagotrophy or heterotrophy diminishes each organism's photosynthetic rate. Bound up with this problem is the production and re-utilization of external metabolites produced by the protoplankton.

**Diurnal Fluctuations in Protoplankton**
Studies of the productivity of an area are rendered more difficult by diurnal variations in the numbers and activity of the protoplankton. Doty and Oguri [27], Yentsch and Ryther [28], and Shimada [29] have recorded a diurnal fluctuation in photosynthetic rates at given stations and depths as measured by $C^{14}$ assimilation. Shimada, Yentsch, and Scagel [30] and Yentsch and Ryther also found corresponding fluctuations in chlorophyll. Wood [31] found that in waters of limited depth, e.g. Lord Howe Island, and on the continental shelf of New South Wales, the total numbers of protoplankton per square metre of surface throughout the photic zone decreased at night and increased during the day, but there was also a vertical migration. The same diurnal variation in numbers and depth was found in the open ocean. Hastings and Sweeney [32, 33] have demonstrated a diurnal rhythm in the bioluminescence of the dinoflagellate *Goniaulax polyedra* with a corresponding rhythm in reproduction and photosynthesis, and similar reproductive rhythms have been recorded for other members of the protoplankton. In the oceans, maxima or minima do not necessarily occur at the same time of day, which makes quantitative studies difficult. Interaction between grazing rhythms and reproductive rhythms out of phase with each other would explain this. Vertical movement of protoplankton, especially of dinoflagellates, has been recorded by Hasle [34, 35] as due to phototactic stimuli and the devices of other groups have been discussed in a previous chapter.

## Concepts of Productivity and Production

It seems desirable at this stage to define the various concepts involved in productivity. Unfortunately, many authors have used the words 'productivity' and 'production' indiscriminately, and the dictionary meanings do not help us much. Some people consider that productivity (or production) applies to plant material only, others to the whole biological sequence from plant to carnivore. My own definition of *productivity* as the *ability or potential to produce per unit of time* is essentially the same concept as that of Ohle [36]: 'the specific bioactivity of a system is its capacity for the formation of potential energy, and the subsequent conversion of this into kinetic energy per unit time and per unit volume (of water) or surface area'. I would define *production* as the *amount of material produced in unit time*. In these definitions, *productivity* is measured in terms of *energy* (energy available, energy used, energy stored, energy wasted), and *production* in terms of *mass*. Gross productivity becomes total energy absorbed, *net productivity* the energy available (after wastage, respiration, etc.). *Plant production* becomes the amount of organic material produced from photosynthesis, *gross production* being the total amount produced in a given time, *net production* that which is available for further use. Davis [37] has recognized the essential differences in the required concepts for a proper appreciation of the whole subject of trophic chains or cycles. His definitions are primarily in terms of energy and mass. He divides productivity into *energoproductivity, energoproduction, organoproductivity,* and *organoproduction.* The terms, though somewhat polysyllabic, are precise. Energoproductivity is the *potential* rate of storage and subsequent dissipation of potential *energy* from sunlight. Energoproduction is the *actual* rate of storage and dissipation of potential *energy.* Organoproductivity is the *potential* rate of formation of organic *matter* and its subsequent reconversion into inorganic. Organoproduction is the *actual* rate of formation and transformation of organic *matter.* In effect, productivity is concerned with potential ability, production with actual ability of the organisms or of the ecosystem as a whole. The terms *gross* and *net* are given their accustomed usage, and he then divides the eight concepts into primary, secondary, and if necessary, tertiary. He points out that one can then define production and productivity in terms of groups, communities, or species. *Standing crop,* defined by Clarke [38] as the amount of organisms existing in a given area at a given time, is related to net production, or in Davis' terms to net organoproduction. There is some difference of opinion as to the preferability of the terms *standing crop* and *standing stock* which might best be resolved by considering *crop* as related to plants, *stock* to animals, so that marine biological terms will be consistent with the agricultural terms for similar concepts. To get net production from standing crop, we need to know the rate of change of this crop, i.e. the production rate, and the material being removed.

The efficiency of production has been variously estimated by different authors for different water environments. Steemann Nielsen [39] considered that it is only 0·02% of the total energy throughout the oceans; Clarke estimates 0·3% for diatoms on George's Bank and 0·31% for Long Island Sound: fresh water phytoplankton has, according to Clarke, an overall efficiency of 0·043% to 0·038%. Clarke estimates the efficiency for fish production on George's Bank at from 0·00005% to 0·00025%.

There has been a tendency in recent years to treat marine biology as an exact science and to assess production and other parameters without due consideration of the biological phenomena involved. While much of this data may still be of limited value, and while the results have given a great stimulus to the study of the oceans, we are not at present in a position to draw too many inferences from the collected data. As Davis [37] points out, productivity has not yet been measured quantitatively and probably never will be measured with any degree of precision. In any ecosystem, there are so many environmental factors acting at a given time, so few of these will be 'average' at one time and the response of any organism to one factor usually varies as other factors vary so that in practice there can never be an 'average' environment. Moreover, there is always more than one species in an ecosystem and the optima of any two species are likely to diverge from the 'average' environment in very different degrees and often in different directions. Davis suggests that we can study the 'best combination' of environmental factors that may be expected in any locality, and that from this we may get an approximation to a productivity figure over a number of years. Even this is more likely to be true in limnology than in oceanography. However, in some cases, orders of magnitude may be significant, and I shall therefore quote some figures which are at least interesting. Riley [40] calculated the production of the oceans as of the order of 300 to 1,500 mg of carbon per metre$^2$ per day, and Steemann Nielsen [39] as about 150 mg per m$^2$ per day. Ryther and Vaccaro [41] reinterpreted Steemann Nielsen's data to give figures much closer to those of Riley. In comparing production of plant material on land and sea, Ryther [42] estimates the standing crop of the oceans as $1 \cdot 1 \times 10^{12}$ kg, of crops as $1 \cdot 5 \times 10^{13}$ kg, and of forests as $1 \cdot 1 \times 10^{15}$ kg. However, he estimates the annual production as $3 \cdot 6 \times 10^{13}$ for the ocean, $2 \cdot 2 \times 10^{13}$ for the forests, and $3 \cdot 0 \times 10^{13}$ for crops. Ryther points out that theoretical production figures mean little in terms of available food for human or animal consumption.

Mathematical models have been made by Cushing [43, 44] and by Steele [45–47] among others. These models apply only to certain places under certain conditions, and may be in error by an order of magnitude under other conditions and in other places. So far, none has been created which has general application even within the limits of an area such as the North Sea. One may be pardoned for doubting whether sufficient data exist, or whether the biological, especially the physiological phenomena associated with plankton are sufficiently known to warrant the creation of models at this stage. Margalef [48, 49] has tried to correlate the biological findings with other measurements such as the diversity index of populations, with chlorophyll and diversity of pigments, and has obtained some interesting results. He has also applied information theory to plankton ecology [50, 51]. Parsons and Strickland [52] have tentatively compared the assimilation of photosynthetic micro-organisms with that of heterotrophs. They gave figures of the order of $0 \cdot 1$ mgC per $m^3$ for the standing crop of heterotrophs, i.e. $0 \cdot 5$ to $1\%$ of photosynthetic production, but point out that photosynthetic and heterotrophic assimilation of carbon per $m^2$ of ocean surface could be of the same order throughout the oceans owing to the depth of the aphotic zone.

**Measurement of Productivity and Production**
A number of methods have been designed to estimate production and the most useful of these are discussed in the chapter on methods. Hydrologists have frequently used phosphate and nitrate analyses to indicate the productivity of an area, assuming that the two substances are limiting. A criticism of this is that phosphate is required by protoplankton only in very small amounts and may remain in organic combination through one or more heterotrophic or phagotrophic cycles, each organism preying on the previous one or utilizing organic phosphorus compounds before any appreciable amount of inorganic phosphate can be released by the bacteria or algae (Provasoli and McLaughlin [53]). Organic phosphate includes that of the living organisms as well as that of dead organisms, particulate organic matter and phosphate adsorbed on organic particles, so analyses for organic phosphate do not strictly represent living organic matter. Many hydrologists have assumed that plants require nitrate or nitrite, and use these as indications of the nitrogen available for plant production. In point of fact, many protoplankters from various groups can use nitrate, nitrite, ammonia, and organic nitrogen compounds. Some flagellates, e.g. *Dunaliella* and blue-green algae, use ammonia only, while some blue-greens fix nitrogen as has been mentioned. Once again, it is not necessary for nitrogen to leave the organic form throughout one to several cycles, as most

organisms can synthesize proteins from amino-acids and polypeptides (Fogg [54], Fogg and Westlake [55], Provasoli and McLaughlin [53]); tyrosine, tryptophane, cystine, and histidine, which have been shown to be present in fresh water lakes by Domogalla, Juday, and Peterson [56] doubtless also occur in salt water. The photosynthetic production of oxygen and utilization of carbon dioxide have been used as indicators of production (Gran [57], Gaarder and Gran [58], Riley, Stommel, and Bumpus [59], Steemann Nielsen [60], Strickland [61], and Allen [62]), and these methods are discussed in some detail in Chapter 9. Organic carbon is also used, but once again it is difficult or impossible to distinguish between that from living and dead organisms and detritus. I shall defer discussion of these measurements until I have described the methods, as some of the limitations are practical, some biological.

Our main concern so far has been with primary production, and the difficulties of determining this with any degree of accuracy have been pointed out. Such difficulties are multiplied when dealing with secondary and even tertiary trophic levels, so that we are far from even a reasonable estimate of production at such levels. It must be obvious that our biological and physiological knowledge of the organisms concerned and their qualitative ecology must be greatly advanced before we seriously attempt a quantitative evaluation of the marine ecosystems.

### Relationships between Plankton Organisms

It will be appreciated from what has been already said that the relationships between plankton organisms is complicated. The large and sudden blooms of single species can be explained by changes in intensity of illumination (Burke, Prager, and McLaughlin [10]), concentrations of nutrients or of growth factors, by 'non-predatory' relationships (Lucas [63]), or by reproductive pulses (Wood [64], Lanskaya [65]) related sometimes at least to lunar or tidal influences as reported for *Goniaulax* by Sommer *et al.* [66] and by Wood [67]. Such blooms may well be assisted by inhibitors excreted by certain species to keep down competitors (see Rice [68]). These inhibitors may be of great importance in lakes, but would tend to be dispersed in the sea until the dominant species had reached considerable numbers – except in calm weather, and it is in calm weather that the Californian red tides and the huge *Trichodesmium* blooms of the tropics occur. Steemann Nielsen [69] has suggested that algal antibiotics keep down bacteria, but phagotrophs such as dinoflagellates may well require bacteria to reach bloom proportions. Oppenheimer found (verbal communication) that bacterial numbers were high in the *Prorocentrum* red tides of California, but the meaning of this is equivocal. The bacteria could have been living on the exocrines from the dinoflagellates or serving as an alternate source of nutrition or both. Bacteria may also act to provide growth factors such as vitamin $B_{12}$ (Burkholder and Burkholder [70]). The form in which the nutrients occur may also be significant, e.g. nitrates to favour diatoms, ammonia to favour blue-greens and so on. Temperature, salinity, trace elements, substances such as iron (as suggested by Ryther and Guillard [71], and Menzel and Ryther [72]), or silica can control both blooms and successions in given cases. The magnitude of the problem of protoplankton blooms and successions is emphasized by the fact that some 200 species of diatoms and another 200 of dinoflagellates are listed as occurring with some frequency in Australasian waters, and some 80 species are abundant or frequent enough to be considered as indicators of water masses, i.e. are limited by temperature or salinity. The influence of exocrines, especially antibiotics and growth factors, will be discussed in Chapter 5.

**Grazing**
In considering protoplankton maxima, and indeed production in general, the effect of grazing by zooplankton must be examined, as the protoplankton we estimate is merely that left behind by the herbivores. It becomes necessary to know, at least roughly, the species present in the samples. According to Harvey [73] copepods and other phytophagous organisms are selective in their feeding, for example, *Calanus finmarchicus* tends to reject the diatom *Chaetoceros*, and it has been found in the author's laboratory that the nauplii of the barnacle *Balanus amphitrite* can live on and digest the diatom *Skeletonema*, but the green alga *Chlorella* passes undigested into the faeces and the animal dies on this diet. Larvae of the tube-worm *Gallionella* prefer *Chlorella* to *Skeletonema*. The grazing rate does not always depend on the nutritional requirements of the organisms. Some authors have found that the rate of feeding of copepods depends frequently on the amount of protoplankton present; when food is sparse, assimilation is more complete than when it is plentiful. Yanovsky [74] found that copepods prefer flagellates, including *Prorocentrum micans*, to diatoms because of the difference in size, and that they consume rounded rather than angular cells, irrespective of size, i.e. that feeding is selective. Single cells are preferred to clumped cells, so that rafts such as those of *Trichodesmium* or *Rhizosolenia* would be unacceptable for that reason alone. The presence of detritus in the gut of copepod nauplii may be due to the use by the copepods of the microbes adsorbed thereon as well as to the dissolved organic matter, rather than to the digestibility of the detritus *per se*. Harvey *et al.* [75] produced evidence which suggests direct grazing by copepods on phytoplankton. They calculated the quantity of phosphate taken from the water by the

phytoplankton and found it far in excess of the diatoms observed. Moreover, the faecal pellets of the herbivorous zooplankton contained diatom fragments, and the authors assumed that the zooplankton was grazing continuously. They also found that the animals ate many times their calculated requirements, provided the food was available. This agrees with the results of other workers who state that a number of plankton feeders pump a given quantity of water irrespective of its nutrient value. Unfortunately, Harvey and his co-workers do not record the microscopic examinations of faecal pellets or gut contents, but Fuller [76] found that faecal pellets of *Calanus* contained about half the nitrogen which had been present in the diatoms ingested.

Hardy [77] proposed the 'animal exclusion' hypothesis, which attempts to explain why zooplankton and phytoplankton maxima are rarely, if ever, concurrent. Hardy states:

> 'Vertically migrating animals which live for part of the 24 hours below the phytoplankton zone come up into that zone for a period inversely proportional to the density of the phytoplankton. The extent of the exclusion from the phytoplankton may vary for different species or for different stages in the development of the same animal.'

Harvey considered the lack of coincidence of phytoplankton and zooplankton swarms to be due to grazing, and there is evidence to support this view. It may well be that colourless protozoa often intervene between the phytoplankton and zooplankton and because they are small they escape the nets which have been usually used to collect phytoplankton. In centrifuged samples, colourless flagellates will usually be found to be numerous when phytoplankton is abundant, but their role has not been investigated. Kozhova [78] found that, during heavy protoplankton blooms, copepods avoid the blooms, but when the protoplankton is scarce or the blooms are light, the numbers of zooplankton increase with increasing protoplankton cells.

At present we have little knowledge of how much phytoplankton is grazed directly by zooplankton or how much is decomposed by bacteria or utilized by other saprophytic or phagotrophic organisms. It is thus very difficult to get a quantitative idea of the efficiency of production in the sea. There are a number of papers dealing with the quantitative aspects, with some good correlations between protoplankton (pigment analyses and numbers) and phosphate (see Riley, Stommel, and Bumpus [59]), but the methods used make it certain that the smaller protoplankton elements were not collected. Failure to include these need not appreciably affect the ratio between the other elements in the protoplankton equation, but must affect the total protoplankton and thus the efficiency. The hypothetical effect of grazing on a protoplankton population has been considered by Braarud [79], who showed that if one of two identical populations of 500 cells per litre suffers a loss by grazing of 10%, the difference between the two populations after 9 successive cell divisions will be 99,159 cells per litre, although only 12,343 cells will have been consumed. This calculation shows the possible effect of grazing on protoplankton populations, and, in the case of selective grazing, on succession of species. Given two species with identical reproductive rates, one being rejected and the other grazed at only a 10% level, the difference in population numbers could be between 1 and 10 million within a week. Lear and Oppenheimer [80] studied the consumption of a *Platymonas*, *P. subcordiformis*, by the copepod *Tigriopus californicus*, using both direct microscopic counts and radiological counts of $Sr^{90}$ and $Y^{90}$ for determining ingestion rates. They considered the direct method to give the most reliable results. Starting with a population of 500,000 *Platymonas* to 100 copepods, the grazed population decreased to 100,000 while the ungrazed control increased to 2,500,000. This gives the total number of cells produced in the grazed population to be between 1,000,000 and 1,100,000, the number grazed per day by each copepod as 4,500 to 5,000 and the *apparent reproduction rate* reduced from 2·25 to 1. The radiological counts gave 1,000 to 1,500 cells per copepod as the grazing rate. Marshall and Orr [81] found that the copepod *Calanus* could ingest up to 50,000 cells per day. Although these *in vitro* experiments cannot be directly related to grazing rates in the ocean, they do show that estimates of productivity taken from existing plant populations could be anything up to an order of magnitude lower than the actual production of protoplankton organisms in heavily grazed populations.

**Reproduction Rates of Protoplankton**
The second biological factor influencing the results of production studies is the rate of multiplication of the organisms, but, apart from a few studies, mainly *in vitro*, we have little information. Most authors who have worked in this field have not given growth curves, but have merely stated the generation times. Wood [64] stated his belief that dinoflagellates (*Goniaulax spinifera*), and diatoms (*Thalassiosira aestivalis*) have biological rhythms in which the rate of reproduction differs, and that there are even periods in which reproduction does not occur. He believes that these rhythms are intrinsic. Lanskaya [65], studying cultures taken from the Black Sea at regular intervals throughout the year, found that the generation time varies up to fourfold for a number of species of diatoms, dinoflagellates, and phytomonads at different seasons of the year. Wood [82] found that *Asterionella japonica* and *Chaetoceros secundum* remained in the logarithmic
G

growth phase during a bloom for 16 hours during which the net generation time was 4 to 5 hours. These counts were made in an estuary and did not take account of grazing. Lanskaya [64] found that *Skeletonema costatum* has a minimum generation time of 3 hours, *Carteria willei* of 6 hours, and *Chaetoceros socialis* of 10 hours, though the average monthly rates are several times as long. The other species that she studied had generation times of up to 48 hours for *Ceratium furca*. Wood, in his experiments, found that nanoplankton had a generation time of the order of 60 minutes. In *in vitro* experiments, under somewhat peculiar circumstances, he found that *Thalassiosira aestivalis* reproduced with a minimum generation time of 30 minutes. In the results of Lear and Oppenheimer, the generation time of *Pyramimonas* was about 10 hours, which is between that of *Carteria* and *Chlamydomonas* as reported by Lanskaya. Soli [83] found a minimum generation time for the diatom *Chaetoceros didymus* in axenic culture to be 11 hours. There are no estimates for generation times of such organisms as *Prorocentrum micans*, *Gymnodinium brevis*, or *Trichodesmium* during 'red tide' formation.

## Micro-organisms in the Food Chain

Grazing has so far been discussed from the viewpoint of its effect on proto-plankton populations, i.e. on primary production. Its bearing on the next trophic level is also worth examining. Considering the large number of marine biologists in the world, surprisingly little is known about food chains in the sea. A great deal of time is spent on the biometrics of fish populations, on studying and interpreting the extremely unreliable fishery statistics, on taxonomy, and on the study of fish eggs and larvae. Plankton too receives a great deal of attention, and estimates of production of seas and lakes are made for what they are worth, but the study of food chains is largely neglected. It is my belief that many cases of the depletion of a fishery are traceable to the mechanical destruction of the feeding grounds of fish and crustacea by man's thoughtless activities. In trawl fisheries, the passage of heavy boards and foot ropes stirs up the bottom and produces several serious effects. It causes turbidity, cuts off the illumination in shallow waters, and brings up the reducing layers of bottom sediments, thus affecting the respiration of bottom-dwelling organisms by lowering the oxygen tension. The suspended mud can well be carried by strong currents over the continental shelf, the trawl acting in the same way as the plough on land to promote soil erosion and devastation. Seaweed beds are destroyed together with the microbes that inhabit them. Evidence of the importance of these beds is given in Mururan Bay and Hakodate Bay in Hokkaido, Japan, where fisheries have been built up over the last century by 'planting' seaweed by strewing the sea bed with rocks suitable for the attachment of *Laminaria*. The seaweed holds the bottom in place, assimilates nutrients from the sea water and forms an ecosystem for the growth of micro-organisms and a shelter for the benthic fauna that feeds on them.

In rivers and estuaries, too, the hand of man can cause serious depletion by altering the course and flow of rivers by retaining walls and flood-prevention schemes, and by the use of heavy nets on the shallows of meandering rivers. Both of these forms of interference have been committed by man in the east coast rivers of Australia, with the result that banks once covered with *Zostera*, and carrying a large population of micro-organisms as epiphytes and in the oxidized surface layer of the sediment, are now devoid of plants and subject to stream erosion. Retaining walls at the mouths of rivers and lagoons have frequently been so placed that the entrances have silted up, e.g. the Manning River and Lake Macquarie in New South Wales. The result is a diminution and sometimes a cessation of interchange of water with the sea, and a consequent change in the biology of the river or lake. Lake Macquarie actually exhibits a landlocked 'oceanic' flora, as already mentioned.

### Diatoms as Food

The role of planktonic diatoms has been studied, especially in the North Sea and the Barents Sea. The ingestion of *Skeletonema* by *Calanus* (see also Harvey [84], Clarke [85], Marshall and Orr [86]) has already been mentioned. Clarke and Clarke and Gellis [87] believe that the diatoms ingested by *Calanus* are largely undigested, and that the organism lives on the bacteria and other components of the nanoplankton which follow the diatom blooms. Marshall and Orr, working with single *Calanus* in beakers, found that these organisms filtered between 1 and 40 ml of water per day, and digested between 59·6 and 74·6% of the *Skeletonema*. With a concentration of $10^5$ cells per ml the filtration was about one-tenth of that with a concentration of $10^4$ cells per ml. These findings do not agree with those of Clarke and Gellis, but the conditions of the experiment were not the same. It seems fair to conclude, however, that diatoms in excess are repugnant to *Calanus*. Manteufel [88] has given an interesting study of the relationship between diatom blooms and the migration of herring in the Barents Sea. The herring feed on *Calanus finmarchicus*, the euphausid *Thysanoessa*, etc., and these organisms feed on the edge of heavy plankton swarms. Table II gives his interpretation of the biological relationships of plankton in the sea. Manteufel makes the point that herring and *Calanus* avoid large blooms of the diatom *Rhizosolenia* and do not shoal while they are in progress. As the plankton bloom declines, the herring move on, in and under the region of the decaying plants, but although they become fatter they do not appear to feed. This paradox is probably due to their ingestion of saprobic organisms which were not found in the gut. Cushing [88] did not confirm the exclusion of herring by blooms of *Rhizosolenia styliformis* on the Dogger Bank at densities up to $5 \times 10^5$ cells per cubic metre. The herring do feed on *Calanus* in May and June, but shoal only after feeding.

In estuarine environments, the diatoms are extremely important as food for the mullets and other phytophagous fish, for molluscs (e.g. the whelk, *Pyrazus*), and probably for other benthic and planktonic animals. The mullets have an exceedingly muscular gut, and use fine particles of mud to grind the tests which are hardly recognizable when they reach the hind-gut. The mullets feed on the epiphytic diatoms rather than the benthic ones, and appear to prefer those epiphytic on *Zostera* and other sea-grasses. Peterson [90] gives a diagram of productivity in coastal waters in which he relates fish production to *Zostera* abundance. I have noted that, in east Australian estuaries (Wood [64, 82]), the fish feed on epiphytic diatoms and rarely if at all on planktonic ones. Darnell [91] recorded that phytoplankton was rare in the stomachs of fish and large invertebrates taken from Lake Pontchartrain, Louisiana; most of the food being organic detritus. In fresh water, diatoms are used as food by aquatic insect larvae, chironomids and Ephemeroptera, while the protozoan *Oxytrichia* can, according to Brook [92], ingest 90 cells of *Nitzschia palea* in 24 hours. *Skeletonema* is used as food by the North Sea herring, and diatoms formed the main food of sardines from the east coast of Australia. It is probable that the clupeoids as a group are phytoplankton feeders.

*Protozoa*

DINOFLAGELLATES. Protoplankton of tropical waters such as the Timor and Coral Seas and the South-west Pacific Ocean consists of large numbers of small, naked flagellates such as *Gymnodinium simplex*, *G. marinum*, and *G. nudum*. Whether these are used as food by zooplankton and fish is not known, but they are certainly of suitable size (between 5 μ and 15 μ). I have not seen the ceratia in fish stomachs, and rather doubt whether such long-horned species would be ingested by copepods or even euphausids. I have seen, but only rarely, large quantities of *Prorocentrum micans* and *Exuviaella marina* in the stomachs of mullet. Some of the *Gymnodinium* and *Goniaulax* species are toxic (see under 'Red Tides'), but whether this applies to oceanic species is not known. Bursa [93] has shown that dinoflagellates ingest other flagellates and diatoms, and I have seen dinoflagellates in salps and tintinnids.

NANOPLANKTON AND MICROBENTHOS. The nanoplankton and microbenthos consist largely of flagellates, and may therefore be considered
here. The work of Bruce, Knight, and Parke [94], Cole [95], Gauld [96],
Raymont and Gross [97], Marshall and Orr [98], and Lear and Oppenheimer [80] shows that the smaller flagellates are useful food for mollusca
and copepods. Davis and Guillard [98] found that while *Isochrysis galbana*
and *Monochrysis lutheri* produced good growth in oyster and clam larvae,
a mixture of these with *Platymonas* and *Dunaliella* gave even better
results. On the other hand, Ryther [99] showed that the flagellates *Nannochloris* and *Stichococcus* could not be assimilated by oysters or clams. We
have had good results in my laboratory by feeding the larvae of sedentary
marine organisms such as *Bugula*, *Watersipora* and *Balanus* with *Dunaliella*,
a coccolithophore, and chrysomonads. Loosanoff and Engle [100] fed
*Ostrea virginica* on a diatom and *Chlorella*, but considered that both were
lethal in excess. I did not confirm his results using *O. commercialis* and
local strains of *Chlorella pyrenoidosa* and *Nitzschia closterium*, but did find
that the pumping rate was increased and became continuous when the
oysters were fed these organisms in excess (Wood [82]).

It is very probable that the microbenthos is of great importance as food
for demersal fish, shrimps, and various molluscs. The 'organic detritus'
recorded by Darnell as forming most of the food of the fish examined by
him was no doubt rich in microbenthos. Oppenheimer and Wood [101]
have shown by fluorescence microscopy the abundance of chlorophyll-
containing microbes in estuarine sediments, especially attached to or
adsorbed on particles of the kind described by Darnell. I have recorded
that the mullets ingest microscopic organisms from the sediments by
stirring the mud with their pectoral fins, allowing the larger particles to
sink, and ingesting only the smaller ones. Analyses showed that these
particles contain the major part of the nitrogen and phosphorus of the
muds, i.e. the organic material including the microbenthic organisms
[82].

CILIATES. Kofoid [102] discussed the importance of ciliates in the
plankton. Of these, the most important group, the tintinnids, which live
in the vicinity of the photic zone in all seas and in all latitudes, graze on
bacteria and the smaller photosynthetic algae, being ingested in turn by
some other organisms such as salps and crustaceans. *Euplotes* and some
other ciliates are rejected as food by larval forms such as *Bugula* and the
barnacles, and in fact the larvae of sedentary forms such as tube worms and
barnacles died when supplied with cultures of *Skeletonema* or *Chlorella* if
the cultures were contaminated with ciliates, though the same stock of
animals lived on the same phytoplankters if the ciliates were absent. Many

ciliates such as *Lionotis*, *Colpidium* and various paramecia are characteristically present in muds and water with a high content of organic material. They graze on algae and bacteria, but their importance as food for higher organisms is not known. Many ciliates may live under anaerobic conditions, but they tend to show the Beijerinck phenomenon, i.e. migration to a zone of optimum oxygen tension, as can be seen by placing them under a microscope slide in water, when they will form a ring at some distance from the centre of the slide irrespective of the illumination. As they use anaerobic bacteria as food, they may be important agents in the translocation of nutrients from the lower to the upper layers of the muds, and from regions of lower to those of higher oxygen tension in necrotic plankton swarms, where they attack the dying phytoplankton and zooplankton in large numbers. Purdy and Butterfield [103], Butterfield and Purdy [104], and Butterfield [105] showed that *Paramecium* and *Colpidium* ingest bacteria in sewage-polluted water. When bacteria were filtered from the water, the ciliates failed to grow, but did grow after the addition of bacteria to the culture. The ciliates did not grow on the products of bacterial metabolism. Luck, Sheets, and Thomas [106] have also grown protozoa on bacteria.

*Blue-green Algae*
The planktonic blue-green algae in the sea do not appear to form an appreciable part of the food chain although *Chanos* may be able to digest them. The possible role of *Trichodesmium* has been discussed in Chapter 2. We do not know if the blue-green Nostocaceae associated with coral reefs are used as food by reef-feeding fish and molluscs, though it would seem probable. In mangrove swamps, estuaries, and rivers, these algae form an important element in the food chains, especially for fish. Brook [92] stated that 10 caddis fly larvae can remove in 14 days a dense felt of blue-green algae from 12 inches of *Myriophyllum* stem, and such rates of consumption can be expected from littoral and benthic animals. In the tambak (pond) fish culture of Java, blue-greens form at certain times the main food of the fish *Chanos* and *Tilapia*, and the ponds are emptied at intervals so that the blue-green algal mats can form on the surface of the muds. This method of fish culture depends on the growth and control of algae which serve as food for the phytophagous fish. For the younger fish, the blue-green algae are the ideal food, as growth and production are continuous, and the growth of the fish is steady; the green algae occur in blooms and are therefore ephemeral. However, the total productivity of the blue-green algae is lower, so it is found profitable to transfer larger fish to ponds where the green algae are blooming (Schuster [107]). Some blue-green algae associated with fresh water ponds are toxic to fish and to animals which may graze on them, but

this does not seem to occur in estuarine or marine species. Many of the Nostocaceae have a very high protein and oil content, and as many of these are nitrogen fixers, it would seem that they, rather than *Chlorella* or *Torulopsis*, would be the ideal forms to study if we are going to produce microbial forms as food. *Nostoc* is eaten by the natives in Fiji.

## Green Algae

The green algae are relatively rare in marine plankton, but are abundant in rivers, estuaries, and lakes, where they are an important food source. The genera *Chaetomorpha*, *Enteromorpha*, *Cladophora*, and *Ulva* are important fish food, though the first two genera often form in the spring the matrix of a heavy slime which deoxygenates the water during the night and during necrosis.

## Red and Brown Algae

*Ceramium, Polysiphonia, Bryopsis,* and *Ectocarpus* are found in the estuarine environment in fish stomachs, but to a lesser degree than the green filamentous algae. *Ectocarpus* is also an important component of blanketing slimes.

## Bacteria

The role of bacteria in making nutrients available for algae and aquatic plants has been discussed elsewhere. Their small size renders the bacteria available as food for all animal groups from the protozoa upwards, but the actual quantity of food material which they represent is the subject of much discussion. In the ocean far from land, bacteria are sparse (ZoBell [108]) and occur in large numbers only when associated with plankton swarms. They are also sparse in sandy bottoms (Wood [109]), but are abundant in estuarine muds and in the turbulent water above the mud. From direct bacterial counts it seems that there are enough bacteria in these turbulent areas to provide 0·1 ml per litre of water, so that, for example, oysters which filter 20 litres a day could obtain 2 ml of bacterial nutriment. Pourbaiz [110] has shown that sponges ingest bacteria, ZoBell and Landon [111] have grown mussels, ZoBell and Feltham [112] worms and oysters, Wood [82] oysters on a bacterial diet, although Gaarder and Spaark [113] believed on field evidence that oysters do not feed on bacteria. The fact that, despite adsorption, oysters can sterilize a body of water and free their own gut of bacteria, as has been shown by Dodgson [114], supports the work of ZoBell and Feltham and Wood. The self-sterilization of fish gut recorded by Wood [109] also suggests the ingestion and digestion of bacteria. Cviic [115] has also shown that bacteria can serve as food for the crayfish *Palinurus vulgaris*. The paucity of bacteria in the open sea may well be due to grazing by the zooplankton, as this scarcity is certainly not due to lack of nutrient material as is shown by the well-known increase of bacterial populations in stored sea water. If the figures of Braarud discussed earlier in connexion with phytoplankton are applied to bacteria with their short generation times, grazing must have an effect on bacterial populations at least 10 to 100 times as drastic as the effect on diatoms.

## Red Tides
So-called 'red tides', which may at times be green or yellow to orange, are a spectacular, and at times important, phenomenon in the oceans of the world. They represent outbursts of phytoplankton production, and are in effect plankton blooms, usually monogeneric or monospecific, being strictly homologous with the coloured plankton blooms in lakes, though on a much vaster scale. The organisms associated with red tides belong to three main groups, diatoms, dinoflagellates, and blue-green algae, though in estuaries, the smaller flagellates may form similar blooms. Of these, the most important in tropical waters are the blue-green *Trichodesmium* spp. which have already been mentioned. In temperate waters, dinoflagellates responsible include *Noctiluca miliaris* (sometimes with a green Euglenid symbiont), *Goniaulax* spp., including *G. catenella*, *G. polyedra*, *G. digitale*, and *G. tamarensis*, *Prorocentrum micans*, *Peridinium triquetrum*, *Gymnodinium brevis*, *G. splendens*. Many of these dinoflagellates are luminescent. Red tides have been recorded from a number of regions in the tropics and temperate waters, but only the *Trichodesmium* red tides would seem to be oceanic, although these do occur in shallow and restricted areas such as the Red Sea, coasts of India, Gulf of Mexico and within the Great Barrier Reef of Australia. Records of red tides are exceedingly numerous and only a few may be mentioned here. I shall quote de Sousa e Silva [116] (Portugal), Margalef [117] (Spain), Ehrenberg [118] (Red Sea), Gunter *et al.* [119], Galtsoff [120, 121], Chew [122], Walton Smith [123] (west coast of Florida), Bary [124] (New Zealand), Baas Becking [125] (tropical southwest Pacific and east Indian Oceans), Brongersma Sanders [126] (Walfisch Bay), Hornell and Nayudu [127] (Malabar coast of India), Subrahmanyan [128], Jacob and Menon [129], Prasad [130] (west coast of India), Carillo [131] (Peru), Mead [132] (Rhode Island), Conover [133] (New Haven, Connecticut), Hirasaka [134] (Japan), Smith [135] (Philippines), Whitelegge [136] (Australia).

Many of these occurrences are associated with the mortality of fish, e.g. Walfisch Bay, Malabar, and Florida. *Trichodesmium* has been associated with such mortality on the Malabar coast of India, *Gymnodinium brevis* in

Florida and probably Port Phillip, Australia. Another *Gymnodinium*, *G. veneficum* is reported to be toxic by Ballantyne [137] and Abbott and Ballantyne [138], but this species does not form heavy blooms, and is not associated with red tides. The red tides which produce mass mortalities of fish are usually of short duration and cause local consternation at the sight of innumerable dead fish washed up on the shores, with a short set-back to fish production. However, in some regions, e.g., on the Gulf coast of Florida, fish mortality is a serious problem. The species *Goniaulax catenella* on the north-west coast of the United States (Sommer *et al.* [66]), *G. tamarensis* on the Atlantic coast (Needler [139]), and *Pyrodinium phoneus* on the north-west coast of Europe (Koch [140]), cause a paralytic shell-fish poisoning which is distinct from the fish mortality. The toxin has been isolated from *G. catenella* and studied by several workers, and shown to be a neurotoxin. Bein [141] isolated a bacterium associated with red tides and toxic to fish. Many red tides are non-toxic. Subrahmanyan [128] considers that the *Noctiluca* blooms do not cause mass mortalities, nor do the *Prorocentrum* blooms of California, nor the *Trichodesmium* blooms in Australian waters.

The occurrence of red tides in the oceans has not been explained. I have seen them only in calm weather, in conditions of stability, but it may well be that they are harder to observe when the weather is rough. It is not easy to conceive a mechanism for the concentration of nutrients or of organisms in the open sea in a manner which would produce these red tides. Moreover, the Coral Sea, one region where they are frequently seen, is poor in nutrients. Ketchum and Keen [142] and Walton Smith [123] consider that phosphate is an important factor, but Chew [122] has stated that 'areas of definite *Gymnodinium* bloom, while high in total phosphorus, did not coincide with areas of maximum total phosphorus which was some ten times the normal value'. Such very high phosphate values could, however, have a depressing effect on red tide formation; I have found such values frequently associated in shallow water with strong sulphate reduction and the release of phosphoric acid (see Chapter 5). The production or concentration of vitamin $B_{12}$ (cyanocobaltamine) by micro-organisms derived from land, and the stimulation of *Gymnodinium* blooms by this substance has also been suggested as the cause of the Florida red tides (Ingle and de Sylva [143]). Innate biological rhythms causing rapid reproduction have also been considered. Ryther [144] (fig. 8) considers that the requirements for a bloom are: (1) a seed population; (2) favourable conditions for dominance, viz. temperature (18°–25°C) which is a little low for *Trichodesmium* and rather high for blooms of Arctic and Antarctic diatoms; salinity less than 30‰ (not applicable to *Trichodesmium*); nutrients, low nitrogen, and phosphate with organic matter (amino-acids); (3) concentration by wind and tide, as it is considered that there would not be enough nutrients in a given area to provide the number of organisms seen. Ryther's suggestions, which are derived from observation of the coastal red tides of the United States, are: (1) an onshore wind, driving surface water shoreward until it forms an undertow, the phytoplankton being concentrated just shoreward of this; (2) vertical (spiral) convection currents bringing the organisms to the surface and depositing them at the edge of the current; (3) river water flowing seaward and turning parallel to the shore line, forming a barrier against ocean water which is moving onshore with the wind, the red tide being concentrated at the interface. Such red tides are confined to a narrow band, usually near the surface of the water (fig. 8). Brongersma

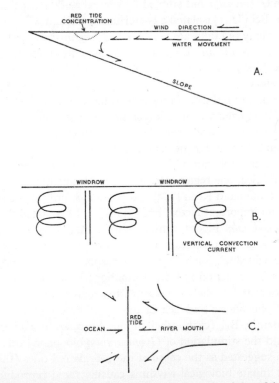

FIG. 8. Schematic representation of the suggested origin of 'red tides'. A. An onshore wind causing an undertow with red tide concentrated between the turn-under of the water and the shore. B. Spiral, vertical convection currents causing the formation of windrows of algae. C. An onshore wind holding river water and turning it along the shore. Red tide forms at boundary between river water and ocean water.

Table II

*Biological seasons of plankton in the Barents Sea (after Manteufel)*

| Property | Winter Dec.–Mar. | Spring April–May | June | Summer July–Sept. | Autumn Oct.–Nov. |
|---|---|---|---|---|---|
| Water temperature in upper strata | Minimum | Low, rising | Rising | Maximum | Decrease |
| Salinity in upper strata | Maximum | Decrease | Decrease | Minimum | Increase |
| PO₄ and NO₃ in upper strata | Increase to maximum | Rapid decrease | Poor | Decrease to minimum | Enrichment begins |
| Light | Minimum | Increase | 24 hours | Decrease | Decrease to minimum |
| Hatching of zooplankton | None | Very intense | | Some | Dying; cessation |
| Phytoplankton | Minimum | Sharp increase to year's maximum | Decrease | Local second maximum | Rapid decrease |
| Zooplankton | Decrease to year's minimum | Low, rising | Increase to year's maximum | Intermittent increase; second local maximum | Steady decrease |
| Production or consumption of zooplankton | Consumption | Production | Production | Consumption–production | Consumption |
| Change in state of plankton | Dying off of summer forms; winter *Calanus* | Flowering; protozoa; multiplication of *Calanus* and *Thysanoessa* | Strong development of *Calanus* and *Thysanoessa* | Summer flowering of warm-loving flora, Atlantic forms; descent of *Calanus* | Dying off of summer forms; winter *Calanus* Halophilic eurytheals |

Sanders [122] in her monograph on the red tides of Walfisch Bay believes they are caused by upwellings and the consequent increase of nutrients. While upwellings do occur in many of the areas associated with red tides, they could not account for the occurrences in Port Phillip, a shallow, almost landlocked bay fronting Bass Strait. Margalef [113] gives an intelligible account of the red tides of the Bay of Vigo. Here, as elsewhere, the blooms are superficial (less than 5 m), and occur when the Bay is stable hydrologically, and there is little interchange with the sea. Intrusion of Atlantic water stopped the red tide, which was not associated with the normal standing crop of phytoplankton, but appears to have an independent entity. The patches of red water were associated with intense vertical thermal gradients, and had a surface of discontinuity with internal waves at a depth of 2 to 3 m. Margalef considers that the prerequisites for a red tide are a phase of stability and a lack of circulation lasting for about 3 weeks; in the Bay of Vigo, the nutrients appear to be sufficient. It would seem that red tides appear under different conditions in different places, but it would be interesting to look for common factors in these occurrences. In most cases, sufficient information is not available. It is obvious that red tides are merely extremely large blooms of phytoplankton, and are governed by the same principles. In the case of the toxic red tides, grazing will be prevented by the exotoxins, but it is not easy to see why non-toxic red tides develop without a rapid concomitant increase in zooplankton production. Such an increase has not been recorded.

## REFERENCES

[1] LARSEN, H. (1953), 'On the morphology and biochemistry of the photosynthetic green sulphur bacteria', *Kgl. Norske Vidensk. Akad. Skr.*, **1**, 1, 199.

[2] STANIER, R. Y. (1961), 'Photosynthetic mechanisms in bacteria; development of a unitary concept', *Bact. Rev.*, **25**, 1–17.

[3] VAN NIEL, C. B. (1931), 'On the morphology and physiology of the purple and green sulphur bacteria', *Arch. Mikrobiol.*, **3**, 1–112.

[4] VAN NIEL, C. B. (1935), 'Photosynthesis of bacteria', *Cold Spring Harb. Symp. Quant. Biol.*, **3**, 138–50.

[5] RYTHER, J. H. (1956), 'Photosynthesis in the ocean as a function of light intensity', *Limnol. Oceanog.*, **1**, 61–70.

[6] SARGENT, M. C. (1941), 'The effect of light intensity on the configuration of the photosynthetic mechanism', *Chronica Botan.*, **6**, 347.

[7] RYTHER, J. H. and MENZEL, D. W. (1959), 'Light adaptation by marine phytoplankton', *Limnol. Oceanog.*, **4**, 492–97.

[8] KOK, B. (1948), 'A critical consideration of the quantum yield of *Chlorella* photosynthesis', *Enzymol.*, **13**, 1.

[9] RODHE, W. (1961, publ. 1963), *AIBS Interdisciplinary Conference in Marine Microbiology*.

[10] BURKE, J. M., PRAGER, J., and MCLAUGHLIN, J. J. A. (1962), 'Preliminary studies on nutritional and physiological factors which determine ecological dominance in phytoplankton blooms', *J. Protozool.*, **8** (suppl.) 7.

[11] KETCHUM, B. H., 'Plankton algae and their ecological significance', in *Manual of Physiology*, Ch. 17, Chronica Botanica, Waltham, Mass.

[12] EMERY, K. O., ORR, W. L., and RITTENBERG, S. C. (1955), 'Nutrient budgets in the ocean', *Essays in Honour of Capt. Hancock*, 229–310. Univ. S. Calif. Press.

[13] LEWIN, JOYCE C. (1953), 'Heterotrophy in diatoms', *J. Gen. Microbiol.*, **9**, 305–13.

[14] LEWIN, JOYCE C. (1963), 'Heterotrophy in marine diatoms', *Symp. Marine Microbiol.*, Ch. 23, C. H. Oppenheimer, ed. Thomas, Springfield, Ill.

[15] LEWIN, JOYCE C. and LEWIN, R. A. (1960), 'Autotrophy and heterotrophy in marine littoral diatoms', *Can. J. Microbiol.*, **6**, 127–34.

[16] BERNARD, F. (1948), 'Réchérches sur le cycle de *Coccolithus fragilis* Lohm. flagellé dominant des mers chaudes', *J. Cons. Int. Expl. Mer*, **15**, 177–88.

[17] BERNARD, F. (1960), 'Rapports charactéristiques entre les principaux unicellulaires du plancton denombrés en sept regions des mers chaudes', *C.R. Acad. Sci.*, Paris, 1–3.

[18] BERNARD, F. (1963), 'Density of flagellates and myxophyceae in the heterotrophic layers related to environment', *Symp. Marine Microbiol.*, Ch. 22, C. H. Oppenheimer, ed. Thomas, Springfield, Ill.

[19] BERNARD, F. and LECAL, J. (1960), 'Plancton unicellulaire recolté dans l'ocean Indien par le *Charcot* (1950) et le *Norsel* (1955–6)', *Bull. Inst. Oceanog.*, Monaco, **1166**, 1–59.

[20] KIMBALL, J. F. JR., CORCORAN, E. F., and WOOD, E. J. F. (1963), 'Chlorophyll-containing micro-organisms in the aphotic zone of the oceans', *Bull. Mar. Sci. Gulf Caribb.*, **13**, 574–77.

[21] KOFOID, C. A. and ADAMSON, A. M. (1933), 'The Dinoflagellata; the family Heterodiniinae of the Peridinioideae', *Mem. Mus. Comp. Zool. Harvard*, **54**, 1–136.

[22] STEEMANN NIELSEN, E. (1934), 'Untersuchungen über die Verbreitung, Biologie und Variation der Ceratien im südlichen Stillen Ozean', *Dana Rept.*, **4**, 1–67.

[23] HUTNER, S. H. and PROVASOLI, L. (1955), 'Comparative biochemistry of the flagellates' in *Biochemistry and Physiology of the Protozoa*, **II**, 17–44. A. Lwoff ed.

[24] WOOD, E. J. F. (1956), 'Diatoms in the ocean deeps', *Pac. Sci.*, **10**, 377–81.

[25] BURSA, A. S. (1963), 'Phytoplankton successions in the Canadian Arctic', *Symp. Marine Microbiol.*, Ch. 58, C. H. Oppenheimer, ed. Thomas, Springfield, Ill.

[26] BUNT, J. S. and WOOD, E. J. F. (1963), 'Micro-algae of Antarctic sea ice', *Nature*, **199**, 1254–55.

[27] DOTY, M. S. and OGURI, M. (1957), 'Evidence for a photosynthetic daily periodicity', *Limnol. Oceanog.*, 2, 37–40.

[28] YENTSCH, C. S. and RYTHER, J. H. (1957), 'Short term variations in phytoplankton and their significance', *Limnol. Oceanog.*, 2, 140–42.

[29] SHIMADA, B. M. (1958), 'Diurnal fluctuation in photosynthetic rate and chlorophyll content of phytoplankton from eastern Pacific waters', *Limnol. Oceanog.*, 3, 336–39.

[30] YENTSCH, C. S. and SCAGEL, R. F. (1958), 'Diurnal study of phytoplankton pigments; an *in situ* study in East Sound, Washington', *J. Mar. Res.*, 17, 567–83.

[31] WOOD, E. J. F. (1963), 'Some relations of phytoplankton to environment', *Symp. Marine Microbiol.*, Ch. 29, C. H. Oppenheimer, ed. Thomas, Springfield, Ill.

[32] HASTINGS, J. W. and SWEENEY, B. M. (1958), 'A persistent diurnal rhythm of luminescence in *Goniaulax polyedra*', *Biol. Bull.*, 103, 440–58.

[33] HASTINGS, J. W. and SWEENEY, B. M. (1958), 'Rhythmic cell division in populations of *Goniaulax polyedra*', *J. Protozool.*, 5, 217–24.

[34] HASLE, GRETHE R. (1950), 'Phototactic vertical migration in marine dinoflagellates', *Oikos*, 2, 162–75.

[35] HASLE, GRETHE R. (1954), 'More on phototactic diurnal migration in marine dinoflagellates', *Nytt Mag. Bot.*, 2, 139–47.

[36] OHLE, W. (1955), 'Beiträge zur Produktionsbiologie der Gewässer', *Arch. Hydrobiol.* (suppl.), 22, 456–79.

[37] DAVIS, C. C. (1963), 'On questions of production and productivity in ecology', *Arch. Hydrobiol.*, 59, 145–61.

[38] CLARKE, G. L. (1946), 'Dynamics of production in a marine area', *Ecol. Monogr.*, 16, 321–35.

[39] STEEMANN NIELSEN, E. (1954), 'On organic production in the ocean', *J. Cons. Int. Expl. Mer*, 49, 309–28.

[40] RILEY, G. A. (1953), 'Letter to the Editor', *J. Cons. Int. Expl. Mer*, 19, 85–89.

[41] RYTHER, J. H. and VACCARO, R. F. (1954), 'A comparison of oxygen and C14 methods of measuring photosynthesis', *J. Cons. Int. Expl. Mer*, 20, 25–37.

[42] RYTHER, J. H. (1960), 'Organic production by plankton algae and its environmental control', *Ecology of Algae*. Pymatuning Symp. Ecol. Spec. Publ. 2, 72–82.

[43] CUSHING, D. H. (1959), 'On the nature of production in the sea', *Min. Agr. Fish. Fish. Inv. Ser.*, 2, 22, 6, 1–40.

[44] CUSHING, D. H. (1959), 'The seasonal variation in oceanic production as a problem in population dynamics', *J. Cons. Int. Expl. Mer*, 24, 455–64.

[45] STEELE, J. (1956), 'Plant production on the Fladen ground', *J. Mar. Biol. Ass. U.K.*, 35, 1–33.

[46] STEELE, J. H. (1958), 'Plant production in the North Sea', *Scottish Home Dept. Mar. Res.*, 7, 1–36.

[47] STEELE, J. H. (1961), 'Primary production', *Oceanography*, A.A.A.S., 519–38.

[48] MARGALEF, R. (1961), 'Correlations entre certains charactères synthetiques des populations de phytoplancton', *Hydrobiol.*, **18**, 155–64.

[49] MARGALEF, R. (1961), 'Communication of structure in plankton populations', *Limnol. Oceanog.*, **6**, 124–28.

[50] MARGALEF, R. (1957), 'Information theory in ecology', *Mem. Real. Acad. Cien. y. Atres*, Barcelona, **23**, 272–449.

[51] MARGALEF, R. (1961), 'Algunas applicationes de la teoria de la informacion en el campo de la biologie y concretamente a la ecologia y al studio de la evolucion', *Scientia*, ser. 6, **55**, 1–7.

[52] PARSONS, R. T. and STRICKLAND, J. D. H. (1962), 'On the production of particulate organic carbon by heterotrophic processes in sea water', *Deep Sea Res.*, **8**, 211–22.

[53] PROVASOLI, L. and MCLAUGHLIN, J. J. A. (1963), 'Limited heterotrophy of some photosynthetic dinoflagellates', *Symp. Marine Microbiol.*, Ch. 10, C. H. Oppenheimer, ed. Thomas, Springfield, Ill.

[54] FOGG, G. E. (1957), 'Relationships between metabolism and growth in plankton algae', *J. Gen. Microbiol.*, **16**, 294–97.

[55] FOGG, G. E. and WESTLAKE, D. F. (1955), 'The importance of extracellular products of algae in fresh water', *Proc. Int. Ass. theor. appl. Limnol.*, **12**, 219–32.

[56] DOMOGALLA, B. P., JUDAY, C., and PETERSON, W. H. (1925), 'The forms of nitrogen found in certain lake water', *J. Biol. Chem.*, **63**, 269–85.

[57] GRAN, H. H. (1927), 'The production of plankton in the coastal waters off Bergen', *Rept. Norweg. Fish. Inv.*, **3**, 8.

[58] GAARDER, T. and GRAN, H. H. (1927), 'Investigations of the production of plankton in Oslo Fjord', *Rapp. et Proc. Verb. Cons. Int. Expl. Mer*, **42**, 1–48.

[59] RILEY, G. A., STOMMEL, H., and BUMPUS, D. F. (1949), 'Quantitative ecology of the plankton of the western North Atlantic', *Bull. Bingham Oceanog. Coll.*, **12**, 3.

[60] STEEMANN NIELSEN, E. (1952), 'The use of radioactive carbon ($C^{14}$) for measuring organic production in the seas', *J. Cons. Int. Expl. Mer*, **18**, 117–40.

[61] STRICKLAND, J. D. H. (1960), 'Measuring the production of marine phytoplankton', *Fish. Res. Bd. Can. Bull.*, **122**, 172 pp.

[62] ALLEN, MARY BELLE (1961), 'Evaluation of the $C^{14}$ technique for measurement of primary production', *1st Radioecol. Symp. Fort Collins*, Sept.

[63] LUCAS, C. E. (1947), 'The ecological effects of external metabolites', *Biol. Rev.*, **22**, 270–95.

[64] WOOD, E. F. J. (1959), 'Some aspects of marine microbiology', *Ind. J. Mar. Biol.*, **1**, 26–32.

[65] LANSKAYA, L. A. (1963), 'Fission rate of plankton algae of the Black Sea in cultures', *Symp. Marine Microbiol.*, Ch. 14, C. H. Oppenheimer, ed. Thomas, Springfield, Ill.

[66] SOMMER, H., WHEDON, W. F., KOFOID, C. A., and STOHLER, R. (1937), 'Relation of paralytic shell fish poison to certain plankton organisms of the genus *Goniaulax*', *Arch. Path.*, **24**, 357–59.

[67] WOOD, E. J. F. (1954), 'Dinoflagellates in the Australian region', *Aust. J. Mar. Freshw. Res.*, **5**, 171–351.

[68] RICE, T. R. (1954), 'Biotic influences affecting fish population growth of planktonic algae', *U.S. Fish. Wildl. Bull.*, **87**, 227–45.

[69] STEEMANN NIELSEN, E. (1955), 'The production of antibiotics by plankton algae and its effect upon the bacterial activities in the sea', *Deep Sea Res.*, **3**, 281–86 (suppl.).

[70] BURKHOLDER, P. R. and BURKHOLDER, LILIAN M. (1956), 'Vitamin $B_{12}$ in suspended solids and marsh muds collected along the coast of Georgia', *Limnol. Oceanog.*, **1**, 202–8.

[71] RYTHER, J. H. and GUILLARD, R. R. L. (1959), 'Enrichment experiments as a means of studying nutrients limiting to phytoplankton production', *Deep Sea Res.*, **6**, 65–69.

[72] MENZEL, D. W. and RYTHER, J. H. (1961), 'Nutrients limiting the production of phytoplankton in the Sargasso Sea with special reference to iron', *Deep Sea Res.*, **7**, 276–81.

[73] HARVEY, H. W. (1937), 'Notes on selective feeding by *Calanus*', *J. Mar. Biol. Ass. U.K.*, **22**, 97–100.

[74] YANOVSKY, A. Y. (1956), 'Grazing of copepods and their larvae in the Black Sea', *Trans. All-Union Hydrobiol. Soc.*, **7**, 271–73.

[75] HARVEY, H. W., COOPER, L. H. N., LEBOUR, MARIE V., and RUSSELL, F. S. (1935), 'Plankton production and its control', *J. Mar. Biol. Ass. U.K.*, **20**, 407–22.

[76] FULLER, J. L. (1937), 'Feeding rate of *Calanus finmarchicus* in relation to environmental conditions', *Biol. Bull.*, **72**, 233–46.

[77] HARDY, A. G. (1935), 'The plankton of South Georgia whaling grounds and adjacent waters, 1926–27', *Discovery Repts.*, **11**, 273–370.

[78] KOSHOVA, O. M. (1957), 'Interrelations of phytoplankton and zooplankton in the Baikal Lake', *Trans. All-Union Hydrobiol. Soc.*, **8**, 278.

[79] BRAARUD, T. (1935), 'The Öst-expedition to the Denmark Strait, II', *Hvalradets Skr.*, **10**, 5–144.

[80] LEAR, D. W. and OPPENHEIMER, C. H. (1962), 'Consumption of microorganisms by the copepod *Tigriopus californicus*', *Limnol. Oceanog.*, **7** (suppl.), 58–66.

[81] MARSHALL, S. M. and ORR, A. P. (1955), 'Studies on the biology of *Calanus finmarchicus* VIII', *J. Mar. Biol. Ass. U.K.*, **34**, 495–529.

[82] WOOD, E. J. F., 'Studies on the microbial ecology of the Australasian region'. MS.

[83] SOLI, G. (1963), 'Axenic cultivation of a pelagic diatom', *Symp. Marine Microbiol.*, Ch. 12, C. H. Oppenheimer, ed. Thomas, Springfield, Ill.

[84] HARVEY, H. W. (1934), 'Measurement of phytoplankton population', *J. Mar. Biol. Ass. U.K.*, 761–73.

[85] CLARKE, G. L. (1939), 'The relation between diatoms and copepods as a factor in the productivity of the sea', *Quart. Rev. Biol.*, **14**, 60.

[86] MARSHALL, S. M. and ORR, A. P. (1955), 'Experimental feeding of the copepod *Calanus finmarchicus* (Gunner) on phytoplankton cultures labelled with radioactive carbon ($C^{14}$)', *Deep Sea Res.*, **3** (suppl.), 110–14.

[87] CLARKE, G. L. and GELLIS, S. S. (1935), 'The nutrition of copepods in relation to the food cycle of the sea', *Biol. Bull.*, **68**, 231–46.
[88] MANTEUFEL, B. P. (1941), 'Plankton and herring in the Barents Sea', *Trans. Knipovitch Pol. Sci. Inst. Sea Fish. Oceanog.*, **7** (Russian).
[89] CUSHING, D. H. (1956), 'Phytoplankton and the herring', *Min. Food Agr. Fish. Inv. Ser.* 2, **20**, 4, 1–18.
[90] PETERSON, C. C. J. (1918), 'The sea bottom and its production of fish food', *Danish Biol. Sta. Rept.*, **25**, 1.
[91] DARNELL, R. M. (1961), 'Tropic spectrum of an estuarine community based on studies of Lake Pontchartrain, Louisiana', *Ecol.*, **42**, 553–68.
[92] BROOK, A. J. (1955), 'The aquatic fauna as an ecological factor in studies of the occurrence of fresh water algae', *Rev. Algol.*, **3**, 414–15.
[93] BURSA, A. S. (1961), 'The annual oceanographic cycle at Igloolik in the Canadian Arctic', *J. Fish. Res. Bd. Can.*, **18**, 563–615.
[94] BRUCE, J. R., KNIGHT, M., and PARKE, MARY (1940), 'The rearing of oyster larvae on an algal diet', *J. Mar. Biol. Ass. U.K.*, **24**, 337–74.
[95] COLE, H. A. (1936), 'Experiments on the breeding of oysters (*Ostrea edulis*) in tanks with special reference to the food of the larvae and spat', *Min. Agr. Fish. Fish. Inv. Ser.* 2, **15**, 4, 1–27.
[96] GAULD, D. T. (1951), 'The grazing rate of plankton copepods', *J. Mar. Biol. Ass. U.K.*, **29**, 695–706.
[97] RAYMONT, J. E. G. and GROSS, F. (1942), 'On the feeding and breeding of *Calanus finmarchicus* under laboratory conditions', *Proc. Roy. Soc. Edin.*, **B67**, 267–87.
[98] DAVIS, H. C. and GUILLARD, R. R. (1958), 'Relative value of ten genera of micro-organisms as food for oyster and clam larvae', *U.S. Fish. Wildl. Serv. Fish. Bull.*, **136**, 293–304.
[99] RYTHER, J. H. (1954), 'The ecology of phytoplankton blooms in Moriches Bay and Great South Bay, Long Island, N.Y.', *Biol. Bull.*, **106**, 198–209.
[100] LOOSANOFF, V. J. and ENGLE, J. B. (1942), 'Use of complete fertilizers in cultivation of micro-organisms', *Science*, **95**, 487–88.
[101] OPPENHEIMER, C. H. and WOOD, E. J. F. (1962), 'Note on the effect of contamination on a marine slough and the vertical distribution of unicellular plants in the sediment', *Z. allg. Mikrobiol.*, **2**, 47–48.
[102] KOFOID, C. A. (1933), 'The distribution of pelagic ciliates in the eastern tropical Pacific', *Proc. 5th Pac. Sci. Cong.*, **3**, 215–19.
[103] PURDY, W. C. and BUTTERFIELD, C. T. (1918), 'The effect of plankton on bacterial death rates', *Amer. J. Publ. Health*, **8**, 449–505.
[104] BUTTERFIELD, C. T. and PURDY, W. C. (1931), 'Some interrelationships of plankton and bacteria in natural purification of polluted water', *J. Ind. Eng. Chem.*, **23**, 213.
[105] BUTTERFIELD, C. T. (1933), 'A report on the food habits of *Colpidium*', *U.S. Publ. Health*, **48**, 28.
[106] LUCK, J. M., SHEETS, G., and THOMAS, J. O. (1931), 'The role of bacteria in the nutrition of protozoa', *Quart. Rev. Biol.*, **6**, 46.
[107] SCHUSTER, W. H. (1952), 'Fish culture in the brackish water ponds of Java', *Indo-Pac. Fish. Counc. Spec. Rept.*, **1**.

H

[108] ZOBELL, C. E. (1946), *Marine Microbiology*, Chronica Botanica Press, Waltham, Mass., 240 pp.

[109] WOOD, E. J. F. (1953), 'Heterotrophic bacteria in marine environments of eastern Australia', *Aust. J. Mar. Freshw. Res.*, 4, 160–200.

[110] POURBAIZ, N. (1932), 'Nota soba la nutricion bacteriaia de las Esponjas', *Notas y Resum. ser. III*, 64, 1–4.

[111] ZOBELL, C. E. and LANDON, W. A. (1937), 'Bacterial nutrition of the Californian mussel', *Proc. Soc. Exp. Biol. Med.*, 36, 607–9.

[112] ZOBELL, C. E. and FELTHAM, C. B. (1938), 'Bacteria as food for certain marine invertebrates', *J. Mar. Res.*, 7, 312–27.

[113] GAARDER, T. and SPAARK, K. (1931), 'Biological investigations of the variations in the productivity of the West Norwegian oyster', *Rapp. et Proc. Verb. Cons. Int. Expl. Mer*, 75, 47.

[114] DODGSON, R. W. (1928), 'Report on Mussel purification', *Fish. Inv. Ser. II*, 10, 535 pp.

[115] CVIIC, V. (1960), 'Contribution à la connaissance du rôle des bactéries dans l'alimentation des larves de langouste (*Palinurus vulgaris* Latr.)', *Rapp. et Proc. Verb. Comm. Int. Expl. Sci. Med.*, 25, 45–47.

[116] DE SOUSA E SILVA, E. (1953) (1956), '"Red water" por *Exuviaella baltica* Lohm. com simultanea mortande de peixe nas aguas litorais de Angola', *Trab. Miss. Biol. Marit.*, 75–90.

[117] MARGALEF, R. (1956), 'Estructura y dinimica de la "purga de mar" en la Ria de Vigo', *Inv. Pesq.*, 5, 113–34.

[118] EHRENBERG, C. G. (1830), 'Neue Beobachtungen über blutartige Erscheinungen in Aegypten, Arabien und Siberien nebst eine Übersicht und Kritik', *Poggendorffs Ann. Phys. Chem.*, 18, 477–515.

[119] GUNTER, G., SMITH, F. G. W., and WILLIAMS, R. H. (1947), 'Mass mortality of marine animals', *Science*, 105, 257.

[120] GALTSOFF, P. S. (1948), 'Red Tide', *Fish. Wildl. Serv. Spec. Rept.*, 46, 1–43.

[121] GALTSOFF, P. S. (1949), 'The mystery of the red tide', *Sci. Month.*, 68, 116–17.

[122] CHEW, F. (1953), 'Results of hydrographic and chemical investigations in the region of the "red tide" bloom on the west coast of Florida in November, 1952', *Bull. Mar. Sci. Gulf Caribb.*, 2, 610–25.

[123] SMITH, F. G. W. (1949), 'Probable fundamental causes of red tide off the west coast of Florida', *Quart. J. Florida Acad. Sci.*, 2, 1–6.

[124] BARY, B. M. (1953), 'Sea water discoloration by living organisms', *N.Z. J. Sci. Tech.*, B34, 393–95.

[125] BAAS BECKING, L. G. M. (1951), 'Notes on some Cyanophyceae of the Pacific region', *Kon. Ned. Akad. Weten.*, 54C, 3.

[126] BRONGERSMA SANDERS, N. (1948), 'The importance of upwelling water to vertebrate palaeontology and oil geology', *Verh. Kon. Ned. Akad. Weten. Naturk.*, 45, 4, i, 112 pp.

[127] HORNELL, J. and NAYUDU, N. (1923), 'A contribution to the life history of the Indian sardine, with notes on the plankton of the Malabar coast', *Bull. Madras Fish.*, 17, 129–97.

[128] SUBRAHMANYAN, R. (1954), 'On the life history and ecology of *Hornellia marina*', *Ind. J. Fish.*, 1, 182–203.

[129] JACOB, P. K. and MENON, M. D. (1948), 'Incidence of fish mortality on the west coast', *J. Bombay Nat. Hist. Soc.*, 47, 455–77.

[130] PRASAD, R. (1953), 'Swarming of *Noctiluca* in Palk Bay and its effect on the Choodai fishery, with a note on the possible use of Noctiluca as an indicator species', *Proc. Ind. Acad. Sci.*, 38B, 40–47.

[131] CARILLO, D. C. N. (1892), 'Estudios sobre las corrientes oceanicas y especialmente de las corriente Humboldt', *Bol. Soc. Geogr. Lima*, 2, 72–110.

[132] MEAD, A. D. (1898), 'Peridinium and red water in Narragansett Bay', *Science*, 8, 707–9.

[133] CONOVER, A. MCM. (1954), 'Observations on the structure of red tides in New Haven harbour, Connecticut', *J. Mar. Res.*, 13, 145.

[134] HIRASAKA, R. (1922), 'On a case of discoloured water', *Annot. Zool. Jap.*, 10, 161–64.

[135] SMITH, H. M. (1908), 'Peridinium', *Philippines J. Sci.*, 3, 187–88.

[136] WHITELEGGE, T. (1891), 'On the organism discolouring the waters of Port Jackson', *Rec. Aust. Mus.*, 1, 144–47; 179–92.

[137] BALLANTYNE, DOROTHY (1956), 'Two new marine species of *Gymnodinium* isolated from the Plymouth area', *J. Mar. Biol. Ass. U.K.*, 35, 467–74.

[138] ABBOTT, B. C. and BALLANTYNE, DOROTHY (1957), 'The toxin from *Gymnodinium venificum* Ballantyne', *J. Mar. Biol. Ass. U.K.*, 36, 169–89.

[139] NEEDLER, A. B. (1949), 'Paralytic shellfish poisoning and *Goniaulax tamarensis*', *J. Fish. Res. Bd. Can.*, 7, 490–504.

[140] KOCH, H. J. (1939), 'La cause des empoisonnéments paralytiques provoqué par les moules', *Ass. Franc. Adv. Sci. Sean. Sess.*, 63, 647–57.

[141] BEIN, S. J. (1954), 'A study of certain chromogenic bacteria isolated from "red tide" water with a description of a new species', *Bull. Mar. Sci. Gulf Caribb.*, 4, 110–19.

[142] KETCHUM, B. H. and KEEN, J. (1948), 'Unusual phosphorus concentrations in the Florida "red tide" sea water', *J. Mar. Res.*, 7, 17–21.

[143] INGLE, R. M. and DE SYLVA, D. P. (1955), 'The red tide', *Fla. Bd. Conserv. Ed. Ser.* 1.

[144] RYTHER, J. H. (1955), 'Ecology of the autotrophic marine dinoflagellates with reference to red water conditions', *Luminescence of Biological Systems*, 378–414. Frank H. Johnson ed.

CHAPTER 5

# Microbial Processes

---

Chapter 4 was devoted to the most important microbial process in the sea, photosynthesis and the immediate consequences of that process, the production and fate of biological material. The present chapter discusses other processes, some autotrophic (in fact, except for the photosynthetic bacteria, chemoautotrophic) and some heterotrophic. These processes were touched upon in Chapter 3, but the emphasis now is on the product rather than the manufacturer.

**The Sulphur Cycle**
The sulphur cycle is, from a geobiological point of view, next in importance to photosynthesis, and its potential milieu is essentially the same (Baas Becking, Wood, and Kaplan [1]). It is in part chemical and part biological (fig. 9). Sulphates are reduced to sulphydryl or sulphides by plants, heterotrophic micro-organisms, and chemoautotrophic anaerobic bacteria, which can act over a wide range of pH, salinity, and temperature, but are finally overcome at a $pH_2S$ of 2. Baas Becking and Wood [2] studied the sulphur cycle in sediments and have drawn up an Eh/pH diagram in which the reactions of the cycle are depicted (fig. 2). The area which delimits sulphate reduction in this diagram contains all the data which could be collated from other workers, field data, data from pure cultures of *Desulphovibrio*, from cultures on inorganic media with iron or hydrogen to provide a hydrogen donor, and on lactate, acetate, cysteine, and other media. In compiling the data, the authors were struck by the repeated coincidence of regions in natural and artificial sediments. This confirmed their opinion that it is the sulphate reduction which controls the pH–Eh of black sulphur-containing muds and thus the biological chemistry of the environment. Although, in the crude cultures, heterotrophic bacteria, ciliates, nematodes, purple bacteria, and thiobacilli were present, sulphate reduction predominated as long as the cultures were not illuminated, or until the sulphate was reduced, but re-oxidation of sulphide to sulphur, and presumably sulphur to sulphate, occurred at the mud-water interface, primarily due to the thiobacilli. In the presence of light, the green and purple sulphur bacteria took

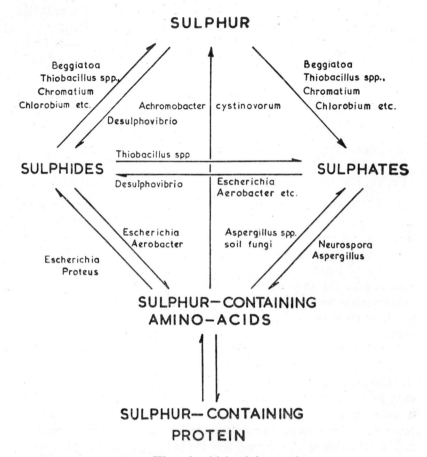

FIG. 9. The microbial sulphur cycle.

over, providing the hydrogen-ion concentration was not too great, i.e. the pH was above 4·8. In seeking an explanation of the action of the thiobacilli, these authors found that, contrary to general belief, these organisms can oxidize sulphur anaerobically, producing sulphates, and at the same time, hydrogen sulphide. This is the first instance of a biological 'auto-oxidation' that appears to have been recorded. The reaction of $H_2S \longrightarrow S$ is chemical reaction under aerobic conditions, i.e. is exothermic, but under anaerobic conditions, it is endothermic and photochemical as Baas Becking and Wood observed, although this had previously been recorded by Bunsen [3]. The green and purple sulphur bacteria catalyse the endothermic anaerobic oxidation of sulphides, while the thiobacilli catalyse the aerobic oxidation of sulphur to sulphate which is also exothermic. The anaerobic oxidation of sulphur to sulphate by the purple bacteria has been discussed.

It will be seen from fig. 2 that the purple sulphur bacteria have a somewhat restricted range of pH (4·8 to 10·5), but that they are active at relatively low and relatively high redox potentials. Actually, there are two regions of activity, one above and one below the $(H_2O_2)\!\rightleftharpoons\!(O_2)$ line, the former representing the oxidation of sulphide to sulphur, the latter sulphur to sulphate. It would appear that the purple sulphur bacteria occur in the region where hydrotroilite $\left( Fe\!\!<^{SH}_{OH} \right)$ predominates over iron sulphydryl $\left( Fe\!\!<^{SH}_{SH} \right)$ as these organisms seem sensitive to high concentrations of SH ion. The green bacteria on the other hand seem to require sulphydryl and are obligate anaerobes. Their activity in sulphide oxidation seems to be limited by very small traces of oxygen, and their upper redox limit is about Eh − 100 mV. That they are not reported more frequently is due to the difficulty of isolating them rather than to their absence. Evidence is accumulating that they may be expected in plankton swarms and in muds below shallow water whenever there is sufficient light, and that they are relatively common in the estuarine environment and on the continental shelf.

Vishniac and Santer [4] state that marine (estuarine) mud is the most reliable source of *Thiobacillus thiooxidans*, and that the marine strains of *T. thioparus* are generally more vigorously motile and grow more rapidly than fresh water isolates. Baas Becking and Wood found that, in the estuarine muds of eastern Australia, the predominant *Thiobacillus* was intermediate between *T. thiooxidans* and *T. thioparus* in its pH range. The original isolation of *T. thioparus* was made by Nathansohn [5] from sea water. The thiobacilli have a very wide range of activity, but this can be divided according to the type of organism and the substrate. The thioparus group has a more restricted range in the region of activity of the purple bacteria, while the thiooxidans group moves away to the acid side, with a steadily increasing Eh up to + 700 mV. The *T. denitrificans* group has a rather lower redox than *T. thioparus*, but occurs in the same pH regime. As its name suggests, it uses the energy of denitrification to oxidize sulphur anaerobically.

It will be observed that there is a considerable area wherein two or more bio-reactions overlap, i.e. they can proceed simultaneously. The greatest degree of overlap occurs in the area of the graph which has the characteristics of sea water and the underlying sediments, i.e. between pH 7 and 8·5 in the water with the sediments about 0·5 pH units lower. Sulphate reduction cannot begin until the Eh is lowered to a certain value (*circa* + 110 mV), and this can occur by bacterial reduction of organic materials such as cellulose, agar, alginic acid, starch, or the production of $H_2S$ or thio-compounds by heterotrophic or other agency. This action by heterotrophic or oxidative autotrophic (Butlin and Postgate [6]) bacteria is necessary to act as a trigger for sulphate reduction by *Desulphovibrio*. Organic matter also tends to poise the system, and thus stabilize it, although sulphate reduction can go on in almost pure sand. Although sulphate reducers can metabolize below pH 5·9, i.e. to about 4·2, no ferrous sulphides will precipitate because of the solubility of these salts at such pH values. However, free $H_2S$ will form, and the pH may drop below 5 and this will continue, the organisms remaining viable provided the pH does not drop too low; addition of alkali will, of course, cause the precipitation of sulphides of iron. Where there is much organic matter, the sulphur-oxidizing colourless blue-greens *Beggiatoa* and *Thiothrix* and the flagellate *Thiovulum* may occur. These organisms tend to form films at certain $SH^-$ tension. Such films are visible to the naked eye, and often form bag-like membranes about the substrate. The film formed by *Thiovulum* has a peculiar striate appearance which is quite characteristic. Skerman et al. [7] describe the oxidation of sulphides by *Sphaerotilus interna* in the presence of peptone. The organism was isolated from river and creek water. The utilization of sulphide by blue-green algae, flagellates, and a diatom has already been mentioned, and it seems that many microscopic algae can grow in high sulphide tensions, probably taking an active part in the sulphur cycle, in the same pH/Eh regime as the photosynthetic sulphur bacteria.

In addition to the autotrophic micro-organisms of the sulphur cycle, a number of heterotrophic organisms can reduce sulphur compounds, and plants, using sulphates as a source of sulphur, reduce these to sulphydryl to provide the reduced compounds of the methionine cycle. Such reduced compounds may be broken down by the plant to mercaptans or thioethers and excreted as such. Among the heterotrophic bacteria recorded as producing hydrogen sulphide are those which do so from organic sulphur compounds and those which reduce inorganic sulphur compounds. Frederick et al. [8] have given us information on the bacterial decomposition of organic sulphur compounds. They found that the ultimate product of microbial decompositions under aerobic conditions was $SO_4$ ion; under anaerobic conditions, $H_2S$ was formed from compounds other than methionine, but that this was broken down into methyl-thiol and dimethyl-sulphide. Artman [9] recorded the reduction of thiosulphates by *Escherichia coli* in the presence of pyruvate or acetaldehyde; sulphite, bisulphite, and sulphates were not reduced. Bromfield [10] recorded the aerobic reduction of sulphates by *Bacillus megaterium* in a medium containing ammonium sulphate and 5% sucrose, and stated that sulphates were not reduced by this organism under anaerobic conditions. However, the conditions of Bromfield's experiments were quite artificial, and I could not obtain sulphate reduction by a marine *B. megaterium* in estuarine sediments. Gunkel and Oppenheimer [11] studied sulphide formation on the German and Texas coasts in estuarine sediments, and found that the sulphide-sulphate ratios were not comparable. In some cases, the sulphide formed is much less than the sulphate utilized, and in others, the reverse is true. This means that in some cases part of the sulphate is used, presumably by plants (including bacteria) to form organic sulphur compounds, and in others, organic sulphur compounds are used to produce sulphides. These experiments do not give a clue to the relative importance of sulphide formation by the general heterotrophic bacterial flora. One would expect that in heavy plant growths, such as sea-grass beds or well-developed algal communities, a great deal of sulphate would be diverted to form the sulphur compounds required by these plants whereas, when organic matter is decomposing, sulphides would be released by the heterotrophic flora from this material as well as from the sulphate. It may be concluded that the chief organisms concerned in the sulphur cycle are the sulphate-reducing *Desulphovibrio*, the action of which is controlled by the preliminary reduction of the substrate by other organisms, and the heterotrophic $H_2S$ producers which may actually reduce oxidized sulphur compounds present in the organic component of the ecosystem or may transform reduced sulphur from the organic to the inorganic form; the oxidative purple and green sulphur bacteria, both anaerobes and both requiring light for their oxidations; and the thiobacilli, which are aerobic except for the *Thiobacillus denitrificans* group.

The effect of sulphides on the growth and silica deposition of diatoms has been noted by Matudaira [12] and Harvey [13] and confirmed by me (see Chapter 3). Lewin [14] has shown that the deposition of silica by diatoms is controlled by sulphydryl in the cell membrane. The tolerance of ciliates, blue-greens, and some flagellates to sulphides and sulphydryl has been mentioned. Braarud [15] found the coccolithophore *Coccolithus huxleyi* actually growing in the absence of oxygen and in the presence of $H_2S$ in Bonne Fjord. Some sea-grasses are very tolerant of $SH^-$, e.g. *Zostera*, *Halophila*, and *Posidonia*. Sometimes, in nature, the anaerobic zone of the black mud is at the mud-water interface as is shown by the activity of the purple bacteria. More usually, there is an oxidized layer, usually more sandy, in which the oxygen tension rises rapidly, and which contains a variety of organisms. *Zostera* seems to be confined to areas where sulphide is present, possibly because of the release of phosphate brought about by sulphate reduction (Baas Becking and Mackay [16]). Because *Zostera* is so important in the economy and ecology of estuaries, the relationship is an important one.

## The Nitrogen Cycle (fig. 10)

*The Distribution of Nitrogen and its Significance*

Nitrate nitrogen is required by most of the higher algae, i.e. most green, brown, and red forms, and is believed to be at times a critical factor in the productivity of certain marine areas. It is more abundant in cooler than in

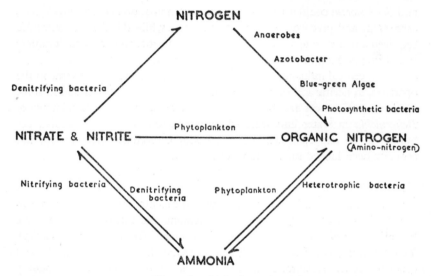

FIG. 10. The microbial nitrogen cycle.

tropical waters, thus no doubt accounting for the frequent replacement in the tropics of diatom blooms (requiring nitrate or nitrite) by blooms of blue-greens which utilize ammonia or nitrogen. Nitrate concentration also increases with depth, or more accurately with closeness to the bottom. This led Brandt [17] to conclude that nitrifying bacteria are lacking in surface waters, but are present in marine sediments, an observation which was confirmed by Waksman *et al.* [18]. In fresh water, in estuaries, and on the continental shelf, the sediment will have a greater effect on the water above than it has in the open sea, so the problem of nitrification is not so important in shallow regions. Moreover, the nitrate so produced will be released in or close to the photic zone, and thus be immediately available to the plant community. It is proven that many algae and phytoplankton organisms may utilize nitrite directly (Ryther [19]), and that, in the absence of nitrate-forming bacteria, the nitrogen cycle continues with minimal nitrate. Hutchinson [20] suggested that the predominance of the blue-green alga *Anabaena* or the diatom *Fragilaria* in fresh-water lakes is dependent on the ammonia–nitrate ratio when the total inorganic content of the water is very low, *Fragilaria* requiring nitrate, *Anabaena* using ammonia. *Anabaena*, however, fixes nitrogen, and the resurgence of *Fragilaria* mentioned by Hutchinson may be due to the fixation of nitrogen by *Anabaena* followed by the bacterial nitrification of the ammonia released during the decomposition of the algal bloom. Ryther [19] has shown that *Nannochloris* and *Stichococcus* could use nitrate, nitrite, ammonia, urea, uric acid, cystine, asparagin, and glycocoll as nitrogen sources, while the diatom *Nitzschia* required either nitrate or nitrite; thus the two former were able to dominate the phytoplankton in polluted Moriches Bay, N.Y.

The microbial influence on the nitrogen cycle is basically the same in the open sea, in neritic and estuarine environments, in fresh water and in soils. The main differences are the absence of *Rhizobia*, and so far as is known of *Beijerinckia* in water and water-dominated environments; *Rhizobia* are hardly to be expected, while *Beijerinckia*, a circumtropical genus, has scarcely been looked for in the water.

*Nitrogen Fixation*

The wide range of micro-organisms which can potentially fix nitrogen in the sea was mentioned in Chapter 3. Among the forms listed were the bacteria *Azotobacter*, *Clostridium*, *Mycoplana* (from *Pavetta* leaves), *Thiorhodaceae*, *Desulphovibrio*, *Nocardia* (Metcalfe and Brown [21]), and other aerobes and anaerobes, the Nostocaceae, *Trichodesmium*, and possibly other blue-green algae. It seems that the microbial fixation of nitrogen is widely distributed among organisms of the marine environment and may be of much greater import than has been generally realized. Quantitative studies on nitrogen fixation in hydrobiology have yet to be made. Jensen [22] remarked concerning agricultural nitrogen fixation: 'The most remarkable gap in our knowledge of the Azotobacteriaceae is probably the fact that after half a century of study we have only vague notions about the quantities of nitrogen actually fixed by *Azotobacter* under natural conditions,' and *Azotobacter* has been much more extensively studied than any other nitrogen-fixing form. The fixation of nitrogen in tambak fish ponds has already been discussed, and nitrogen fixation by Nostocaceae of the coral reef niggerheads may be of very great importance in the reef ecosystem, and so may the overall fixation by *Trichodesmium*. The mechanism of nitrogen fixation especially in *Azotobacter* has been extensively studied, and it has been shown that fixation may be inhibited by nitrate and ammonia. This probably fixes an upper limit of redox potential at which the reduction of nitrogen can occur. Molybdenum is known to be essential for nitrogen fixation, but should not be limiting in the sea.

I have failed to isolate *Azotobacter* from marine sources, including the estuarine environment and oceanic water at a number of depths to 10,000 m, using benzoate medium for the attempts at isolation. On a few occasions in the shallows I found bacteria morphologically resembling *Azotobacter*, but they either did not reduce nitrogen or else grew readily in fresh water and were probably of terrestrial origin. On the other hand Pshenin [23] recorded *Azotobacter* in all depths of water and sediment in the Black Sea, even in the presence of hydrogen sulphide, surely a strange environment for an aerobe, if it were active in nitrogen fixation! This author reported up to 24,000 cells per litre. He claims that the *Azotobacter* maximum occurred in summer, associated with the larger phytoplankton elements, which he believes supply the carbon required by the bacteria concentrated on the algae and in the sediments. Nitrogen-fixing clostridia have been recorded from the marine environment by Waksman, Hotchkiss, and Carey [24], moreover, Proctor and Wilson [25], and Hino and Wilson [26] have found other aerobes and facultative anaerobes which can fix nitrogen, though it has yet to be shown that such organisms are significant in marine environments. The actual role of sulphate reducers and purple and green sulphur bacteria in fixing nitrogen under marine conditions is not known, although Sisler and ZoBell [27] and Gest, Kamen, and Bregoff [28] have recorded the ability of these organisms to do so.

*Nitrification*

Nitrification is brought about by bacteria which oxidize ammonia to nitrite or nitrate. Carey [29] summarized the information available at the time on nitrification in the sea, and found that nitrifying bacteria occur in sediments and inshore waters but not appreciably in the open ocean. Nitrification was also associated with plankton. Spencer [30] confirmed that the addition of plankton, particularly of diatoms, stimulated the production of nitrite from ammonia in non-sterile but not in sterile sea water. The same effect was produced by sterile diatom cultures and iron. He concluded that iron, probably even particulate iron, is required for nitrification in the sea. Watson [31] has cultivated autotrophic nitrifying bacteria from onshore and offshore waters in the Atlantic Ocean and is studying their physiological characters. Hutton and ZoBell [32] found that autotrophic methane-oxidizing bacteria isolated from marine sediments could oxidize ammonia to nitrite and that the nitrite formed was quantitatively related to the methane oxidized. Fisher, Fisher, and Appleman [33] have shown that heterotrophic gram-negative pleomorphic rods similar to the *Mycoplana* forms recorded by Wood from marine sources, oxidized ammonia to nitrate in the presence of, but not without, soil extract, and such bacteria may also assist in nitrification in the oceans. We have, however, no evidence of the extent of nitrification in the sediments or of how frequent or active are the nitrifying bacteria in the oceans. As the nitrogen balance in the sea seems to have reached a steady state we must conclude that the process is adequate to maintain the ecosystem.

## Denitrification

Plants use nitrate by assimilation and conversion to amino-substances, and by photosynthesis using nitrate as the hydrogen acceptor in the presence (van Niel *et al.* [35]) or absence (Davis [36]) of oxygen, provided glucose and phosphate are present.

$$KNO_3 + 2(CH_2O) \longrightarrow NH_3 + KOH + 2CO_2$$

$$2CO_2 + H_2O \xrightarrow{\text{light}} 2(CH_2O) + 2O_2$$

Some bacteria convert part of it to nitrate, ammonia, gaseous nitrogen, or oxides. The importance of these bacteria was stressed by Brandt [17] who considered that denitrifying bacteria controlled the available nitrogen in the sea, and therefore phytoplankton production, and by Drew [37] who postulated that denitrifiers were the main cause of calcium carbonate deposition in the sea. Venkataraman and Sreenivasan [38] isolated 20 strains of denitrifying *Pseudomonas* from shallow water, but these strains required 1,000 p.p.m. of peptone for denitrification, and such a concentration would be rare in the ocean, but more frequent in plankton swarms, estuaries, and marine sediments. Vargues and Brisou [39] also discussed the presence of marine nitrate-reducing pseudomonads in the marine environment. Kefauver and Allison [40], in a study of *Bacterium denitrificans*, found that this organism, though it reduces the Eh from $+ 300$ mV to $+ 50$ mV, denitrifies only a little at $10\%$ oxygen, but does so markedly at $6\%$ oxygen. This would mean about one-fifth saturation of oxygen, a figure which would be reached only when accompanied by considerable catabolic biological activity. Waksman *et al.* [19] found no complete denitrifiers in the sea, and only one species in the sediments, though the organisms reducing nitrate to nitrite were relatively common, again being more numerous in the sediments than in the water. The bacteria decomposing non-nitrogenous plant remains utilize nitrate from the sea, and thus the nitrate of the water will be kept low in the vicinity of dying plankton swarms. In the sediments, the reduced zone contains ammonia rather than nitrate nitrogen, and in the surface layers, where denitrification to nitrogen is theoretically possible, there is usually a strong oxidative tendency, which is more likely to give nitrification. Denitrification can in theory be caused by a number of eubacteria, though only a few species, even of *Pseudomonas*, give nitrogen as the end product. Most organisms reduce nitrate only to nitrite.

*Use of Organic Nitrogen and Ammonia*

Heterotrophic bacteria make great use of organic nitrogen and there are many marine bacteria which use peptone and protein nitrogen, while others use amino-acid and urea nitrogen. Wood found that most marine corynebacteria can utilize urea nitrogen and so can many pseudomonads and other gram-negative rods and some cocci. Lysis of fish protein, gelatin, and milk is quite a common property among water bacteria (Wood [41, 42], Liston and Colwell [43]), while autotrophs and many heterotrophs can use ammonia to synthesize their own cell substance. The ability of many phytoplankters to use organic forms of nitrogen has already been mentioned. Guillard [44] studied the ability of a number of unicellular marine organisms to utilize organic forms of nitrogen. Of his cultures, the phyto-monad *Carteria* could use uric acid when adapted to it. This may have been due to the history of the strain as Guillard found great differences in the action of various strains of the coccolithophore *Coccolithus huxleyi*, depending, apparently, on their origin. Benthic species such as *Melosira*, *Coscinodiscus asteromphalus*, and *Cyclotella* could utilize various organic nitrogen sources quite readily. Estuarine and neritic strains used urea or uric acid quite readily, but the Sargasso Sea strains did not, though some of these could use glutamine. It seems that the ability to use organic nitro-gen sources varies with the origin of the clone tested, and such experiments as those of Guillard cannot provide information on the actual importance of such compounds in phytoplankton nutrition.

The effect of hydrogen-ion concentration and redox potential have been little studied in connexion with the nitrogen cycle in the sea. As all inorganic nitrogen compounds are soluble, this cycle will not have the same limiting effect on the environment that the sulphur cycle has, and it is highly probable that the poising of the sediment–water system by other reactions will control the nitrogen cycle.

## The Phosphorus Cycle

The phosphorus cycle in water and bottom deposits is believed to be a limiting factor in productivity, and there is some evidence for this. Taylor [45] has shown that phosphorus can limit bacterial decomposition of organic matter in fresh water, and other authors (Atkins [46], Redfield [47]) have shown the same thing for sea water. Plants require inorganic phosphate for their nutrition, and plankton swarms often deplete the water of available phosphate. The animals (including the protista) graze on the plants, and thus use organic phosphate, while the bacteria break down plant and animal phosphate to the inorganic state. Thus, the phosphate cycle differs from the sulphur and nitrogen cycles in not involving any change in the state of oxidation. Redox potential therefore will not affect the issue except indirectly, but hydrogen-ion concentration has an all-powerful effect owing to the insolubility of the phosphates of calcium and iron at the pH of most hydrobiological systems. It was formerly believed that ferric phosphate was only available to micro-organisms with difficulty if at all, although it is recognized that bacteria may regenerate calcium phosphate in several ways as stated by ZoBell [48]. These are: (1) generation of acids; (2) decomposition of organic matter associated with the calcium phosphate of bones mechanically liberating calcium phosphate; (3) production of ammonium salts; (4) conversion of insoluble tri-calcium phosphate into cell proteins and phospholipids by direct assimilation. Wood [49] has carried out some experiments which throw a little light on the question. By using a calcium or ferric phosphate medium with asparagin as the carbon source, the bacteria grew at a pH of 8·5. This corresponds to ZoBell's reaction (4). After some time, these bacteria, which had been cultured on the ferric phosphate medium for 12 months, were able to grow more actively on the calcium phosphate medium than they did on nutrient agar, and continued to grow quite happily on the ferric phosphate medium. With glucose or other carbohydrate as a carbon source, and calcium phosphate, the medium was reduced to pH 5·5, i.e. ZoBell's reaction (1) occurred. In nature, this could only happen in a micro-environment or in bays and lagoons at times of great stability, as sea-water is well buffered. Incidentally, agar-liquefying organisms lost the property of liquefaction on ferric phosphate agar, from which it would appear that phosphate can be a limiting factor in agar liquefaction. In sediments, the high iron content would bind most of the phosphate, except where there is sulphate reduction, but the fact that the bacteria can 'solubilize' phosphate allows for their abundance in these environments, and no doubt they serve as a phosphate source for higher organisms.

Phosphate utilization by the marine diatom *Asterionella japonica* has been studied by Goldberg, Walker, and Whisenand [50]. These authors found that in minimal amount required for growth, phosphate is firmly bound, but if excess is present this is taken up in the labile, water-soluble form. The strongly bound phosphate returns only very slowly to solution on placing the diatoms in the dark. This phosphate may be transferred to bacteria living on the decayed diatoms. Provasoli and Pintner [51] found narrow optimal ranges of phosphate of 4 µg to 10 µg per litre in natural waters, and consider that the amount required for maximum growth of phytoplankton is governed by the K/Mg ratio in the culture fluid. Goldberg *et al.* found that reproduction could still occur in phosphorus concentrations of less than 0·1 µg per litre. It is obvious that marine and fresh water micro-organisms require only minute amounts of phosphate for growth and reproduction, and that they can utilize even the most 'insoluble' compounds as a source of that element. Thus chemical insolubility is not a limiting factor to microbial growth, and phosphate could only become limiting in large blooms of phytoplankton where the demands are particularly heavy, and possibly where grazing is preventing the return of organic phosphate to the inorganic state. The turnover time of phosphate in surface water is measured in minutes and in the water system as a whole is about 4 to 5 days. It is known that some micro-organisms can assimilate phosphate still in the organic state and short-circuit the phosphorus cycle. To what extent this happens, and whether it can be a limiting factor in phytoplankton blooms, we do not know.

## Carbon Dioxide Utilization

Because the reduction of carbon dioxide is exothermic, animals are primarily dependent on organic substances for their carbon. It is left for the plants and micro-organisms to reduce carbon dioxide by means of photosynthesis or some other energy-giving (exothermic) reaction. Apart from the seaweeds and sea-grasses, micro-organisms are responsible for the assimilation of carbon dioxide in aqueous environments. Photosynthesis and its biological implications in hydrobiology were discussed in the previous chapters. The assimilation of carbon dioxide, using hydrogen sulphide or an organic hydrogen donor is of interest to us as microbiologists. It is now known that carbon dioxide is assimilated by both autotrophs and heterotrophs, although the heterotrophs do require an organic carbon source in addition to $CO_2$, while many if not all autotrophs can use organic carbon in place of or as well as $CO_2$, thus largely invalidating the distinction between heterotrophy and autotrophy (see Woods and Lascelles [52], Stanier [53]). As a result of the researches of Werkman and his co-workers

(see Werkman and Wilson [54]), we now know that all bacteria and protozoa require carbon dioxide and cannot live without it, and that it is possible
that all living cells need it. The last statement does not invalidate the distinction between plants and animals as the need for carbon dioxide is
primary in the photosynthetic and chemo-autotrophic organisms, possibly
primary but not evident in the Wood–Werkman phenomenon, and
carboxylation of bacteria and holozoic protozoa, and secondary in animal
cells.

The micro-organisms mentioned as members of the water environment
have the function of reducing carbon dioxide to provide the greatest part
of the energy for the whole aquatic biosphere, except in such areas as the
sea-grass and algal meadows, where larger plants make a significant contribution. In the deeper lakes, whether fresh or salt, in rivers and in the
open ocean, the planktonic and benthic micro-organisms form the lifeline
for carbon assimilation.

## Organic Matter

Organic matter is decomposed by bacteria and other members of the protoplankton, including many sedentary diatoms, which can utilize glucose,
fructose, and tryptone in the dark. Bacteria are certainly concentrated
packets of enzymes and can catalyse transformations which are otherwise
only possible by abiological reactions, which are often considerably less
efficient. Heterotrophic bacteria have in the degradation and translocation
of organic matter a biological and chemical importance equal to that of the
autotrophs, and like these they may perform many transformations that
cannot be brought about by larger organisms. I have mentioned heterotrophy among the diatoms and the possibility that fungi may play an
important part in the degradation of organic matter in the sea, especially
in the surface sediments. Unfortunately we do not know whether these
organisms are important in this process, so it is not profitable to discuss
them further at this stage. We do know a great deal about the effectiveness
of the marine bacteria in such processes from the work of ZoBell and his
colleagues over the years, and that of Cviic, Kriss and of those who have
studied fish spoilage and the heterotrophic bacterial flora of fish and other
marine animals. Liston and Colwell [44] found that, as Wood had predicted,
the bacterial flora varied with different hosts and that there was also
considerable geographic variation. As well as a difference in generic ratios,
there is a difference in proteolytic and reductive capacity of the organisms;
bacteria from vertebrate hosts were generally more active biochemically
than those from invertebrates.

In the degradation of organic matter, the end products differ according to the environment. Under anaerobic conditions, such as occur in sediments and red tide blooms, the final products are methane and hydrogen, together with a certain amount of carbon dioxide, nitrogen, and hydrogen sulphide produced directly or indirectly from organic matter. Much of the nitrogen thus formed is no doubt combined again by anaerobic nitrogen fixers, the sulphides are oxidized by the sulphur bacteria, and the methane and hydrogen are normally used by the 'knallgas' bacteria as they are formed. However, if there is a great excess of organic matter, some of these gases are given off, resulting in marsh gas in swamps and shallow lagoons, and natural gas where coal formation has begun. Under aerobic conditions, however, the decomposition of organic matter is incomplete. Carbohydrates are broken down by heterotrophs to lactic, pyruvic, butyric, and other acids, and by some bacteria, principally gram-negative rods, to carbon dioxide. Strangely enough, the carbon-dioxide forming bacteria are not autochthonous in sea water and probably not in fresh water. Proteins are broken down to simpler amino-compounds or oxidized to nitrate by nitrifying bacteria in the sediments and shallow waters. The release of inorganic phosphate from organic has been mentioned. Bacteria can use minute quantities of phosphate, e.g. the ionized amount of ferric phosphate, either by making direct use of its very limited solubility or by solubilizing it with hydroxy-acids. The release of phosphate by sulphate reducers has already been discussed.

All these reactions are of the utmost importance in maintaining productivity and are necessary for the continued growth of higher organisms in the sea. The bacterial substance is also used by protozoa and other holozoic organisms as food.

In addition to the activity of aquatic bacteria in assisting plant production by producing or converting inorganic substances, their capability of attacking and altering organic compounds is also interesting. The greatest concentration of bacteria in association with plankton swarms is found during the death phase of the latter and in the bottom deposits or sediments, especially at the water interface (see ZoBell [48]), wherever, in fact, their potential activity is greatest. They make use of dead and dying plant and animal material and their active enzymes are to some extent assisted by autolysis. In aqueous environments, one finds bacteria with enzymes capable of attacking all organic substances present in the milieu, with the exception perhaps of some of the carotenoids which have been reported from ancient sediments by Fox and Anderson [56], Fox, Updegraff, and Novelli [57], and Fox [58]. Of course no strain possesses all the enzymes, but one often finds bacteria with enzymes which are of no use in their

I

particular regimes, e.g. the agar digesters frequently found in soils and plankton swarms.

The saprophytic heterotrophs may be divided as follows:

Proteolytic: Gelatin liquefying bacteria
Bacteria digesting fish protein but not necessarily gelatin
Bacteria attacking peptones, polypeptides, amino-acids, and thio-compounds
Urea digesters and trimethylamine-oxide reducers
Carbohydrate hydrolysers: Bacteria attacking sugars, starches, celluloses, agar, alginic acid, chitin, lignin
Fat Splitters
Bacteria decomposing aromatic compounds such as phenols.

Various authors have ascribed carbohydrate hydrolysis specifically to the micrococci, trimethylamine-oxide reduction to *Achromobacter*, and proteolysis to *Pseudomonas*, but this segregation of generic activity breaks down so frequently that it is unwise to carry such generalizations too far. Wood [34, 41] has found micrococci which attack protein, and trimethylamine-oxide, proteolytic corynebacteria, and more occasionally saccharolytic pseudomonads. Even cellulose digestion is not confined to a single genus, since both the eubacteria and the cytophagas have representatives which carry out this important degradation.

## Iron

Iron bacteria oxidize ferrous iron to ferric, forming tubes of pectic material impregnated with ferric hydroxide, the bacteria occurring at the ends of these tubes. Pringsheim believed that these organisms could not occur in sea water owing to the absence of ferrous carbonate. However, Baas Becking, Wood, and Kaplan [59] have recorded their occurrence in estuarine waters at a pH above 8 and shown that they are gradient organisms as already stated.

## Methane and Hydrogen

Methane and hydrogen, produced by a number of microbial degradations, are oxidized by certain autotrophic bacteria, *Methanomonas* and *Hydrogenomonas*. Hutton and ZoBell [60] have shown the existence of these in marine environments. In addition, hydrogen is, of course, oxidized by the bacteria of the sulphur cycle.

## Luminescence of Micro-organisms

Apart from insects and fungi, most luminous organisms occur in water. This is probably highly significant, and it is generally considered that sodium chloride is required in the luciferin–luciferase reaction to produce luminescence. Plant luminescence is continuous, while animal luminescence is discontinuous and requires a trigger mechanism. Some forms of animal luminescence are caused by bacteria as in the case of certain fish which have luminous glands which sustain luminous bacteria, and are either reversible or fitted with a blind, so that the discontinuity is mechanical while the luminosity is continuous. Luminous bacteria occur, not only in fish glands, but also in sea water, rotting fish, and other places. As a group, they do not retain their luminosity in sub-culture. I have isolated a number of luminous cultures, but they have all lost this property after a time on artificial media. In 1954, Dr Haneda of Tokyo presented Scripps Institution of Oceanography with some of his cultures of luminous bacteria isolated from fish, but all the strains soon lost their luminescence. Sea water media were used in all cases.

Among luminous micro-organisms are the dinoflagellates *Noctiluca*, many species of *Peridinium, Goniaulax, Ceratium*, and *Prorocentrum*, several of which form red tides, and some of the Radiolaria. These require a stimulus, e.g. a rowing boat passing through the plankton bloom. The same result can be obtained in cultures of *Ceratium tripos* and *Peridinium triquetrum* by shaking the cultures, the stimulus being oxygen which is required for the luciferin–luciferase reaction.

## REFERENCES

[1] BAAS BECKING, L. G. M., WOOD, E. J. F., and KAPLAN, I. R. (1957), 'Biological processes in the estuarine environment, X', *Kon. Ned. Akad. Weten. Proc.*, **B60**, 88–102.
[2] BAAS BECKING, L. G. M. and WOOD, E. J. F. (1955), 'Biological processes in the estuarine environment, I, II', *Kon. Ned. Akad. Weten. Proc.*, **B58**, 160–181.
[3] BUNSEN, H. (1893), 'Über der Einfluss des Lichtes auf Bakterien und über die Selbstreinigung der Flusse', *Arch. Hydrobiol.*, **17**, 179.
[4] VISHNIAC, W. and SANTER, M. (1957), 'The Thiobacilli', *Bact. Rev.*, **21**, 195–213.
[5] NATHANSOHN, A. (1902), 'Über eine neue Gruppe von Schwefelbakterien und ihre Stoffwechsel', *Mitt. Zool. Sta. Neapel*, **15**, 655–80.
[6] BUTLIN, K. R. and POSTGATE, J. R. (1954), 'The microbiological formation of sulphur in the Cyrenaican lakes', *Biology of Deserts*, **112**, Inst. Biol. Lond.
[7] SKERMAN, V. B. D., DEMENTJIVA, G., and CAREY, BARBARA J. (1957), 'Intracellular deposition of sulphur by *Sphaerotilus nitans*', *J. Bact.*, **73**, 504–12.

[8] FREDERICK, L. R., STARKEY, R. L., and SEGAL, W. (1957), 'Decomposibility of some organic sulphur compounds in soil', *Proc. Soil Sci. Soc. Amer.*, 21, 287–92.

[9] ARTMAN, M. (1956), 'The production of hydrogen sulphide from thiosulphate by *Escherichia coli*', *J. Gen. Microbiol.*, 14, 315–22.

[10] BROMFIELD, S. M. (1953), 'Sulphate reduction in a partly sterilized soil exposed to air', *J. gen. Microbiol.*, 8, 378–90.

[11] GUNKEL, W. and OPPENHEIMER, C. H. (1963), 'Experiments regarding the sulphide formation in sediments of the Texas Gulf coast', *Symp. Marine Microbiol.*, Ch. 63, C. H. Oppenheimer, ed. Thomas, Springfield, Ill.

[12] MATUDAIRA, T. (1942), 'On organic sulphides as a growth promoting ingredient for diatoms', *Proc. Imp. Acad. Tokyo*, 18, 108–116.

[13] HARVEY, H. W. (1955), *The Chemistry and Fertility of Sea Water*, Cambridge University Press, 244 pp.

[14] LEWIN, JOYCE C. (1954), 'Silicon metabolism in diatoms', *J. Gen. Physiol.*, 37, 589–99.

[15] BRAARUD, T. (1955), 'The effect of pollution by sewage on the waters of Oslo Fjord', *Proc. Int. Ass. theor. appl. Limnol.*, 12, 811–13.

[16] BAAS BECKING, L. G. M. and MACKAY, MARGARET (1956), 'Biological processes in the estuarine environment. V', *Kon. Ned. Akad. Weten. Proc.*, **B59**, 109–23.

[17] BRANDT, K. (1923–1937), 'Stickstoffverbindungen im Meere', *Wiss. Meeres. Kiel.*, 20, 202.

[18] WAKSMAN, S. A., REUSZER, H. W., CAREY, C. L., HOTCHKISS, M., and RENN, C. E. (1933), 'Studies on the biology and chemistry of the Gulf of Maine, III', *Biol. Bull.*, 64, 183–205.

[19] RYTHER, J. H. (1954), 'The ecology of phytoplankton blooms in Moriches Bay and Great South Bay, Long Island, N.Y.', *Biol. Bull.*, 106, 189–209.

[20] HUTCHINSON, G. E. (1944), 'Limnological studies in Connecticut, VII', *Ecology*, 23, 3–26.

[21] METCALFE, G. and BROWN, M. E. (1957), 'Nitrogen fixation by a new species of *Nocardia*', *J. Gen. Microbiol.*, 17, 567–72.

[22] JENSEN, H. L. (1954), 'The Azotobacteriaceae', *Bact. Rev.*, 18, 195–210.

[23] PSHENIN, L. N. (1963), 'Distribution and ecology of *Azotobacter* in the Black Sea', *Symp. Marine Microbiol.*, Ch. 36, C. H. Oppenheimer, ed. Thomas, Springfield, Ill.

[24] WAKSMAN, S. A., HOTCHKISS, MARGARET, and CAREY, CORNELIA L. (1933), 'Marine bacteria and their role in the cycle of life in the sea, II', *Biol. Bull.*, 65, 137–67.

[25] PROCTOR, M. H. and WILSON, P. W. (1958), 'Nitrogen fixation by gram-negative bacteria', *Nature*, 182, 891.

[26] HINO, S. and WILSON, P. W. (1958), 'Nitrogen fixation by a facultative bacillus', *J. Bact.*, 75, 403–8.

[27] SISLER, F. D. and ZOBELL, C. E. (1951), 'Nitrogen fixation by sulphate-reducing bacteria indicated by nitrogen/argon ratios', *Science*, 113, 511–12.

[28] GEST, H. KAMEN, D., and BREGOFF, H. M. (1950), 'Studies in the meta-bolism of photosynthetic bacteria, V', *J. Gen. Physiol.*, 26, 241.

[29] CAREY, CORNELIA L. (1938), 'The occurrence and distribution of nitrifying bacteria in the sea', *J. Mar. Res.*, 1, 291–304.

[30] SPENCER, C. P. (1956), 'The bacterial oxidation of ammonia in the sea', *J. Mar. Biol. Ass. U.K.*, 35, 621–30.

[31] WATSON, S. W. (1963), 'Autotrophic nitrification in the oceans', *Symp. Marine Microbiol.*, Ch. 7, C. H. Oppenheimer, ed. Thomas, Springfield, Ill.

[32] HUTTON, W. E. and ZOBELL, C. E. (1953), 'Production of nitrite from ammonia by methane-oxidizing bacteria', *J. Bact.*, 65, 216–19.

[33] FISHER, T., FISHER, E., and APPLEMAN, M. D. (1952), 'Nitrification by certain heterotrophic bacteria present in soil', *J. Bact.*, 64, 596 (note).

[34] WOOD, E. J. F. (1953), 'Heterotrophic bacteria in marine environments of eastern Australia', *Aust. J. Mar. Freshw. Res.*, 4, 160–200.

[35] VAN NIEL, C. B., ALLEN, MARY BELLE, and WRIGHT, B. E. (1953), 'On the photochemical reduction of nitrate by algae', *Biochem. Biophys. Acta.*, 12, 67–74.

[36] DAVIS, E. A. (1953), 'Nitrate reduction by *Chlorella*', *Plant Physiol.*, 28, 539–44.

[37] DREW, C. H. (1914), 'On the precipitation of calcium carbonate in the sea by marine bacteria and the action of denitrifying bacteria in tropical and temperate seas', *Pap. Tortugas Lab. Wash.*, 5, 7–45.

[38] VENKATARAMAN, R. and SREENIVASAN, A. (1955), 'Utilization of various nitrogenous compounds by certain *Pseudomonas* cultures from marine environments', *Proc. Ind. Acad. Sci.*, 42, 31–38.

[39] BRISOU, J. and VARGUES, H. (1963), 'Proteolysis and nitrate reduction in sea water', *Symp. Marine Microbiol.*, Ch. 38, C. H. Oppenheimer, ed. Thomas, Springfield, Ill.

[40] KEFAUVER, MARGARET and ALLISON, F. E. (1957), 'Nitrate reduction by *Bacterium denitrificans* in relation to oxidation-reduction potential and oxygen tension', *J. Bact.*, 73, 8–14.

[41] WOOD, E. J. F. (1940), 'Studies on the marketing of fish in eastern Australia, II', *C.S.I.R.O. Bull.*, 100, 92.

[42] WOOD, E. J. F. (1950), 'The bacteria of shark spoilage', *Aust. J. Mar. Freshw. Res.*, 1, 129–38.

[43] LISTON, J. and COLWELL, R. R. (1963), 'Host and habitat relationships of marine commensal bacteria', *Symp. Marine Microbiol.*, Ch. 57, C. H. Oppenheimer, ed. Thomas, Springfield, Ill.

[44] GUILLARD, R. R. L. (1963), 'Organic sources of nitrogen for marine centric diatoms', *Symp. Marine Microbiol.*, Ch. 9, C. H. Oppenheimer, ed. Thomas, Springfield, Ill.

[45] TAYLOR, C. B. (1949), 'The effect of phosphorus on the decomposition of organic matter in fresh water', *Proc. Soc. Appl. Bact.*, 1, 4–10.

[46] REDFIELD, A. C. (1934), *On the proportions of organic derivatives in sea water and their relation to the composition of plankton*, James Johnstone Memorial Volume, Liverpool Univ. Press, 176–92.

[47] ATKINS, W. R. G. (1926), 'A quantitative consideration of some factors concerned with plant growth in water', *J. Cons. Int. Expl. Mer*, 1, 99–126.

[48] ZOBELL, C. E. (1946), *Marine Microbiology*, Chronica Botanica Press, Waltham, Mass., 240 pp.
[49] WOOD, E. J. F. (1951), 'Bacteria in marine environments', *Proc. Indo-Pac. Fish. Counc.*, 69–71.
[50] GOLDBERG, E. D., WALKER, T. J., and WHISENAND, A. (1951), 'Phosphate utilization by diatoms', *Biol. Bull.*, **101**, 274–84.
[51] PROVASOLI, L. and PINTNER, IRMA J. (1953), 'Ecological implications of *in vitro* nutritional requirements of algal flagellates', *Ann. N.Y. Acad. Sci.*, **36**, 839–51.
[52] WOODS, D. D. and LASCELLES, JUNE (1954), 'The no-man's land between the autotrophic and heterotrophic ways of life', *Autotrophic Microorganisms*, 1–27. Cambridge University Press.
[53] STANIER, R. Y. (1961), 'Photosynthetic mechanisms in bacteria; development of a unitary concept', *Bact. Rev.*, **25**, 1–17.
[54] WERKMAN, C. H. and WILSON, P. W. (1951), *Bacterial Physiology*, Academic Press, New York.
[55] ZOBELL, C. E. and FELTHAM, C. B. (1934), 'Preliminary studies on the distribution and characteristics of marine bacteria', *Bull. Scripps Inst. Oceanog. Tech. Ser.*, **3**, 279–96.
[56] FOX, D. L. and ANDERSON, L. J. (1941), 'Pigments from marine muds', *Proc. Nat. Acad. Sci.*, **27**, 333–36.
[57] FOX, D. L., UPDEGRAFF, D. M., and NOVELLI, C. D. (1944), 'Carotenoid pigments in the ocean floor', *Arch. Biochem.*, **5**, 1–23.
[58] FOX, D. L. (1944), 'Biochemical fossils', *Science*, **100**, 111, 113.
[59] BAAS BECKING, L. G. M., WOOD, E. J. F., and KAPLAN, I. R. (1956), 'Biological processes in the estuarine environment, VIII', *Kon. Ned. Akad. Weten. Proc.*, **B59**, 398–407.
[60] HUTTON, W. E. and ZOBELL, C. E. (1949), 'The occurrence and characteristics of methane oxidizing bacteria in marine sediments', *J. Bact.*, **58**, 463–73.

# CHAPTER 6

# The Effects of Physical and Chemical Factors on Micro-organisms

## Temperature

The temperature of sea water ranges from $-2°$ to $40°C$, the former being reached in the polar regions, the latter only in very shallow tropical waters. The maximum ranges are recorded in shallow waters at or near the surface; in deeper waters, the temperature is constant within a degree or so. With regard to marine bacteria, Wood [1] found that 42% were killed at $37°C$ and 15% survived $45°C$ in the warm currents of eastern Australia. ZoBell [2] recorded that growth and reproduction of marine bacteria were optimal around $18°C$ and that a temperature of $30°C$ for 10 minutes inhibited the reproduction of 20% of bacteria from sea water and 30% from deep sea sediments off the Californian coast where the water is much cooler than in the Australian region sampled by Wood. A temperature of $4°C$ caused a marked diminution both in numbers and rate of development, though Sanborn [3] and Bedford [4] found marine bacteria which caused spoilage of fish at $-5°C$, and ZoBell showed that 76 out of 88 marine bacterial strains grew at $-4°C$. Liston [6] found that bacteria from Aberdeen Bay grew best between $0°$ and $20°C$, and nearly all were killed at $37°C$. He considers that the differences in temperature tolerance that have been observed in different localities are due to selection by environment. In estuaries, especially in the tropics, temperatures up to $50°C$ can very occasionally be reached in the shallows on a sunny day, and some micro-organisms can withstand these temperatures though others are killed. Such temperatures are, however, very exceptional. Estuarine strains of sulphate-reducing bacteria reduced sulphate at temperatures up to $65°C$ (Wood unpublished) at which terrestrial temperature *Desulphovibrio orientis* is also active (Adams and Postgate [7, 8]).

Among the diatoms, flagellates, and blue-green algae, some species are stenothermal, while others are eurythermal; some species have tropical and Antarctic strains, separated apparently by temperature barriers which cause a geographic separation. Such species are *Corethron criophilum* and

*Dactyliosolen mediterraneus.* Stenothermal diatoms include *Rhizosolenia castracanei, Chaetoceros messanense* (tropical), *R. robusta* (temperate), *R. hebetata* f. *hiemalis* (cool to cold water), and *R. curvata, Chaetoceros dichaeta, Fragilariopsis antarctica* (Antarctic). Eurythermal species include *Nitzschia closterium, Planktoniella sol, Rhizosolenia alata,* and *R. styliformis.* Many of the pennate diatoms are eurythermal because, in their usual shallow water habitat, they are subject to rapid and continual changes of temperature. However, species such as the pelagic *Synedra reinboldii, Thalassiothrix antarctica,* and *Amphiprora kerguelensis* are stenothermal, most of these being Antarctic species.

Of the dinoflagellates, the Dinophysidae are as a group stenothermal. *Dinophysis miles,* the genera *Histioneis, Ornithocercus, Triposolenia,* and *Heterodinium* (Peridineaceae) are tropical, *Phalacroma mawsonii* and *P. cornutum* are Antarctic. Some ceratia are stenothermal, e.g. *C. cephalotum, C. gravidum, C. breve, C. carriense, C. incisum,* others eurythermal, e.g. *C. tripos, C. furca,* and *C. fusus,* which are cosmopolitan. The same applies to the genus *Peridinium* except for a few species such as *P. turbinatum* and *P. obovatum* (Antarctic). From my own observations, the Gymnodiniaceae are more abundant and the 'species' more numerous in tropical waters than in cool-temperate and Antarctic waters. Bipolarity of some species such as *Ceratium lineatum* is probably due to temperature. The stenothermal diatoms and dinoflagellates are used by phytoplanktologists as indicator species to determine the identity of biological water masses.

It is often considered that the spring bloom of phytoplankton is triggered by temperature, and it is true that, in the warmer regions where the temperatures are constantly higher, phytoplankton production is more constant than in higher latitudes. Temperature has an effect on the rate of reproduction and total populations of diatoms as Lund [10] has shown for fresh water diatoms, e.g. *Asterionella formosa.* It can also affect the dominance of protoplankton groups, and in shallow waters can change successions by inhibiting or killing off the more sensitive species. Such changes, e.g. from diatoms to flagellates, could have an effect throughout the whole trophic chain. A sudden rise in temperature will kill off some organisms, cause others to form spores and leave a third group unaffected, an obvious way of influencing succession in estuaries.

**Pressure**
The effect of pressure on the microflora of fresh water and estuarine environments is negligible, since the increase of hydrostatic pressure with depth is approximately one atmosphere per 10 m depth, and, so far as is known, pressure changes of a few atmospheres do not appreciably affect

enzyme reactions (see Johnson et al. [11]). In the oceans, with depths of up to 10,000 m and consequent pressures of up to 1,000 atmospheres or 15,000 lb/in$^2$, hydrostatic pressure could be of great importance in ecology. In the photic zone, hydrostatic pressure would be less than 40 atmospheres, and its effect has been neglected. Some preliminary experiments have been made which suggest that there may be a differential retardation of photosynthesis and respiration due to pressure; if this is so it could significantly alter the compensation depth.

The effect of pressure on micro-organisms has been studied by a number of workers. The literature was reviewed by Cattell [12], who showed that single-celled micro-organisms can tolerate pressures greater than 3,000 atmospheres. However, though a percentage of organisms will survive great pressures, ZoBell and Johnson [13] found that terrestrial bacteria and some strains from shallow water were killed by pressures of 600 atmospheres and were retarded by 300 atmospheres. Strains isolated from water at 500 to 600 atmospheres grew more readily at such pressures than at 1 atmosphere and many marine strains were intermediate. Generally speaking, high pressures raised the optimum temperature for growth, and in one case cultures developed at 40°C at 400 to 600 atmospheres, though they failed to grow at that temperature at atmospheric pressure. These authors used the term 'barophilic' for the organisms that grew better under pressure, and attributed the effect of pressure to changes in the rates and equilibria of chemical reactions governed by molecular volume changes. ZoBell and Oppenheimer [14] confirmed the previous work and showed that most bacteria from surface water or terrigenous environments are killed by prolonged exposure to pressures of from 200 to 600 atmospheres during the logarithmic growth phase. Different biological processes such as nitrate reduction, starch hydrolysis, or methylene blue reduction are differentially affected by increased hydrostatic pressure. Frequently, there is a preliminary acceleration of reaction rate by pressures of the order of 100 to 200 atmospheres followed by a reduction of rate by higher pressures. Morita and ZoBell [15] found that the reduction of methylene blue by Escherichia coli was retarded by pressures of 200 atmospheres or more; the degree of inhibition of enzyme activity increased with time. Haywood et al. [16] recorded that increased pressures up to 10 atmospheres reversibly decreased the luminescence of Achromobacter fischeri. Morita [17] found that the activity of succinic, formic, and malic dehydrogenases increased with decreasing hydrostatic pressure in resting cells of non-barophilic organisms. Morita and Howe [18] reported, however, that phosphatase activity depended more on the strain or culture than on hydrostatic pressure.

ZoBell [19] found bacteria living and growing at depths up to 10,000 m in the ocean in numbers between $10^3$ and $10^6$ per gm of wet sediment, some being obligate barophils (ZoBell and Morita [20]), and many of these organisms were found to be alive and motile after 2 years' incubation at 750 atmospheres and 10°C. Sulphate reduction was still occurring in this material. Growth is very slow at high pressures. The organisms consist of aerobes and anaerobes, the latter mostly facultative, with a few true anaerobes (*Clostridium* and *Desulphovibrio*). Many of the barophilic bacteria reduce nitrates at high pressures. Wood (unpublished) found that sulphate reduction of shallow water strains of *Desulphovibrio*, including freshly isolated strains from Mission Bay, California, was not retarded by 500 atmospheres or over; cultures incubated at 500 to 1,000 atmospheres for 2 days and after that at 1 atmosphere were not killed.

Wood [21] has produced evidence that diatoms can also live and reproduce at pressures up to 500 atmospheres and probably higher while growing in the dark in a medium containing glucose, and that they will continue to produce chlorophyll. The species observed in material from the ocean deeps (7,000 m to 10,000 m) collected by the Danish research ship *Galathea* were *Coscinodiscus marginatus*, *C. centralis*, *Melosira granulata*, *Navicula*, *Synedra*, *Nitzschia*, *Cocconeis*, *Diploneis*, *Pinnularia*, *Trachyneis*, *Pleurosigma*, and *Ethmodiscus*, all benthic or epontic species. Protoplasmic material was seen in *Coscinodiscus*, *Synedra*, and *Navicula*. A few, apparently living foraminifera were present in this material. Bernard's findings at great depths (4,000 m) and pressures of coccolithophores, dinoflagellates, and blue-green algae, and the confirmation of these findings, have already been discussed.

The microbial flora so far observed in the ocean deeps suggests that the microbial processes with the possible exception of photosynthesis can and do occur at the highest oceanic pressures and the greatest depths. Hydrostatic pressures will, of course, have an effect on the thermodynamics of chemical equilibria and enzymic processes at such depths and these effects must be known before we can interpret the ecology of microorganisms in these environments.

## Salinity

The salinity tolerance of marine bacteria has been the subject of some discussion. Wood [22, 23], working on fish-spoilage bacteria, did not find any marked difference between bacterial growth on sea water and fresh water media, but later, unpublished, work showed that many bacteria isolated from Australian coastal waters grew more readily on sea water than on fresh water agar. ZoBell [2], Shewan [24], and Liston [25] found that sea water media gave higher counts than fresh water media, and ZoBell maintained that this was sufficient evidence for the existence of a truly marine flora. Wood's earlier findings were based on a bacterial flora that was largely estuarine, which probably accounts for the differences observed. There are also conflicting reports of the effect of hypertonic salt concentrations on marine bacteria. Some authors, e.g. ZoBell [2], record that marine strains are easily killed by somewhat higher salt concentrations, and others, e.g. Castell and Mapplebeck [26], and Venkataraman and Sreenivasan [27], state that many cocci and bacilli are able to tolerate up to 10% and some up to 15% salt. Halvorson [28] has suggested that gram-positive bacteria are on the whole more salt-tolerant than gram-negative ones. As the majority of truly marine bacteria are gram-negative (except for certain peculiar environments) ZoBell's contention finds confirmation (see also Wood [23], Table I). The gram-positive, largely pigmented flora of fish (Wood [22, 23]) is a separate biocoenosis within the marine ecosystem, and this is the flora studied by Castell and Mapplebeck. It seems certain that, just as fresh water bacteria can be trained to grow in sea water, many bacteria can be trained to grow at higher salinities than their normal habitat. True halophils can also give cultures which can grow at low salt concentrations. It has already been stated that sulphate-reducing bacteria from estuaries have been grown in salinities with 0% to 24% sodium chloride. Likewise, sulphur bacteria from Owens, Searles, and Mono Lakes, California, have been grown in media of low salinity and even tap water media, usually after a staging process, but more rarely directly (Wood unpublished). McLeod and Onofrey [29] considered that certain marine bacteria have an absolute requirement for sodium ion even though mutants could be obtained which could do without it. Even then, the addition of $Na^+$ improved their growth. We can sum up by saying that there are distinct bacterial elements in the flora of fresh water, sea water, and brines, but that they may best be regarded as eco-forms rather than distinct species. However, the same microbial processes occur in each environment, and the same groups of micro-organisms are responsible. Salinity itself does not affect bacterial processes, but merely regulates the strains of bacteria responsible for them. The blue-green algae occur through a very wide range of salinity. They are found in saturated brines of salt lakes, such as Owens Lake, in artificial salterns, in the oceans, in estuaries, and in fresh water lakes and streams. From some experiments conducted in my laboratory, it would seem that many species are tolerant of wide changes in salinity, though no specific experiments have been carried out to determine the salt-tolerance of individual strains.

Some diatom species are recorded from both fresh and salt water environments, others are stenohaline. Some species vary in their salinity requirements, e.g. the genera *Rhopalodia* and *Epithemia* are restricted to fresh water environments in eastern Australia and are endemic in the evaporite Laguna Madre and Aransas Bay environments of South Texas (Wood [30]). This is probably a case of adaptation. Planktonic diatoms in the ocean appear to be restricted in their distribution by temperature rather than salinity, probably because the salinity changes are not sufficient.

Of the flagellates, *Dunaliella salina* is characteristic of strong brines such as those of Owens Lake, but some strains of this species will grow at lower salinities, and other species of the genus are common in the sea. The coccolithophores and most other flagellate groups are recorded from both fresh and sea water, but there would appear to be a much more varied flora in fresh water than in the oceans. This may, in part, be due to the lack of study of marine forms. The dinoflagellates have marine and fresh water forms, with many stenohaline species such as *Ceratium hirundinella*, a fresh water species in Europe and Africa, but found occasionally in the sea in the Australian region. Many of the *Glenodinium* and *Peridinium* species are confined to fresh water, while most of the Dinophysidae and Ceratiaceae are restricted to marine environments. While the distribution of dinoflagellates seems to be temperature-controlled in oceanic environments, salinity, or a factor governed by salinity, governs the distribution in estuaries (Wood in press).

Among the ciliate protozoa, Tintinnids have fresh and salt water species and other ciliate groups appear to be euryhaline. Of the Sarcodina, the armoured forms are usually ascribed to marine localities and the naked ones to fresh or brackish water, but in fact naked amoebae are not uncommon in oceanic plankton.

**Ionic Concentrations** (other than sodium chloride)
The effect on microbes of cation balance, which is different in fresh and sea water, has been studied for the bacteria by McLeod and Onofrey [29, 31, 32], Tomlinson and McLeod [33], McLeod, Hogenkamp, and Onofrey [34], McLeod, Hori, and Fox [35, 36], and McLeod and Hori [37]. These authors consider that the marine bacterial flora is characterized by specific requirements for sodium, potassium, and magnesium ions, the last being required for endogenous but not for exogenous oxidations, and being replaceable by manganese to prevent cytolysis. Chlorine ion was also necessary, while calcium and magnesium ions had sparing effects or were antagonistic according to concentration. There is evidence, too (Jones [38]), that ionic balances are at least in part responsible for the bactericidal activity of sea water reported by ZoBell, at least as far as *Escherichia coli* is

concerned. The requirements for heavy metals must be considered. McLeod and his group found that one of their bacteria had an absolute requirement for ferrous iron but that nickel and cobalt were toxic at the same levels. The ionic requirements of marine bacteria did not differ from their terrestrial counterparts with regard to the tricarboxylic acid cycle.

In the algae, most work regarding monovalent–bivalent cation ratios has been done using fresh water species. This work has been summed up very ably by Provasoli [39]. These ratios among the algae are very complicated, and different species vary greatly in their requirements. For example, in *Ankistrodesmus* and *Oscillatoria*, calcium stimulates growth and reproduction at first, but later loses that function, and the density of final growth depends on magnesium, and with magnesium and calcium at suboptimal levels, each has a sparing effect on the other. In favourable total solid concentrations, and monovalent–bivalent cation ratios, many organisms are tolerant of wide calcium–magnesium ratios, and brackish and marine species require far less of these elements than are present in the environment. Sodium is essential for certain known species, and probably for many more which have not been studied. The trace metals Mo, Cu, Mn, V, and Co are probably essential to all algae, but the maximum quantity which can be tolerated differs from group to group and probably from species to species. The effect of these elements is probably cushioned by chelating agents, many of which may be produced by the organisms themselves, or by commensals. Provasoli points out that no one has cultivated true oceanic species in bacteria-free culture, and this may be due to the production of extracellular chelating agents rather than that of growth factors which are probably present in sufficient quantity anyway.

The mineral nutrition of phytoplankton has been the subject of a review by Ketchum [40]. Marine organisms, e.g. *Nitzschia closterium*, require more calcium and magnesium than fresh water diatoms. Just how widely this applies among marine plants is not known. Manganese is required by *Chlamydomonas* and *Chlorella* up to 0·2 to 2·0 mg per m$^3$, but is not so essential for *Coscinodiscus excentricus* according to Harvey [41]. Halldal [42] has shown that calcium and magnesium ions induce phototaxis in the motile green algae. Goldberg [43] found that the marine diatom *Asterionella japonica* did not grow until the initial iron concentration of the water exceeded 8 mol per litre, i.e. 10 × 10$^{-8}$ mol per cell. The ratio of minimal iron to minimal phosphate was found to agree with that of natural plankton samples. Only particulate or colloidal iron was available to diatoms, chelate iron being unavailable. This fits the findings of Baas Becking and Mackay mentioned previously. The same mechanism seems to be used by the iron bacteria, as the iron of the sheath can be dissolved out with acid, leaving a pectinoid sheath which stains with ruthenium chloride. Iron also seems to be necessary for the formation of cytochrome $c_3$ by *Desulphovibrio* and for normal sulphate reduction by that organism (Postgate [44]). Copper is recorded as essential for some littoral diatoms by Hendey [45] and many diatoms are tolerant to copper and mercury, as are certain marine bacteria (Wood [1]). Fogg [46] has shown that *Anabaena* and other algae excrete free polypeptides into the water, and these can reduce the toxicity of copper and other metallic ions. Molybdenum is an essential element for the nitrogen cycle, both for aerobic nitrogen fixation and for denitrification (Mulder [47]). Silicon is used by diatoms to form their frustules and according to Lund [48] is a limiting factor in diatom populations in lakes. Hart [49, 50] believed that silica was also limiting to the rate of diatom growth in the Antarctic in summer when the tests are very thin. It is certain that diatom blooms deplete the water of silica, which increases below the photic zone, due no doubt to the re-solution of the siliceous frustules. Silica is appreciably soluble at the pH of sea water. Pearsall [51] and Lund [48] place the minimal quantity of silica required for blooms of *Asterionella formosa* at $0·5$ mg per litre. As has been shown, the metabolism of silica is controlled by sulphydryl in the cell membrane. Radiolaria also require silica for their skeletons, and the quantity removed from the water by these organisms has been colossal as is evidenced by the deposits of radiolarian cherts and jaspers, e.g. the Jenolan series in Australia which is 1,000 feet thick.

Baas Becking, Wood, and Kaplan [52] have suggested that the potential aqueous environment is delimited by certain inorganic reactions which affect the pH/Eh relationships of the system (fig. 11). These reactions are the oxidation and reduction of sulphur compounds, oxidation and reduction of iron, buffer capacity of the medium as controlled by the $CO_2 \rightleftharpoons HCO_3^-$ and $CO_3^=$ relationships, and concomitantly with the last, photosynthesis. Photosynthesis acts on the system by utilizing $CO_2$ and $HCO_3^-$ and releasing oxygen or removing hydrogen. The lower limit of the potential environment is probably dictated by the toxicity of sulphydryl at low electrode potentials, i.e. at a high pSH. The acid limit appears to be set by the sulphydryl, sulphur, bisulphite equilibrium and the alkaline limit by ferrous–ferric and carbonate equilibria. In environments where calcium is high, as in sea water, calcium carbonate will precipitate at about pH $9·4$ and the lack of carbon dioxide and bicarbonate will limit photosynthesis. In regions of low calcium (alkaline evaporites) bicarbonate is absent at about pH $10·5$, and as carbonate ion is not assimilated by plants, this should mark the absolute limit of photosynthesis under such conditions. The reason for the delimitation of the

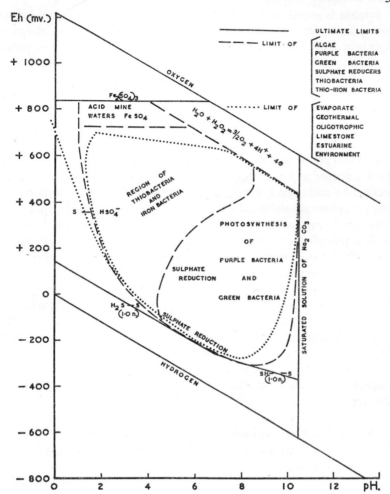

FIG. 11. The pH–Eh limits of the natural environment, showing the relation between microbial distribution and the limits of biological reactions.

environment by the three equilibria is twofold. Firstly, both iron and sulphur are capable of oxidation and reduction, the reactions consuming or releasing large quantities of energy, and secondly, there are large differences in the solubilities of the series of compounds formed by iron and sulphur and of the carbonates and bicarbonates. The nitrogen cycle also has potentialities for oxidation and reduction, but all nitrogen compounds are soluble, and all ions concerned in the cycle remain available.

Sulphur is usually considered to be available to plants as sulphate ion, but organic sulphur compounds are also available to many microbes, especially in the aqueous environment. It is possible that plants first reduce sulphate to sulphydryl and take it in as such. At any rate, sulphur more usually appears in the plant in the reduced state, e.g. methionine, taurine, glutathione, cysteine, cystine, though it does occur also as sulphates or sulphonic acids. Selenate has been shown by Postgate [53] to be a competitive inhibitor of sulphate reduction in *Desulphovibrio* and is known to affect the uptake of sulphur in other plants.

As stated previously, phosphate is required by micro-organisms in very small amounts and the organisms store phosphate by chelation in the pectinoid sheath which many possess (Baas Becking and Mackay [54]). The phosphate is solubilized by hydroxy-acids present in the sheath and is frequently precipitated as ferric phosphate. For this reason, ferric and calcium phosphates are readily available to bacteria (Wood [55]) and to unicellular algae. It is probable that phosphates in the ocean are utilized to a large extent by microbes while still in the organic state.

Many micro-organisms are specific in their nitrogen requirements: diatoms as a class preferring or requiring nitrates, blue-green algae needing ammonia. The activity of nitrogen-fixing micro-organisms is often governed by the amount of ammonia or nitrate present in the substrate. This makes it very difficult to estimate the actual significance of nitrogen-fixation by micro-organisms in the sea. We do know, however, that a number of marine organisms have that ability at least in theory (see Chapter 4).

**Hydrogen-ion Concentration and Redox Potential**

It has become clear to marine and fresh water microbiologists that oxidation-reduction potentials (redox) of the water and the bottom have ecological significance, and the same applies to hydrogen-ion concentration.

Cooper gives the Eh of Atlantic sea water as between +402 and +432 mV at pH 7·62 to 8·15, and my own values for the south-west Pacific are of this order. Marine sediments have been studied by ZoBell [56] who found the Eh to lie between +350 mV and −500 mV with the pH ranging from 6·4 to 9·5, the majority of sediments lying between 7·5 and 9·0. Siebert and Schwartz [57] made artificial sediments using sand, sea water, or fresh water with *Laminaria* or *Fucus* to provide organic matter, varying the calcium content and pH. After 12 months, the pH ranged between 6·8 and 8·4 and the Eh from + 65 mV to − 374 mV. These figures are in substantial agreement with those of ZoBell, and with the natural and synthetic sediments of Baas Becking and Wood [58]. The sediments of the continental shelf off Cronulla, Australia, range from pH 6·6 to 7·3 and the Eh from + 50 mV to + 250 mV; Emery and Rittenberg [59] record Eh values from − 300 mV to + 300 mV and pH from 7·3 to 8·5 in cores from the California Basin up to 100 in deep. The low Eh values were associated with the presence of $H_2S$. In general, Eh decreased with depth, though in one case where there was considerable pollution at the surface the Eh was highest at the lowest part of the core. In freshly formed sediments, the Eh tends to be positive at the surface and rapidly becomes negative in areas of active sulphate reduction below, but in more stable sediments the Eh may be positive to considerable depths, or there may be layers of alternatively positive and negative Eh values due to seasonal or periodic layering of the sediments.

Many authors have studied the pH/Eh relationships of water and bottom deposits in terms of biological activity, but Baas Becking and Wood and Baas Becking, Wood, and Kaplan produced a scheme correlating the limits of microbial processes in aqueous environments with the pH and Eh. These authors have delineated the autotrophic and quasi-autotrophic biological processes in terms of pH and Eh (fig. 2) and the aquatic environments and governing chemical reactions (fig. 11) in the same terms, as has been discussed to some extent previously. The potential aquatic environment is somewhat wider than the actual environment. This is due to the fact that, in nature, pure cultures very rarely exist and the controlling factors are biologically reversible. The following environments have been studied by Baas Becking, Wood, and Kaplan; limestone waters, estuarine sediments, estuarine waters, geothermal regions, oligotrophic waters, and evaporites (desert brines and salterns). Limestone waters are typified by the Jenolan Caves of New South Wales, in which organic matter is very low and sulphate ion absent. Organisms of the sulphur cycle could not be isolated, and there was no evidence of the existence of iron bacteria. The absence of the latter is interesting as the pH lies between 5·5 and 9·0 and the Eh between + 150 mV and + 500 mV, and it is within this region that the iron bacteria are usually found. The explanation appears to be that iron bacteria are gradient organisms (Baas Becking, Wood, and Kaplan [62]) and there is no gradient in this environment. The mean Eh of the limestone environment is between + 300 mV and + 350 mV and the mean pH between 6·5 and 7·0. The relatively low mean pH is due to the domination of the aqueous system by bicarbonate ion. The limestone environment would be the limiting case of the coral-reef environment in which the mean Eh is much lower but the pH of the same order, though it can go as low as 5 with free $H_2S$.

Oligotrophic waters include high moors, peat bogs, and regions such as
K

the Hawkesbury Sandstones of New South Wales. In these waters the pH and Eh ranges are somewhat wider, lying between pH 4·0 and 7·4, and Eh + 550 mV to − 50 mV with means of pH 6·0 to 6·5 and Eh bimodal between + 450 mV and + 500 mV, and + 300 mV and + 350 mV. In this environment there may be an Eh gradient and iron bacteria therefore occur, while sulphate reduction is possible if sulphate is present. In certain high moors (e.g. in Tasmania) sulphate is absent. Such oligotrophic environments can influence estuarine environments of drowned valleys such as those near Sydney where the drainage comes from the Hawkesbury sandstones.

Estuarine waters have a character more closely approaching that of sea water and are usually well buffered and poised. They are more alkaline than oligotrophic waters, and slightly more alkaline than limestone waters, possibly due to the effect of photosynthesis on the carbon dioxide equilibrium. The maximum pH of 9·4 is reached in algal-filled rock pools and on shallow sea-grass beds as recorded from Lake Illawarra and Lake Macquarie, New South Wales by Wood [60], from Redfish Bay, Texas, by Oppenheimer and Debyser from the French coast. The Eh is controlled by photosynthesis on the positive side and by respiration and organic reducing systems on the negative. At certain times, when colloidal iron sulphydryl and free hydrogen sulphide occur in the water, the Eh may fall to − 100 mV in the water. This limiting case also lowers the pH to 5·8 by liberating phosphoric acid from the ferric phosphate in the water and the sediment. This phenomenon has been studied in deep, almost landlocked basins, and may occur in artificial fish ponds of the tambak type. Estuarine waters have a pH range from 7·0 to 9·4 and a mean between 8·0 and 8·5, with an Eh range from + 150 mV to + 500 mV and a mean between + 350 mV and + 400 mV under normal conditions. Estuarine sediments have a very wide range of both pH and Eh, the former ranging from 5·3 to 9·4 (mean 7·3) and the latter from + 600 to − 350 mV with means at + 300 to + 350 mV and − 50 to − 100 mV. The acid values are no doubt due to the release of phosphoric acid by sulphate reduction and perhaps in part to nitrification, which is largely confined to the sediments, though Spencer [64] has shown that nitrification can occur in the sea water environment. In shallow water sediments there is a seasonal change in Eh from negative in the late summer to positive in the late winter. This is due to the reducing effect of decomposing algae and sea-grasses, which wash up and become embedded in the sediments at the end of summer growth, and to the lack of organic matter after the winter (Wood [60]). Estuarine sediment profiles usually show a positive Eh at the surface unless there is an algal felt immediately over the sediment, when the Eh will be negative throughout. The Eh at lower levels depends on the presence or absence of sulphate reduction. The pH usually shows a minimal value from 5 cm to 20 cm below the surface. Debyser [65] found that the pH dropped from between 7·5 and 8·0 at the surface to between 6·6 and 6·8 at 5 cm and rose to 7·0 at a depth of 20 cm in the sediment. We have recorded very similar figures with a minimum at 5 cm from Botany Bay, New South Wales. There is little correlation between Eh, particle size and the number of microbes, these depending rather on the history of the sediment, i.e. newly formed sediments tend to have a low Eh and a high microbial content.

In geothermal regions, the Eh ranges from + 650 mV to − 100 mV and the pH from 1·5 to 9·4. In the area studied by Kaplan [66] and discussed by Baas Becking, Wood, and Kaplan [52] there were three Eh means at + 300 mV, + 100 mV, and − 50 mV, and two pH means at 1·5 (obviously representing sulphur oxidation by *Thiobacillus thiooxidans*), and at 6·0 to 6·5 which could be associated with travertine formation.

Evaporites have a pH range from 5·5 to 8·5 and an Eh range from + 650 mV to − 150 mV. There are two Eh means, one at + 450 mV the other at + 300 mV. The high Eh is associated with the flagellate *Dunaliella salina*. The pH mean is between 7·0 and 7·5. At Sand Springs, Nevada, the pH recorded was 10·4 (Baas Becking [67]) in alkaline brines poor in calcium and magnesium, i.e. with high sodium and potassium. If the micro-organisms are considered with regard to their pH–Eh limits, it is possible to predict the type of environment in which they may be found. The photosynthetic micro-organisms show the greatest range of pH and Eh (1·5 to 10·5 and − 170 mV to + 700 mV), followed by the thiobacilli (− 0·5 to 9·4 and − 170 mV to + 700 mV). The purple sulphur bacteria range from pH 4·5 to 10·5 and − 180 mV to + 350 mV. *Desulphovibrio* does not become active above + 110 mV (Postgate gives a lower figure for pure cultures), and its activity ceases at about − 350 mV, while the green sulphur bacteria have a narrow milieu between − 100 mV and − 300 mV and pH 6·5 to 10·0. This Eh range suggests that they require sulphydryl while the purple sulphur bacteria require hydrotroilite, i.e. a certain amount of OH ion. The iron bacteria (*Sphaerotilus* and *Gallionella*) and the organo-sulphur microbes *Beggiatoa, Thiothrix,* and *Thiovulum,* appear to be gradient organisms, requiring a large drop in Eh between the two surfaces of the film which they form. The anaerobic heterotrophs, e.g. the clostridia, produce very low potentials of the order of − 350 mV to − 450 mV (Gillespie and Rettger [68]). The potentials required for the growth of anaerobes must be produced by the facultative anaerobes or microaerophilic organisms. Bahr and Schwartz

[69] delimit the habitat of *Beggiatoa* and *Thiothrix* as between pH 6·7 and 7·3 and Eh + 350 mV and + 450 mV in sulphur springs, eutrophic waters, and faecal slimes. The optimum pH/Eh for *Beggiatoa* lay between 6·8 and 7·2 at + 360 mV to + 480 mV. Baas Becking and Wood have not recorded sulphate reduction at an Eh lower than about − 350 mV so that the Eh of − 500 mV recorded by ZoBell was probably due to heterotrophic anaerobes rather than *Desulphovibrio*.

With the knowledge of possible environments and the limits of the microbial components of the aqueous ecosystem, one can predict the probable flora of a given water or sediment, and estimate the resultant of the metabiotic interaction of this flora. In sea water and fresh water, except under certain catastrophic conditions such as those occasionally met with in red tides or heavy plankton blooms, the Eh is positive and relatively constant, so the main biological reaction will be photosynthesis, raising the Eh and pH during the day, with respiration lowering both during the dark. The sulphur and iron cycles will be unimportant or absent though the micro-organisms concerned may still be present. Wood [60] isolated strict anaerobes, *Desulphovibrio* and *Thiobacillus denitrificans*, from estuarine water 90% saturated with oxygen.

In bottom deposits, changes in Eh appear to be more significant than pH changes, and express the resultant of the processes going on within the sediment, because the controlling processes are oxidative and reductive. Most of the processes are biological, sulphate reduction being entirely so, while the oxidation of sulphides can proceed abiologically, but is frequently made use of by bacteria and certain algae as a source of energy (see Chapter 3). The activity of *Desulphovibrio*, as has been stated, requires a preliminary lowering of redox, and this is produced by heterotrophic bacteria and algae. The breakdown of carbohydrate, e.g. agar, alginate, and starch by bacteria (Baas Becking and Wood [58]) or the production of dimethyl sulphide or other substances by living *Zostera* or other sea-grasses (Wood [70]) or algae (Bywood and Challenger [71]), causes the initial lowering of the redox potential. At pH values above 4·8, i.e. all environments except acid peat bogs and some geothermal regions, the $H_2S$ is bound by the heavy metals present, the chief of which is iron. Ferric iron is reduced to ferrous and this reacts to form $Fe{<}^{SH}_{SH}$ (iron sulphydryl), a very unstable compound, the instability of which causes active bleaching of the sediments on exposure to air. This may oxidize to $Fe{<}^{SH}_{OH}$ (hydrotroilite) and more slowly to pyrite ($FeS_2$). Because of the greater insolubility of the sulphides of copper, cobalt, lead, and nickel, these metals may replace iron. Bottom deposits of stagnant waters have a consistently low Eh if the organic content of the sediment is consistently high. The 'Hole' in Lake Macquarie has sediments with an Eh varying from $-$ 130 mV to $+$ 160 mV at the surface and from $-$ 125 mV to $+$ 55 mV at 20 cm depth. It is an almost landlocked basin within the lake and has a high organic content. In places where there are large blooms of algae or sea-grass, and this material is washed into shallow water by wind and wave action, such as Swansea, Lake Macquarie, the Eh of the sediment surface rises from $+$ 50 mV in late spring to $+$ 200 mV in late autumn, and at 20 cm depth from $-$ 120 mV to $+$ 230 mV in the same seasons. Here, accumulations of rotting *Zostera* and *Enteromorpha* occur in late spring and summer, and occasionally in late autumn. In the latter case, the Eh drops to values between $-$ 80 mV and $+$ 50 mV. In sandy sediments, the Eh is higher than in muds, or, if the Eh is low, it rises rapidly on aeration. This is due to the low organic content of sandy bottoms and a consequent lack of poising. Low Eh in sands can be shown by oxidation tests to be due almost entirely to sulphate reduction, as these sands will bleach rapidly on oxidation. Algal felts, e.g. of *Enteromorpha*, *Vaucheria*, *Gloeocapsa*, or *Oscillatoria*, which produce mercaptans or thioethers will have an Eh of $-$ 100 mV or lower at the sediment surface directly below the felt. This low Eh usually gives rise to sulphate reduction, and purple and green bacteria can be expected immediately below the felt.

## Organic Compounds

The availability and utilization of dissolved and particulate organic matter in the seas has been the subject of controversy since Putter [72] put forward his theory that marine animals could make use of dissolved organic carbon. Krogh [73, 74] disputed this, and his findings were generally accepted. Recently, however, Provasoli and Shirahashi [75], Provasoli, Shirahashi, and Lance [76], and Shirahashi and Provasoli [77] have shown that the brine-shrimp and the copepod *Tigriopus* can be grown in axenic culture with nothing but dissolved organic material *as food*, and that they can also take in growth factors from the water. In addition, organisms of the proto-plankton, including diatoms, can assimilate dissolved organic compounds heterotrophically, and these compounds must certainly be an important source of nourishment to protoplankton and possibly to higher organisms in the aphotic zone.

The quantity of dissolved and particulate organic matter present in the sea, or its rate of production and consumption, are inadequately known. Krogh estimated dissolved organic matter as representing 1·2 mg to 2·0 mg of organic carbon per litre and 0·2 mg organic nitrogen, i.e. about

1·5 kg dissolved organic matter per sq m of surface, and believed that particulate carbon was 0·3 of this in the deeper parts of the ocean. Plunkett and Rakestraw [78] state that the dissolved organic matter in the sea varies from 1·41 mg to 2·82 mg organic carbon per litre with a minimum between 500 m and 750 m depth, and at a depth of 6,290 m there was 1·18 mg carbon per litre. Inshore, of course, the amount of dissolved and particulate carbon will be much higher and will vary owing to a number of factors. Particulate organic matter is available to phagotrophic organisms and to zooplankton, and there are, at all depths in the oceans, organisms such as the flagellates and ciliates, which can take advantage of this. The role of such organisms in the open ocean has been ignored or under-estimated, and it must be remembered that the amount of organic matter found will represent the residual after the feeding of the organisms present. As grazing may be regarded for our purposes as continual, the ratio of the amount consumed to the residue could be very high, and we have, at the present time, no method of estimating it.

Dissolved organic matter may for convenience be classified as nutri-tional (e.g. amino-acids, polypeptides, carbohydrates), auxotrophic or growth-assisting, and antibiotic or growth-inhibiting. Such organic matter may be derived from the decomposition of organisms by microbial or autolytic processes, or from excretion by living organisms. Lucas [79–81] pointed out the possible importance of external metabolites in the sea, especially in controlling or initiating biological succession in plankton blooms. Fogg [82, 83] and Fogg and Westlake [84] stressed the importance of excreted substances, and showed that the polypeptides excreted by certain blue-green algae help to solubilize tricalcium phosphate, are good chelators and may help to store required metals or to inactivate toxic ones such as copper. Duursma [85] contends that these authors have not shown that such extracellular substances are produced by living phyto-plankton in the ocean, and that the organic matter produced is derived from dead or dying organisms. He offers no satisfactory proof of his thesis which is probably not important from the ecological point of view. He also minimises the presence of particulate organic matter in the open ocean, but his method of preserving samples with N/10 sulphuric acid would hydrolyse a good deal of such particulate matter. The fact is that organic particles are abundant in the open ocean, and do act as surfaces for adsorp-tion and consequent interaction.

Microbial decomposition, except under anaerobic conditions, will be incomplete, i.e. the products will contain oxygen. Organic matter in the water will probably be only partly broken down to carbon dioxide, the rest being released as carbohydrate, amino-acids, and other simple organic compounds. These organic substances, whether produced by excretion, by autolytic or microbial action, are easily assimilable by organisms capable of heterotrophy, and as Provasoli [38] points out, 'if we do not find more organic substances it is because they are utilized as fast as they are released into the water'. Smayda [86], basing his discussion on Duursma's figures and conclusions, does not consider that Lucas' external metabolites are likely to be of importance in determining succession, because of their paucity and dilution. Fogg, however, quotes experiments to show that extracellular products may amount to 50% of the total material assimilated, but that the net extracellular material in lakes appears to be of the order of 2%. The difference would be represented in part at least by consumption by heterotrophs. McLaughlin et al. [87], working with the dinoflagellate Katodinium dorsisulcatum, found that $5 \times 10^6$ cells per litre yielded 1·4 gm of polysaccharide per litre, and that this material altered certain characters of some marine bacteria, stimulated some species, and inhibited or had no effect on others. When we remember that many dinoflagellates, especially the naked ones, have mucoid sheaths, that such species of plank-tonic diatom as Thalassiosira subtilis, T. decipiens, and Bacteriastrum hyalinum, and the blue-green algae Katagnymene and Haliarachne occur embedded in mucoid material which they secrete, we will realize how important such material may be in the marine ecosystem. Although other materials may not be produced in such bulk as these mucoid substances, the importance of many of them in growth and succession may be prodi-gious.

Vallantyne [88] has listed a large number of organic compounds that have been released from hydrolysates of seston and of sediments. Papers by such workers as Ericson and Lewis [89], Burkholder and Burkholder [90], Cowey [91], Wangersky [92], Starr [93], Fogg and Westlake [84], Droop [94], Guillard and Wangersky [95], Lewin [96], and Fogg and Boalch [97] list an ever-increasing number of organic substances, some essential to growth, some antagonistic, so that the quantity, especially in plankton blooms, may be at times of primary importance in determining succession. It may indeed be that such substances are too dilute in the open ocean to initiate protoplankton blooms on most occasions, but, once a bloom is gaining impetus, excreted material could well have a great effect in selecting the species which will follow, as the Katodinium material does in the case of the bacteria tested by McLaughlin et al. As well as direct growth-promoting or antibiotic effects, chelation of metals as storage, or removal of toxic or beneficial ions must be considered. Dissolved organic substances which can be used as nutrients include amino-acids, urea and uric acids which can be used as nitrogen sources by some algae (Provasoli

[38]), organic phosphates such as glycerophosphate, monoethyl-phosphate, guanilic, cytidilic, and yeast nucleic acids, and it is possible that ability to use organic phosphates may play an important part in protoplankton succession during blooms. Glucose is required by plants to produce chlorophyll in the dark, and as we have seen, chlorophyll-bearing plants occur in the ocean well below the photic zone and deep in certain sediments. One would assume that the protoplankton organisms found in deep waters by Bernard [98, 99] and others are living largely on the dissolved organic matter and that it is mainly autochthonous. However, we do not know the rate of growth, metabolism, or reproduction of these organisms, so cannot estimate the amount of organic matter required for their maintenance even to the nearest order of magnitude.

It may now be accepted as a truism that there are very few true autotrophs in the marine environment. The work of Provasoli, Hutner, Droop and many others is evidence of this. Provasoli [38] has given a very useful review of the ever-increasing literature on the subject, and a list of the groups and species of organisms which have been tested. It is unfortunate for us that so many of these are fresh water species. However, it would seem that most of the marine species are auxotrophic, exceptions being *Navicula pelliculosa* (estuarine), and *Nitzschia closterium* v. *minutissima* (*Phaeodactylum tricornutum*) which is ubiquitous. The Chlorophyceae as a group are true autotrophs or facultative heterotrophs, i.e. do not require growth factors, but these organisms are sparse in the ocean. Provasoli points out that the species with myxotrophic or heterotrophic tendencies are usually auxotrophic, but this is not universal. The most important growth factors are cyano cobaltamine, thiamine, biotin and possibly *p*-amino-benzoic acid (Hutner [100]). Provasoli shows that auxotrophy does not correlate with any particular environment, and raises a number of ecological questions. Droop [101] considered that vitamin $B_{12}$ is always in sufficient supply in the ocean, but Daisley [102] questioned this. Provasoli considers that Droop's conclusion is valid for coastal waters at least. The abundance of other growth factors in the oceans has yet to be considered. Vitamin $B_{12}$ is produced by bacteria, algae, and certain of the larger seaweeds. The fact that so many microbes are adsorbed on particles may assist in the assimilation of such substances, as the chances are that they will be adsorbed also, and thus available in concentrated form. Burkholder and Burkholder [90] found that suspended solids in estuarine waters and sediments are poor in cyano-cobaltamine but relatively rich in its analogues. Auxins have been demonstrated in phytoplankton, zooplankton, and sea water by Bentley [103]. She found that offshore sea water contained 0·375 µg in 100 litres, and that the minimal amount required to give observable improvement in the growth of *Skeletonema* is 1 μg to 10 μg per 100 litres, i.e. the amount detected is one-tenth of that required for improved growth. On the other hand, probable losses due to the preparation and assay of the samples may account for the discrepancy noted. In blooms or zooplankton swarms, the auxin content of sea water could be much higher.

The production of extracellular substances may be regarded as an example of metabiosis, but such products may not always be favourable for the growth of the organisms present. Lefevre and Farrugia [104] point out that algae, fungi, and bacteria may produce substances which are stimulatory for growth in minimal concentrations and later become toxic, and Jörgensen and Steemann Nielsen [105] show that they may excrete both stimulatory and inhibitory substances. Some of the material produced is auto-antagonistic (i.e. restricts the growth and reproduction of the organism producing it), some is hetero-antagonistic (i.e. restricts other species – is antibiotic), while some is both auto- and hetero-antagonistic.

This brings us to a consideration of antibiotics as such. Rosenfeld and ZoBell [106] showed that antibiotics were produced by certain marine bacteria, though earlier authors had suggested that antibacterials existed in aquatic environments. Grien and Meyers [107] obtained antibiotics from estuarine actinomycetes, and Demny, Miller, and Woodruff [108] isolated 154 antibiotic-producing strains out of 1,414 isolates of actinomycetes from salt marsh, sea water, littoral, and estuarine areas and deep cores. However, Carlucci and Pramer [109] did not find any antibiotic active against *Escherichia coli* or *Bacillus subtilis* from 200 isolates of bacteria from marine sources. Algae also produce bactericidal and fungicidal substances. Steemann Nielsen [110] suggested that fresh water *Chlorella* and a marine *Thalassiosira* produce in the light antibiotics which keep down bacteria. Sieburth [111] found that Antarctic phytoplankton has strong antibacterial effects, Allen and Dawson [112], Chesters and Scott [113], and Burkholder, Burkholder, and Almodovar [114] found red, green, and brown algae with bactericidal properties, while Welch [115] found that 11 out of 35 marine algae which she studied produced fungistatic substances. There is no record of the testing of bacterial or fungal antibiotics against algae, except in the routine use of certain antibiotics of terrestrial origin for procuring pure cultures of algae. In these cases, the antibiotics are selective against the algae and are toxic to varying extents according to the species present, i.e. could be active in promoting the succession of certain species.

It may be concluded that antibiotics are produced by a number of microbes in the sea, and by macroscopic organisms also, that these are selectively toxic and may be autotoxic, that they may be beneficial in small doses, and that they may play an important part in plankton succession, especially in association with the phenomena of adsorption. Adsorption could act in two ways: by removing toxins from the vicinity of free-floating organisms, or by concentrating them in close proximity to attached or adsorbed organisms on particles.

## Adsorption

Rubentschik et al. [116], Henrici [117], ZoBell [2], and Wood [1] are among those who have stressed the importance of adsorption to microbial processes in water. In both water and sediments, most particles are microscopic, and thus afford a tremendous surface for adsorption phenomena. Such phenomena, by differential adsorption, can entirely alter the chemical and biological relationships of an environment. Wood [60] found that sulphide-containing sediments with a large silt fraction are far more difficult to oxidize than those with a small silt fraction, both hydrogen-ion concentration and redox potential being more stable in the former case. There is some correlation too (Wood [1], fig. 2) between the number of silt particles per cubic centimetre of sediment and the bacterial population. In cultures of Desulphovibrio, reduction is almost entirely confined to surfaces as shown by film-formation on the walls of the vessel or on added steel wool, and by inoculation experiments. The latter usually failed unless the surfaces were scraped, or the culture shaken to provide an inoculum. Further, ferrous sulphide was produced far more rapidly when washed steel wool was used in the cultures than when iron was added as *ferrum reductum*, which formed a heap in the bottom of the vessel. Increased reaction rates were produced if the *ferrum reductum* were mixed with glass wool or ballotini. This is due to the increased surface available both for hydrogen production (Fe + $H_2O \longrightarrow Fe^{++} + 2H^-$), and for the bacteria themselves.

Studies have been made on the adsorptive capacity of sediments for bacteria; Rubentschik et al. [116] found that bacteria in salt lakes are adsorbed on mud particles which are positively charged. They found that the viability of bacteria is not adversely affected by adsorption and suggested that in certain cases the muds may adsorb metabolic products. In the case of the sulphate reducers, the sulphide is certainly adsorbed on the glass, steel wool, or ballotini. Desorption also occurs and adsorption and desorption may occur simultaneously. Rubentschik et al. found an adsorption of 99·2% of bacteria at an optimum concentration of 10 × $10^6$ bacteria in 5 gm of mud. Wood [1] adsorbed bacterial suspensions of known populations on autoclaved estuarine sediments of measured particle size obtained by shaking and sedimentation. The bacteria were gently shaken with the sediment for half an hour, centrifuged at a speed just sufficient to settle the mud particles, the supernatant plated, and the bacteria counted. It was found by microscopic examination that optimum adsorption occurred on particles of 1 to 2 $\mu$ diameter (up to 99·8% of bacteria adsorbed), but that good adsorption occurred on particles between 5 and 20 $\mu$. Also there appears to be, as Rubentschik stated, an optimum concentration of bacteria for maximum adsorption. Adsorption was higher (99·8%) in concentrations of $5 \times 10^5$ bacteria per ml than in concentrations of $4 \times 10^4$ (95·9%) or $5 \times 10^6$ (91·2%). Adsorption also occurred on diatomaceous earth which had been washed with strong hydrochloric acid and distilled water, but the amount of adsorption was not as great as on muds. The difference may be due to the buffering or poising capacity of the organic matter in the muds, to surface charge or possibly to both.

A microscopic study of sediments with the bacteria stained with fuchsin or acridine orange showed adsorption of the order of 90%, the number of bacteria adsorbed on each particle being independent of particle size within wide limits. As a general rule, most bacteria were adsorbed on particles showing some traces of organic structure, though this was not universally true. It is probable that, in shallow water, the adsorptive ability of sediments reduces the bacterial population of the overlying waters in tidal areas where there is some turbulence. Henrici [116] attributed the rapid decrease of bacterial populations in river water after it enters lakes to the precipitation of organisms adsorbed on silt particles. At any rate, the population is greatest in the water above, usually immediately above the sediment which contains most silt particles. In the case of estuarine flats where the tide rises and falls in a series of cross-currents, the turbulence and bacterial counts may be complicated, but there is nearly always a minimal count somewhere between the surface of the water and that of the sediment. Because diatoms and other particles are held at the surface of the water by surface tension, the bacterial count here is often much higher than it is just below – another case of adsorption. The number of particles and of bacteria decrease further from land, and the distribution of bacteria on particles appears from microscopic observation to become more even, and clumping becomes less important. Because the particles in the sediment and in water consist of different chemical aggregations, the bacteria will orientate themselves accordingly. Thus, phosphate-dissolving organisms are associated with particles high in calcium- or ferric-phosphate, e.g. portions of bone or faecal pellets, while the sulphate-reducers are associated with the presence of iron, heterotrophs with organic particles and so on.

Adsorption of micro-organisms on sediment particles may be shown in another way, by determining the nitrogen on various silt fractions. Wood (in press) has shown that the nitrogen of estuarine sediments increases sharply with decreasing particle size. This is of great importance in the food chain since many animals, e.g. the mullets, can select these fine particles. The use of fluorescent microscopy to count organisms in the sediments shows that photosynthetic micro-organisms as large as the smaller diatoms are adsorbed on the sediment particles to the extent of 80% to 90% (see Wood and Oppenheimer [118]). Microscopic examination of living material from the photic zone of the oceans shows that here too adsorption of the smaller nanoplankton on non-living particles is very important.

Provasoli and Shirahashi [75] made the very interesting observation that *Artemia* cannot be grown to the adult stage on dissolved organic substances alone. If starch particles are added, these are excreted in the faeces, but stimulate the filter-feeding of the brine-shrimp by stimulating the act of swallowing and no doubt by increasing the amount of available solute by adsorption on the particles and transfer in the gut.

# REFERENCES

[1] WOOD, E. J. F. (1953), 'Heterotrophic bacteria in marine environments of eastern Australia', *Aust. J. Mar. Freshw. Res.*, 4, 160–200.

[2] ZOBELL, C. E. (1946), *Marine Microbiology*, Chronica Botanica Press, Waltham, Mass., 240 pp.

[3] SANBORN, J. R. (1930), 'Certain relationships of marine bacteria to the decomposition of fish', *J. Bact.*, 19, 375–82.

[4] BEDFORD, R. H. (1933), 'Marine bacteria of the north Pacific Ocean. The temperature range of growth', *Contr. Can. Biol. Fish.*, n.s. 7, 431–38.

[5] ZOBELL, C. E. (1934), 'Microbiological activities at low temperatures with particular reference to marine bacteria', *Quart. Rev. Biol.*, 9, 460–66.

[6] LISTON, J. (1957), 'The occurrence and distribution of bacterial types on flatfish,' *J. Gen. Microbiol.*, 20, 252–57.

[7] ADAMS, MARY E. and POSTGATE, J. R. (1959), 'A new sulphate-reducing vibrio,' *J. Gen. Microbiol.*, 20, 252–57.

[8] ADAMS, MARY E. and POSTGATE, J. R. (1959), 'On sporulation in sulphate-reducing bacteria', *J. Gen. Microbiol.*, 24, 291–94.

[9] WOOD, E. J. F. (1954), 'Dinoflagellates in the Australian region', *Aust. J. Mar. Freshw. Res.*, 5, 171–351.

[10] LUND, J. W. G. (1949), 'Studies on *Asterionella formosa*, I', *J. Ecol.*, 37, 389–419.

[11] JOHNSON, F. H., EYRING, H., and POLISSAR, M. J. (1954), *The Kinetic Basis of Molecular Biology*, Wiley, New York, 874 pp.

[12] CATTELL, M. (1936), 'The biological effects of pressure', *Biol. Rev.*, 11, 411–76.

[13] ZOBELL, C. E. and JOHNSON, F. H. (1949), 'The influence of hydrostatic pressure on the growth and viability of terrestrial and marine bacteria', *J. Bact.*, 57, 179–190.

[14] ZOBELL, C. E. and OPPENHEIMER, C. H. (1950), 'Some effects of hydrostatic pressure on the multiplication and morphology of bacteria', *J. Bact.*, 60, 771–81.

[15] MORITA, R. Y. and ZOBELL, C. E. (1956), 'The effect of hydrostatic pressure on the succinic dehydrogenase system of *Escherichia coli*', *J. Bact.*, 71, 668–72.

[16] HAYWOOD, C., HARDENBERG, H. C., and HARVEY, E. N. (1956), 'The effect of increased pressure of oxygen on the luminescence of *Achromobacter fischeri*', *J. Cell. Comp. Physiol.*, 47, 289–94.

[17] MORITA, R. Y. (1957), 'The effect of hydrostatic pressure on the succinic, formic, and malic dehydrogenases in *Escherichia coli*', *J. Bact.*, 74, 251–55.

[18] MORITA, R. Y. and HOWE, R. ARLENE (1957), 'Phosphatase activity by marine bacteria under hydrostatic pressure', *Deep Sea Res.*, 4, 254–58.

[19] ZOBELL, C. E. (1952), 'Bacterial life at the bottom of the Philippines Trench', *Science*, 115, 507–8.

[20] ZOBELL, C. E. and MORITA, R. Y. (1957), 'Barophilic bacteria in some deep sea sediments', *J. Bact.*, 73, 563–68.

[21] WOOD, E. J. F. (1956), 'Diatoms in the ocean deeps', *Pac. Sci.*, 10, 377–81.

[22] WOOD, E. F. F. (1940), 'Studies on the marketing of fish in eastern Australia, II', *C.S.I.R. Aust. Pam.*, 100, 92 pp.

[23] WOOD, E. J. F. (1950), 'The bacteriology of shark spoilage', *Aust. J. Mar. Freshw. Res.*, 1, 129–38.

[24] SHEWAN, J. M. (1953), 'Some recent progress on the bacteriology of marine fish', *Proc. Int. Cong. Microbiol.*, 7, 361–65.

[25] LISTON, J. (1956), 'Quantitative variations in the bacterial flora of flatfish', *J. Gen. Microbiol.*, 15, 305–14.

[26] CASTELL, C. H. and MAPPLEBECK, E. G. (1952), 'The importance of *Flavobacterium* in fish spoilage', *J. Fish. Res. Bd. Can.*, 9, 148–56.

[27] VENKATARAMAN, R. and SREENIVASAN, A. (1954), 'Salt tolerance of marine bacteria', *Food Res.*, 19, 311–13.

[28] HALVORSON, H. O. (1944), *The Chemistry and Technology of Food and Food Products*, Interscience Publishers, New York, I, 356–91.

[29] MACLEOD, R. A. and ONOFREY, EVA (1956), 'Nutrition and metabolism of marine bacteria. II', *J. Bact.*, 73, 661–67.

[30] WOOD, E. J. F. (1963), 'A study of the diatom flora of fresh sediments of the South Texas Bays and adjacent waters', *Inst. Mar. Sci. Publ.*, 9, 237–310.

[31] MACLEOD, R. A. and ONOFREY, EVA (1957), 'Nutrition and metabolism of marine bacteria. VI', *Can. J. Microbiol.*, 3, 753–59.

[32] MACLEOD, R. A. and ONOFREY, EVA (1963), 'Studies on the stability of the sodium requirements of marine bacteria', *Symp. Marine Microbiol.*, Ch. 45, C. H. Oppenheimer, ed, Thomas, Springfield, Ill.

[33] TOMLINSON, N. and MACLEOD, R. A. (1957), 'Nutrition and metabolism of marine bacteria, IV', *Can. J. Microbiol.*, **3**, 627–38.

[34] MACLEOD, R. A., HOGENKAMP, H., and ONOFREY EVA (1958), 'Nutrition and metabolism of marine bacteria, VII', *J. Bact.*, **75**, 460–66.

[35] MACLEOD, R. A., HORI, A., and FOX, SYLVIA M. (1960), 'Nutrition and metabolism of marine bacteria, X', *Can. J. Microbiol.*, **6**, 639–44.

[36] MACLEOD, R. A., HORI, A., and FOX, SYLVIA M. (1960), 'Nutrition and metabolism of marine bacteria, IX', *Can. J. Biochem. Physiol.*, **38**, 693–701.

[37] MACLEOD, R. A. and HORI, A. (1960), 'Nutrition and metabolism of marine bacteria, VIII', *J. Bact.*, **80**, 464–71.

[38] JONES, G. E. (1963), 'Suppression of bacterial growth by sea water', *Symp. Marine Microbiol.*, Ch. 53, C. H. Oppenheimer, ed. Thomas, Springfield, Ill.

[38] PROVASOLI, L. (1958), 'Nutrition and ecology of protozoa and algae', *Ann. Rev. Microbiol.*, **12**, 279–308.

[40] KETCHUM, B. H. (1954), 'Mineral nutrition of phytoplankton', *Ann. Rev. Plant Physiol.*, **5**, 55–74.

[41] HARVEY, H. W. (1947), 'Manganese and the growth of plankton', *J. Mar. Biol. Ass. U.K.*, **26**, 562–79.

[42] HALLDAL, P. (1957), 'Importance of calcium and magnesium ions in phototaxis of marine algae', *Nature*, **179**, 215–16.

[43] GOLDBERG, E. D. (1952), 'Iron assimilation by marine diatoms', *Biol. Bull.*, **102**, 243–48.

[44] POSTGATE, J. R. (1956), 'Iron and the synthesis of cytochrome $c_3$', *J. Gen. Microbiol.*, **15**, 186–193.

[45] HENDEY, N. I. (1951), 'Littoral diatoms of Chichester Harbour with special reference to fouling', *J. Roy. Micro. Soc.*, **71**, 1–86.

[46] FOGG, G. E. (1955), 'The importance of extracellular products of algae in fresh water', *Proc. Int. Ass. theor. appl. Limnol.*, **12**, 219–32.

[47] MULDER, E. E. (1948), 'Importance of molybdenum in the nitrogen metabolism', *Plant and Soil*, **1**, 94–119.

[48] LUND, J. W. G. (1950), 'Studies on *Asterionella formosa* Haas, II', *J. Ecol.*, **38**, 1–35.

[49] HART, T. (1934), 'On the phytoplankton of the south-west Atlantic and the Bellingshausen Sea, 1929–1931', *Discovery Repts.*, **8**, 3–268.

[50] HART, T. (1942), 'Phytoplankton periodicity in Antarctic surface waters', *Discovery Repts.*, **21**, 261–356.

[51] PEARSALL, W. H. (1932), 'Phytoplankton in the English Lakes, II', *J. Ecol.*, **20**, 241–62.

[52] BAAS BECKING, L. G. M., WOOD, E. J. F., and KAPLAN, I. R. (1957), 'Biological processes in the estuarine environment, X', *Kon. Ned. Akad. Weten. Proc.*, **B60**, 88–102.

[53] POSTGATE, J. R. (1952), 'Competitive and non-competitive inhibitors of bacterial sulphate reduction', *J. Gen. Microbiol.*, **6**, 128–42.

[54] BAAS BECKING, L. G. M. and MACKAY, MARGARET (1956), 'Biological processes in the estuarine environment, V', *Kon. Ned. Akad. Weten. Proc.*, **B59**, 109–23.

[55] WOOD, E. J. F. (1946), 'Bacteria in marine environments', *Proc. Indo-Pac. Fish. Counc.*, 69–71.

[56] ZOBELL, C. E. (1946), 'Studies on redox potentials of marine sediments', *Bull. Amer. Ass. Petrol. Gas Geol.*, **30**, 477–513.

[57] SIEBERT, G. and SCHWARTZ, W. (1956), 'Untersuchungen über das vorkominen von Mikroorganismen in entstehenden Sedimenten', *Arch. Hydrobiol.*, **52**, 321–66.

[58] BAAS BECKING, L. G. M. and WOOD, E. J. F. (1956), 'Biological processes in the estuarine environment, I, II', *Kon. Ned. Akad. Weten. Proc.*, **B58**, 168–81.

[59] EMERY, K. O. and RITTENBERG, S. C. (1952), 'Early diegenesis of California Basin sediments in relation to the origin of oil', *Bull. Amer. Soc. Petrol. Geol.*, **36**, 735–806.

[60] OPPENHEIMER, C. H. (1960), 'Bacterial activity in sediments of shallow marine bays', *Geochim. Cosmochim. Acta.*, **19**, 244–60.

[61] WOOD, E. J. F. (1959), 'Some aspects of the ecology of Lake Macquarie, N.S.W. VI', *Aust. J. Mar. Freshw. Res.*, **10**, 322–40.

[62] BAAS BECKING, L. G. M., WOOD, E. J. F., and KAPLAN, I. R. (1956), 'Biological processes in the estuarine environment, VIII', *Kon. Ned. Akad. Weten. Proc.*, **B59**, 398–407.

[63] DEBYSER, J. (1952), 'Le pH de la péllicule superficielle d'une vase fluviomarine', *Compt. Rend. Acad. Sci.*, **254**, 864.

[64] SPENCER, C. F. (1956), 'The bacterial oxidation of ammonia in the sea', *J. Mar. Biol. Ass. U.K.*, **35**, 621–30.

[65] DEBYSER, J. (1952), 'Variation de pH dans l'épaisseur d'une vase fluviomarine', *Compt. Rend. Acad. Sci.*, **254**, 741.

[66] KAPLAN, I. R. (1956), 'Evidence of microbiological activity in some of the geothermal regions of New Zealand', *N.Z. J. Sci. Tech.*, **37**, 639–62.

[67] BAAS BECKING, L. G. M. (1934), *Geobiologie of Inleiding tot de Milieukunde*, van Stockum, The Hague.

[68] GILLESPIE, R. W. H. and RETTGER, L. F. (1938), 'Bacterial oxidation-reduction studies', *J. Bact.*, **36**, 605–38.

[69] BAHR, H. and SCHWARTZ, W. (1956), 'Untersuchungen zur Ökologie farblöse Schwefelmikroben', *Biol. Zeit.*, **75**, 452–64.

[70] WOOD, E. J. F. (1953), 'Reducing substances in *Zostera*', *Nature*, **172**, 916.

[71] BYWOOD, R. and CHALLENGER, F. (1953), 'The evolution of dimethyl sulphide by *Enteromorpha intestinalis*', *Biochem. J.*, **55**, 4, xxiii (abs.).

[72] PUTTER, A. (1908), 'Die Ernährung des Wassertiere', *Z. allg. Physiol.*, **7**, 283.

[73] KROGH, A. (1931), 'Dissolved substances as food for aquatic organisms', *Biol. Rev.*, **6**, 412–42.

[74] KROGH, A. (1934), 'Conditions of life at great depths in the ocean', *Ecol. Monogr.*, **4**, 430–39.

[75] PROVASOLI, L. and SHIRAHASHI, K. (1959), 'Axenic cultivation of the brine shrimp *Artemia salina*', *Biol. Bull.*, **117**, 345–55.

[76] PROVASOLI, L. SHIRAHASHI, K., and LANCE, J. R. (1959), 'Nutritional idiosyncrasies of *Artemia* and *Tigriopus* in monoxenic culture', *Ann. N.Y. Acad. Sci.*, **77**, 250–61.

[77] SHIRAHASHI, K. and PROVASOLI, L. (1959), 'Growth factors as supplements for inadequate algal foods for Tigriopus japonicus', Tohoku J. Ag. Res., 10, 89–96.
[78] PLUNKETT, M. A. and RAKESTRAW, N. W. (1955), 'Dissolved organic matter in the sea', Deep Sea Res., 3 (suppl.), 12–14.
[79] LUCAS, C. E. (1947), 'The ecological effect of external metabolites', Biol. Revs. Camb. Phil. Soc., 22, 270.
[80] LUCAS, C. E. (1961), 'Interrelationships between aquatic organisms mediated by external metabolites', Oceanography, A.A.A.S., 499–517.
[81] LUCAS, C. E. (1961), 'On the significance of external metabolites in ecology', Symp. Soc. Exp. Biol., 15, 190–206.
[82] FOGG, G. E. (1952), 'The production of an extracellular nitrogenous substance by a blue-green alga', Proc. Roy. Soc., B139, 272–97.
[83] FOGG, G. E. (1958), 'Extracellular products of phytoplankton and the estimates of primary production', Rapp. et Proc. Verb. Cons. Int. Expl. Mer, 144, 56–60.
[84] FOGG, G. E. and WESTLAKE, D. F. (1955), 'The importance of extracellular products of algae in fresh water', Proc. Int. Ass. appl. Limnol., 12, 219–32.
[85] DUURSMA, M. (1960), 'Dissolved organic carbon, nitrogen and phosphorus in the sea', Thesis Univ. Amsterdam, Wolters, Groningen, 147 pp.
[86] SMAYDA, T. J. (1963), 'Ectocrine substances and limiting factors as determinants of succession in natural phytoplankton communities', Symp. Marine Microbiol., Ch. 27, C. H. Oppenheimer, ed. Thomas, Springfield, Ill.
[87] MCLAUGHLIN, J. J. A., ZAHL, P. A., NOWAK, A., MARCHISOTTO, J., and PRAGER, J. (1960), 'Mass cultivation of some phytoplanktons', Ann. N.Y. Acad. Sci., 90, 856–65.
[88] VALLANTYNE, J. R. (1957), 'The molecular structure of organic matter in lakes and oceans, with lesser reference to sewage and soils', J. Fish. Res. Bd. Can., 14, 33–82.
[89] ERICSON, L. E. and LEWIS, L. (1953), 'On the occurrence of vitamin $B_{12}$ factors in marine algae', Arch. Kemi., 6, 427–42.
[90] BURKHOLDER, P. R. and BURKHOLDER, LILIAN M. (1956), 'Vitamin $B_{12}$ in suspended solids and marsh muds collected along the coast of Georgia', Limnol. Oceanog., 1, 202–8.
[91] COWEY, C. B. A. (1956), 'A preliminary investigation of the variation of vitamin $B_{12}$ in oceanic and coastal waters', J. Mar. Biol. Ass. U.K., 35, 609–20.
[92] WANGERSKY, P. J. (1952), 'Isolation of ascorbic acid and rhamnosides from sea water', Science, 115, 685.
[93] STARR, T. J. (1959), 'Some ecological aspects of vitamin $B_{12}$ active substances', Texas Repts. Biol. Med., 17, 49–59.
[94] DROOP, M. R. (1961), 'Vitamin $B_{12}$ and marine ecology; the response of Monochrysis lutheri', J. Mar. Biol. Ass. U.K., 41, 69–76.
[95] GUILLARD, R. R. L. and WANGERSKY, P. J. (1958), 'The production of extracellular carbohydrate by some marine flagellates', Limnol. Oceanog., 3, 449–54.

[96] LEWIN, R. A. (1956), 'Extracellular polysaccharides of green algae', *Can. J. Microbiol.*, 2, 655–72.
[97] FOGG, G. E. and BOALCH, G. T. (1958), 'Extracellular products in a pure culture of a brown alga', *Nature*, 181, 789.
[98] BERNARD, F. (1948), 'Réchérches sur le cycle de *Coccolithus fragilis* Lohm. flagellé dominant des mers chaudes', *J. Cons. Int. Expl. Mer*, 15, 177–88.
[99] BERNARD, F. (1963), 'Density of flagellates and myxophyceae in the heterotrophic layers related to environment', *Symp. Marine Microbiol.*, Ch. 22, C. H. Oppenheimer, ed. Thomas, Springfield, Ill.
[100] SCHER, S., SCHER, BARBARA, and HUTNER, S. H. (1963), 'Notes on the natural history of *Rhodopseudomonas palustris*', *Symp. Marine Microbiol.*, Ch. 54, C. H. Oppenheimer, ed. Thomas, Springfield, Ill.
[101] DROOP, M. R. (1957), 'Vitamin $B_{12}$ in marine ecology', *Nature*, 180, 1041–42.
[102] DAISLEY, K. W. (1957), 'Vitamin $B_{12}$ in marine ecology', *Nature*, 180, 1042–43.
[103] BENTLEY, JOYCE A. (1960), 'Plant hormones in marine phytoplankton, zooplankton, and sea water', *J. Mar. Biol. Ass. U.K.*, 39, 433–44.
[104] LEFEVRE, M. and FARRUGIA, GISÈLE (1958), 'De l'influence sur les algues de l'eau douce des produits de la composition spontanée des substances organiques d'origin animale et végétale', *Hydrobiol.*, 10, 49–65.
[105] JÖRGENSEN, E. G. and STEEMANN NIELSEN, E. (1961), 'Effects of filtrates from cultures of unicellular algae on the growth of *Staphylococcus aureus*', *Physiol. Plant*, 14, 896–908.
[106] ROSENFELD, W. D. and ZOBELL, C. E. (1947), 'Antibiotic production by marine organisms', *J. Bact.*, 54, 393–98.
[107] GRIEN, A. and MEYERS, S. P. (1958), 'Growth characteristics and antibiotic production of actinomycetes isolated from littoral sediments and materials suspended in sea water', *J. Bact.*, 76, 457–63.
[108] DEMNY, T. C., MILLER, I. M., and WOODRUFF, H. B. (1961), 'Occurrence of a variety of Actinomycetes isolated from marine materials', *Symp. Marine Microbiol.* (abs.) *S.A.B. Bact. Proc.* D10, 47.
[109] CARLUCCI, A. F. and PRAMER, D. (1960), 'An evaluation of factors affecting the survival of *Escherichia coli* in sea water', *Appl. Microbiol.*, 8, 247–56.
[110] STEEMANN NIELSEN, E. (1955), 'The production of antibiotics by plankton algae and its effect upon bacterial activities in the sea', *Deep Sea Res.*, (suppl.), 3, 181–86.
[111] SIEBURTH, J. MCN. (1959), 'Gastro-intestinal flora of antarctic birds', *J. Bact.*, 77, 521–31.
[112] ALLEN, MARY BELLE and DAWSON, E. Y. (1960), 'Production of antibacterial substances by benthic tropical marine algae', *J. Bact.*, 79, 459–60.
[113] CHESTERS, C. G. C. and SCOTT, J. A. (1956), 'The production of antibiotic substances by sea weeds', *2nd Internat. Seaweed Symp.*, Pergamon Press, New York.
[114] BURKHOLDER, P. R., BURKHOLDER, LILIAN M., and ALMODOVAR,
L

L. R. (1960), 'Antibiotic activity of some marine algae of Puerto Rico', *Botan. Marina*, **2**, 149–56.

[115] WELCH, ANNE M. (1962), 'Preliminary survey of fungistatic properties of marine algae', *J. Bact.*, **83**, 97–99.

[116] RUBENTSCHIK, L., ROISIN, R. B., and BIELJANSKY, F. J. (1936), 'Adsorption of bacteria in salt lakes', *J. Bact.*, **32**, 11.

[117] HENRICI, A. T. (1939), 'Distribution of bacteria in lakes', *Amer. Ass. Adv. Sci.*, **10**, 39–64.

[118] WOOD, E. J. F. and OPPENHEIMER, C. H. (1962), 'Note on fluorescence microscopy in marine microbiology', *Z. allg. Mikrobiol.*, **2**, 164–65.

CHAPTER 7

# Pathological Micro-organisms in Hydrobiology

The effects of diseases and parasites on the populations in the seas are fundamental to the ecology of marine environments.

## Diseases of Marine Animals

The study of diseases of marine animals is somewhat fragmentary, as such work has been done in response to particular needs, i.e. on particular diseases affecting an animal of economic importance, such as the furunculosis of salmon and trout (Duff [1]) or the 'milkiness' of barracouta, also known as 'pap snoek' (Gilchrist [2], Willis [3]). There are several reasons for this. As ZoBell [4], p. 175, remarks: 'Conditions in the sea are not conducive to the production of pathogenic micro-organisms' because many sick animals drop out of the school or are soon caught and eaten by predators and so removed from contact with the rest of the population. Most diseases are specific and the predator is unaffected by it. When the fish are herded or occur in schools in confined locations away from predators (e.g. salmon), microbial diseases do become important. In the case of barracouta (*Thyrsites atun*), these fish are predators with a large mouth and unpleasant teeth, and it is a courageous predator who will attack them; therefore epizootics do occur. Another reason for lack of interest in animal pathology in the sea is that little can be done to control diseases there, as no selection or segregation is possible, nor are therapeutic measures practicable, except perhaps in certain estuarine fisheries. Further, there is no instance of a disease of fish attacking man or land animals apart from *Goniaulax* toxification of shellfish. This rules out any serious investigations by the two most numerous groups of microbiologists, the veterinary and the medical, while marine microbiologists are too few and the general field of research too wide to justify an intense investigation by these workers into animal pathology in the sea. A few workers have carried out limited investigations out of interest, but this has largely been confined to new growths in an attempt to increase our knowledge of cancer. In 1953, a symposium was held under the auspices of the American Fisheries Society, and the work of this is summarized in the *Transactions*. Oppenheimer [5, 6] has studied some marine fish diseases in order to find out whether epizootics may contribute to such phenomena as the disappearance of pilchards from the Californian coast.

## Bacterial Diseases

One frequently reads in the literature about diseases in fresh and salt water aquaria. Usually, however, the epizootic is over before the microbiologist is called in. In many cases a fluorescent *Pseudomonas* is isolated, but it is not always possible to satisfy Koch's postulates, i.e. reinoculate a healthy fish from the culture and reproduce the disease, and then re-isolate the organism from the infected fish. I have encountered this difficulty on several occasions. The probable reason for this is given by Duff [7], who has shown that *Pseudomonas (Bacillus) salmonicida*, the causal organism of furunculosis, tends to change from the pathogenic S- to the non-pathogenic R-form on prolonged cultivation. although it was possible by suitable means to reproduce the pathogenic S-form. The same phenomenon is also frequent in the *Pseudomonas (Phytomonas)* strains causing plant diseases, so it may be very difficult to establish the aetiology of a disease although the causal organism has been isolated in pure culture.

Among the records of bacterial diseases of salt water fish may be cited: A tumour-like lesion in *Trachurus* from which Fabre-Domergue [8] isolated a fluorescent *Pseudomonas*; furunculosis of salmon and trout on which a great deal of work has been done in Europe and America and is caused by a *Pseudomonas (Acetomonas)*, Griffin *et al.* [9], although called *Bacillus salmonicidus* by Williamson [10] and *Bacterium salmonicida* by Duff. This disease has been described in Europe by Emmerich and Weibel [11], Babes and Riegler [12], Plehn [13], in Britain by Patterson [14], Arkwright [15], Williamson [10], and in America by Marsh [16], Drew [17], Harrison [18], Duff and Stewart [19]. Blake and Anderson [20] showed that the Scottish strains are serologically homogenous and Plehn and Trommdorf [21] state that although *P. salmonicida* and *P. fluorescens* are both pathogenic to trout, they do not cross-agglutinate and so must be distinguished. ZoBell and Wells [22] found *Pseudomonas ichthyodermus* to be the causal agent of a dermatitis in *Fundulus parvipennis*, and Hodgkiss and Shewan [23] found a *Pseudomonas* infection in plaice, while Oppenheimer [24] recorded one causing tail rot on cod. It would appear that there are at least four species of fluorescent *Pseudomonas* which can and do cause diseases of fish, and that there is a considerable variation in the pathogenicity of these species. Horne [24] found apparently healthy salmon which gave blood cultures positive for *P. salmonicida* and he regards such fish as reservoirs of infection (carriers). Apparently there is an immunity similar to that post-infectional immunity which characterizes certain diseases of humans.

A *Hemophilus, H. piscium*, has been recorded as infecting fish by Snieszko and Friddle [26] and Griffin and Friddle [27]. There are several records of Mycobacteria in salt water fish. Moore [28] described tuberculous lesions in cod, and isolated a *Mycobacterium* and a *Staphylococcus*; Calmette [29] recorded diseases of fish, amphibia, and reptiles due to Mycobacteria. Aronson [30] described *Mycobacterium marinum* as a fish pathogen and other pathogenic mycobacteria have been described by Baker and Hagan [31] and Earp, Ellis, and Ordal [32]. Anderson [33] described a skin ulcer in fish, associated with *Staphylococcus aureus* and *Escherichia coli* and Davis [34], Garnjobst [35], and Nigrelli and Hutner [36] describe a myxobacterium, *Chondrococcus columnaris* (Davis, Ordal, and Rucker), causing an infection of the skin, gills, and fins of salt water fish.

Bacterial diseases of lobsters have been recorded by Snieszko and Taylor [37] who found a non-pigmented *Staphylococcus* which gave acid from carbohydrates, and by Hess [38] who found a chitinovorous bacterium apparently attacking the shell of live lobsters, and in one case causing an epizootic; the organism was not described. Inman [39] recorded a luminous bacterium which he considered pathogenic to sand fleas, confirming the findings of Giard and Billet [40]. Apparently the relation between the crustacea and the bacterium is symbiotic or commensal with an occasional upset of the balance towards pathogenicity.

### Virus Diseases

Virus diseases have been recorded from several marine fish. The lympho-cystis disease of pike-perch (*Stizosteidon vitreum*) and flounder reported by Nigrelli and Smith [41], of mullet (*Mullexus surmuletus*) by Alexandrowicz [42] and of the file fish (*Ceratocanthus schoepfii*) by Weissenberg [43] appears to be a virus disease and produces cell inclusions in the tumours. Other suspected virus diseases are fish pox, infectious dropsy of carp, kidney disease, etc. (Watson [44]). Moewus [45] has shown how viruses could be transmitted from one marine animal to another by means of an intermediate host, in this case a ciliate.

### Fungus Diseases

Fungi belonging to the Saprolegniaceae are commonly found associated with diseases of fresh water fish, but do not seem to occur in marine fish.

Sproston [46] recorded an *Ichthyosporidium* and Fish [47] another fungus on salt water fish, and Newcombe and Rogers [48] found *Lagenidium callinectes* parasitic on blue crab eggs. It is possible too that *Erysipelothrix* may attack fish and be transferred by them to fishermen (Sheard and Dicks [49], Oppenheimer [50]). A fungus parasite has been described as infecting sponges in the Bahamas (Brown *et al.* [50]) and in British Honduras (Smith [51]). Smith considers that the high salinities and temperatures were the primary causes of the epizootic, allowing the fungus, which is always present, to become pathogenic.

*Protozoan Diseases*

Wenyon [52] lists 180 species of fish in which blood parasites of the genera *Haemogregarina*, *Trypanosoma*, *Trypanoplasma*, *Globidium*, *Haemohormidium*, and *Herpetomonas* have been observed. This author records that trypanosomes have been recorded from the blood but not intestines of fresh water fish, and from the intestines but not the blood of marine fish. Among marine invertebrates, schizogregarines are present as parasites on tunicates, arthropods, and annelids, while the spirochaete *Cristispira balbianii* was recorded from oysters by Certes [53]; spirochaetes have been recorded from fish by Henry [54].

Although records of protozoan infections of fish are exceedingly numerous, reports of serious epizootics are not frequent. *Chloromyxum* infections in snoek or barracouta and other scombroid fishes have been recorded by Gilchrist [2], Perard [55], McGonigle and Leim [56], Woolcock [57], Hahn [58], Fujita [59], and Willis [3], and can cause serious destruction in commercial fisheries, and *Eimeria* of herring and pilchards (Fujita [60]) also affects commercial fisheries at times.

## Diseases of Marine Plants

*Bacterial Diseases*

Bacterial diseases of marine plants are few, although bacterial decomposition of dead and dying algae on the beaches is so rapid as to indicate that the bacteria must have been present in the living algal community. Brandt [61] found a bacterial infection causing 'black rot' of kelp (*Macrocystis pyrifera*) on the Californian coast. More careful cutting of the beds and cooler water brought the disease under control, so the organism would seem to be a facultative parasite. Catacuzene [62] related bacterial infection with tumours on Irish Moss (*Chondrus crispus*) and *Sarcorhiza bulbosa*. In other cases, actual pathogenicity of bacteria on marine plants does not seem to have been proved. Many algae which produce antibiotics probably do so to keep down bacterial or fungal infections.

## Virus Diseases

Phages have been recorded from *Chondrococcus columnaris*, which is itself a pathogen, by Anacker and Ordal [63]. Marine phages for *Photobacterium fischeri* and other marine bacteria are reported by Kriss and Rukina [64], and Spencer [65–68]. In his latest paper [68], Spencer gives detailed methods for the isolation of phages from the sea. Lewin [69] recorded a virus infection of a blue-green alga.

There seems to be sufficient evidence that marine viruses and phages may be more important in the sea than has been realized, as there has been no effort to estimate possible virus infections in plankton swarms or phytoplankton blooms, where one would expect them to have maximum effect, or to study the occurrence of phages in decomposing plankton blooms or organic sediments. They might well play a major part in succession.

## Fungal Diseases

Parasitic and often pathogenic fungi would seem to be both numerous and frequent in estuarine and marine plants, and have been recorded by a number of authors including Sutherland [70], Scherfel [71], Sparrow [72], Cienkowski [73], Petersen [74], Kibbe [75], Zeller [76], Renn [77], Aleem [78], Arasaki *et al.* [79], and Tutin [80]. The slime fungus (Myxomycete) *Labyrinthula* was found associated with *Ophiobolus salinus* in *Zostera* suffering from 'wasting disease' and both these fungi were regarded by different workers as the cause of the disease. The *Zostera* beds of Europe and north-east America were completely devastated, as has been stated in a previous chapter, and as the sea-grasses frequently govern the plant and animal associations of the estuaries, this devastation had a most serious effect on the ecology and economy of the areas concerned, an effect which in some areas has persisted to the present day. Sparrow recorded a *Labyrinthula* from the diatom *Rhizosolenia* and the green alga *Cladophora*; he also found a number of chytridiaceous fungi which differ from fresh water chytrids in having biciliate zoospores, i.e. represent truly marine forms. Many of these are parasitic, and some, e.g. *Ectrogella perforans* and *Rhizophydium* spp., are regarded by him as likely to cause serious epiphytotics of diatoms, especially *Licmophora abbreviata*, *Striatella unipunctata*, and *Rhizosolenia* spp. He considers that these fungi might well be limiting factors in diatom production under certain conditions, and that they might also be important in the degradation of plant remains in marine sediments. Most of these forms were found on both sides of the Atlantic, and Sparrow considers that they are probably widely distributed in the sea, and therefore of considerable ecological importance. He was not able to prove that living diatoms in the plankton were heavily infested, though he had some evidence that this was so at times. Other algae attacked by pathogenic fungi (*Chytridium* and *Rhizophydium*) include *Codium*, *Pelvetia*, *Ceramium*, *Polysiphonia*, *Ectocarpus*, *Sphacelaria*, *Callithamnion*, *Alaria*, and *Bryopsis*, all important algae in the estuarine environment. Sparrow found a *Pleolpidium* (*Rozella*) as a parasite on *Chytridium polysiphoniae*, itself a parasite on *Polysiphonia fibrillosa*. *Ectrogella perforans* was found to attack the ciliate *Vorticella* as well as diatoms, having been ingested by the ciliate along with the diatom.

*Protozoan Diseases*
Sparrow has reported a Protomyxa-like form as symbiotic with a fungus *Sirolpidium bryopsidis* parasitic in the alga *Bryopsis*.

*Algae*
A blue-green alga, *Richelia intracellularis*, occurs in the cells of several species of the diatoms *Rhizosolenia* and *Pleurosigma*. It is probably endophytic rather than parasitic. At times, the diatoms contain very little chlorophyll, so the *Richelia* may help to provide the diatom with photosynthate.

**Some Conclusions**
Plant diseases in marine environments could have recognizable ecological effects in several ways:

(*a*) They could lower productivity by destroying major planktonic or periphytic elements, or lower certain ecological ratios, thus altering the association or even the ecosystem. Canter and Lund [81] have shown that chytrid infection of *Asterionella formosa* does not alter the maximum production of the bloom, as this is controlled by nutrients, but it does delay the bloom, so that, if there were in the lake another unparasitized competitor, e.g. *Anabaena*, a marked change could result. This might be the explanation of some of the results recorded by Hutchinson and others studying the periodicity of plankton blooms in lakes. The same general principles would apply in estuaries and in the sea, but the effects might be more complex and harder to resolve.

(*b*) They could remove deleterious organisms such as the slime-forming algae of the sea-grass flats, and thus improve the pasture.

(*c*) They could indirectly affect the chemical and physical environment by premature destruction of the host, e.g. oxygen tension, phosphate availability, redox potential, or pH.

# REFERENCES

[1] DUFF, D. C. B. (1932), 'Furunculosis or fish boils in game fish', *Vancouver Mus. Art Notes*, **7**, 16.

[2] GILCHRIST, J. D. F. (1924), 'A protozoal parasite *Chloromyxum thyrsites* sp. n. of the Cape sea fish the Snoek (*Thyrsites atun* Euphr.)', *Trans. Roy. Soc. S. Africa*, **11**, 263.

[3] WILLIS, A. G. (1949), 'On the vegetative forms and life history of *Chloromyxum thyrsites* Gilchrist and its doubtful systematic position', *Aust. J. Sci. Res.*, Ser. **B**, **2**, 379.

[4] ZOBELL, C. E. (1946), *Marine Microbiology*, Chronica Botanica Press, Waltham, Mass., 240 pp.

[5] OPPENHEIMER, C. H. (1953), 'Why study marine fish diseases?' *J. Cons. Int. Expl. Mer*, **29**, 39–43.

[6] OPPENHEIMER, C. H. (1955), 'The effect of marine bacteria on the development and hatching of pelagic fish eggs and the control of such bacteria by antibiotics', *Copeia*, **1**, 43–49.

[7] DUFF, D. C. B. (1937), 'Dissociation in *Bacillus salmonicida*', *J. Bact.*, **34**, 49.

[8] FABRE-DOMERGUE, M. (1890), 'Sur une tumeur d'origine bactérienne obsérvée chez *Caranx trachurus* (Lacep.)', *C.R. Mem. Soc. Biol.*, Paris, **42**, 391–93.

[9] GRIFFIN, P. H., SNIESZKO, S. F., and FRIDDLE, S. B. (1953), 'A more comprehensive description of *Bacterium salmonicida*', *Trans. Amer. Fish. Soc.*, **82**, 128–38.

[10] WILLIAMSON, I. J. F. (1929), 'A study of the bacterial infection in fish and certain other lower invertebrates', *Fish. Bd. Scot. Salmon Fish.*, **II**, 1–28.

[11] EMMERICH, R. and WEIBEL, E. (1894), 'Über eine durch Bakterien erzeugte Seuche under den Forellen', *Arch. Hyg.*, **21**, 1.

[12] BABES, V. and RIEGLER, P. (1909), 'Über ein Fischepidemie bei Bukharest', *Zent. Bakt.*, **I**, **33**, 438.

[13] PLEHN, MARIANNE (1909), 'Die Furunkulose bei Salmoniden', *Zent. Bakt.*, **II**, **52**, 468.

[14] PATTERSON, J. (1903), 'On the cause of salmon disease', *Rept. Fish. Bd. Scot. 1903*, 1–21.

[15] ARKWRIGHT, J. A. (1912), 'An epidemic disease affecting the salmon and trout in England during the summer of 1911', *J. Hyg.*, **12**, 391.

[16] MARSH, M. C. (1902), 'A more complete description of *B. truttae*', *Bull. U.S. Comm.*, **22**, 411.

[17] DREW, G. H. (1909), 'Some notes on parasitic and other diseases of fish', *Parasitol.*, **2**, 193.

[18] HARRISON, F. C. (1918), 'Examination of affected salmon, Miramichi Hatchery, N.B.', *Contr. Can. Biol. Fish.*, **38A**, 149–68.

[19] DUFF, D. C. B. and STEWART, B. J. (1933), 'Studies on the furunculosis of fish in British Columbia', *Contr. Can. Biol. Fish.*, **8**, 105.

[20] BLAKE, I. and ANDERSON, E. J. M. (1930), 'The identification of *Bacillus salmonicida* by the complement fixation test', *Fish. Scot. Salmon Fish.*, **1**.

158 · MARINE MICROBIAL ECOLOGY

[21] PLEHN, MARIANNE and TROMMDORFF, R. (1916), 'Bacterium salmonicida und Bacterium fluorescens zwei wohldifferentierte Bakterien', Zent. Bakt., I, 78, 142.
[22] ZOBELL, C. E. and WELLS, N. A. (1934), 'An infectious dermatitis of certain marine fishes', J. Inf. Dis., 55, 199.
[23] HODGKISS, W. and SHEWAN, J. M. (1950), 'Pseudomonas infection in a plaice', J. Path. Bact., 62, 655.
[24] OPPENHEIMER, C. H. (1958), 'A bacterium causing fin rot in the Norwegian cod', Publ. Inst. Mar. Sci. Texas, 5, 160–62.
[25] HORNE, J. H. (1938), 'Furunculosis in trout and the importance of carriers in the spread of the disease', J. Hyg., 28, 67.
[26] SNIESZKO, S. F. and FRIDDLE, S. B. (1948) 1950, 'A contribution to the etiology of ulcer disease of trout', Trans. Amer. Fish. Soc., 78, 56–63.
[27] GRIFFIN, P. J. and FRIDDLE, S. B. (1950), 'A new bacterium (Hemophilus piscium n. sp.) from ulcer disease of trout', J. Bact., 59, 699–710.
[28] MOORE, A. D. (1912), 'A review of piscine tubercle with a description of an acid-fast bacillus found in cod', Liverpool Biol. Soc., 27, 219–25.
[29] CALMETTE, A. (1923), Tubercule Bacillus and Tuberculosis, Williams Wilkins, Baltimore.
[30] ARONSON, J. D. (1926), 'Spontaneous tuberculosis in salt water fish', J. Inf. Dis., 39, 315.
[31] BAKER, J. A. and HOGAN, W. K. (1942), 'Tuberculosis of the Mexican Platyfish Platypoecilus maculatus', J. Inf. Dis., 70, 248–52.
[32] EARP, B. J., ELLIS, C. H., and ORDAL, E. J. (1953), 'Kidney disease in young salmon', Wash. Dept. Fish. Spec. Rept. Ser. 1, 74 pp.
[33] ANDERSON, A. G. (1909), 'Bacteriological investigations as to the cause of an outbreak of a disease amongst fish at the marine laboratory, Bay of Nigg, Aberdeen', Ann. Rept. Fish. Bd. Scot., 28, 38–45.
[34] DAVIS, H. S. (1922), 'A new bacterial disease of fresh water fishes,' U.S. Bur. Fish., 88, 261.
[35] GARNJOBST, L. (1945), 'Cytophaga columnaris in pure culture; a myxomycete pathogenic to fish', J. Bact., 49, 113.
[36] NIGRELLI, R. F. and HUTNER, S. H. (1945), 'The presence of a myxobacterium Chondrococcus columnaris (Davis) Ordal and Rucker, 1944, on Fundulus heteroclitus L.', Zoologica, 30, 101.
[37] SNIESZKO, S. F. and TAYLOR, C. C. (1947), 'A bacterial disease of the lobster Homarus americanus', Science, 105, 500.
[38] HESS, E. (1937), 'Chitinovorous bacteria on live lobsters', Biol. Bd. Can. Prog. Rept., 19.
[39] INMAN, O. L. (1927), 'A pathogenic luminous bacterium,' Biol. Bull., 53, 97.
[40] GIARD, A. and BILLET, A. (1889), 'Obsérvations sur la maladie phosphorescènte des talitres et autre crustacea', Compt. Rend. Soc. Biol., Paris, 1, 39, 593.
[41] NIGRELLI, R. F. and SMITH, G. M. (1939), 'Studies on the Lymphocystis disease in the orange filefish Ceratocanthus schoepfii (Walbaum) from Sandy Hook Bay, N.J.', Zoologica, 24, 255.
[42] ALEXANDROWICZ, J. S. (1951), 'Lymphocystis tumours in the red mullet (Mullexus surmuletus, L.)', J. Mar. Biol. Ass. U.K., 30, 315.

[43] WEISSENBERG, R. (1945), 'Studies on virus diseases of fish, IV. Lymphocystis disease in the Centrarchidae', Zoologica, 30, 169.

[44] WATSON, S. W. (1953), 'Virus diseases of fish', Trans. Amer. Fish. Soc., 83, 331–41.

[45] MOEWUS LISELOTTE (1963), 'Studies on a parasitic marine ciliate as a possible virus vector', Symp. Mar. Microbiol., Ch. 35, C. H. Oppenheimer, ed. Thomas, Springfield, Ill.

[46] SPROSTON, NORA G. (1947), 'Ichthyosporidium hoferi Plehn and Mulsow, 1911, an internal fungal parasite of the mackerel', J. Mar. Biol. Ass. U.K., 26, 72.

[47] FISH, F. F. (1934), 'A fungus disease of fishes in the Gulf of Maine', Parasitol., 26, 1.

[48] NEWCOMBE, C. L. and ROGERS, M. B. (1947), 'Studies on a fungus parasite which infects blue crab eggs', Turtox News, 25, 9.

[49] SHEARD, K. and DICKS, H. G. (1949), 'Skin lesions among fishermen at Houtmans Abrolhos, W.A., with an account of Erysipeloid of Rosenbach', Med. J. Aust., 2, 352.

[50] BROWN, H. H., GALTSOFF, P. S., SMITH, C. C., and SMITH, F. G. W. (1939), 'Sponge mortality in the Bahamas', Nature, 143, 807.

[51] SMITH, F. G. W. (1941), 'Sponge disease in British Honduras and its transmission by water currents', Ecology, 22, 415.

[52] WENYON, C. M. (1925), Protozoology, Williams Wilkins, Baltimore.

[53] CERTES, A. (1884), 'Sur la culture à l'abri des germes atmosphériques des eaux et des sédiments rapportés par les expéditions du Travailleur et du Talisman', C. R. Acad. Sci., Paris, 98, 690.

[54] HENRY, H. (1910), 'On the haemoprotozoa of British sea fish', J. Path. Bact., 14, 463.

[55] PERARD, C. H. (1928), 'Sur une maladie du Macquereau (Scomber scomber L.) due à une microsporidie Chloromyxum histolyticum n. s.', Compt. Rand. Acad. Sci., Paris, 186, 108.

[56] MCGONIGLE, R. H. and LEIM, A. H. (1937), 'Jellied swordfish', Prog. Rept. Atl. Biol. Sta. Can., 19, 3.

[57] WOOLCOCK, V. (1936), 'Chloromyxum pristiophori, a new species of Myxosporidian parasitic in the gall bladder of Pristiophorus cirratus (Saw shark),' J. Parasitol., 28, 72.

[58] HAHN, C. W. (1917), 'On sporozoan parasites of fishes of Woods Hole and vicinity, III', J. Parasitol., 4, 13.

[59] FUJITA, T. (1913), 'On a new species of Chloromyxum from the gall bladder of carp', Annot. Zool. Jap., 8, 257.

[60] FUJITA, T. (1933), 'Note on Eimeria of herring', Proc. 5th Pacific Sci. Cong. V., B8, 4135.

[61] BRANDT, R. P. (1923), 'Potash from Kelp. Early growth and development of the giant kelp, Macrocystis pyrifera', U.S. Dept. Agr. Bull., 1, 1191.

[62] CANTACUZENE, A. (1932, 1930), 'Contributions à l'étude des tumeurs bactériennes chez les algues marines', Theses Univ. Paris (abst. in Bibliog. Oceanog., 3, 246).

[63] ANACKER, R. L. and ORDAL, E. J. (1955), 'Study of bacteriophage infecting the Myxobacterium Chondrococcus columnaris', J. Bact., 70, 738–41.

[64] KRISS, A. E. and RUKINA, E. A. (1947), 'Bacteriophage in the sea', *Doklady Akad. Nauk. S.S.S.R.*, 57, 833–36.

[65] SPENCER, R. (1955), 'Marine bacteriophage', *Food Inv. Bd. Mem.*, 916.

[66] SPENCER, R. (1957), 'Thermal inactivation of a "marine" bacteriophage', *J. Gen. Microbiol.*, 16, proc. vi-vii.

[67] SPENCER, R. (1960), 'Indigenous marine bacteriophages', *J. Bact.*, 79, 614–17.

[68] SPENCER, R. (1963), 'Bacterial viruses in the sea', *Symp. Marine Microbiol.*, Ch. 34, C. H. Oppenheimer, ed. Thomas, Springfield, Ill.

[69] LEWIN, R. A. (1962), 'Viruses of marine algae', *Symp. Marine Microbiol.*, Chicago, abstr.

[70] SUTHERLAND, G. K. (1915), 'New marine fungi in *Pelvetia*', *New Phytol.*, 14, 33.

[71] SCHERFEL, A. (1925), 'Endophytische Phycomyceten. Parasiten der Bacillariaceen und eine neue Monadinen', *Arch. Protist.*, 52, 1.

[72] SPARROW, F. K. (1936), 'Biological observations on marine fungi of Woods Hole waters', *Biol. Bull.*, 70, 236.

[73] CIENKOWSKI, K. (1867), 'Über den Bau und die Entwicklung der Labyrinthulen', *Arch. Mikro. Anat.*, 3, 274.

[74] PETERSEN, H. E. (1905), 'Contributions à la connaissance des phycomycètes marins (Chytridineae, Fischer)', *Overs. Kgl. Danske Vidensk. Selsk. Forh.*, 439–88.

[75] KIBBE, ALICE (1916), '*Chytridium alarum* on *Alaria fistulosa*', *Publ. Puget Sod. Biol. Sta.*, 1, 221–26.

[76] ZELLER, S. M. (1916), 'Fungi found on *Codium mucronatum*', *Publ. Puget Sod. Biol. Sta.*, 2, 121–25.

[77] RENN, C. E. (1936), 'The wasting disease of *Zostera*', *Biol. Bull.*, 70, 148.

[78] ALEEM, A. A. (1953), 'Marine fungi from the west coast of Sweden', *Ark. Bot.*, 3, 1, 1–32.

[79] ARASAKI, S., INOUYE, A., and KOCHI, Y. (1960), 'The disease of cultured *Porphyra* with special reference to the cancer-disease and the chytrid disease which occurred in the culture field in Tokyo Bay in 1950–60', *Bull. Jap. Soc. Sci. Fish.*, 26, 1074–81.

[80] TUTIN, T. G. (1934), 'The fungus on *Zostera marina*', *Nature*, 134, 573.

[81] CANTER, H. M. and LUND, J. W. G. (1951), 'Studies in plankton parasites, III', *Ann. Bot.*, 15, 359–71.

# CHAPTER 8

# Ecosystems of the Marine World

It is possible, of course, to consider the marine world as a single ecosystem, but such an ecosystem would be far too vast and complicated. Dividing this into smaller ecosystems means that these will not be mutually independent, and the degree of independence will differ from one to the next. It is probably best, and in accord with general practice, to separate oceanic and estuarine communities, and then planktonic and benthic communities. We can thus consider these four communities and their habitats as four ecosystems, and must, in the light of our present knowledge, add a fifth, the *aphotic* ecosystem of the oceans. It may, however, be more convenient to consider the benthic and planktonic habitats of the estuaries as a single ecosystem, and to add to this the habitat of the *periphyton* (the epontic organisms). There will be at times an aphotic region in the estuarine ecosystem, but it is much more a transition area between the planktonic and benthic communities than a separate habitat or community.

## The Oceanic Planktonic Ecosystem

It will be realized from what has already been said in the discussion of productivity and production, that our quantitative knowledge of this ecosystem is negligible, though, at that, it is greater than that of the other ecosystems. On the qualitative side, we are a little better off, and the reader will see the deficiencies for himself as they occur.

Because of the relative constancy of the oceanic environment, as pointed out in Chapter 2, a large number of species are to be found through all latitudes, and in all oceans, although other forms, more sensitive to temperature or other factor are restricted by latitude, but may be bipolar or circumpolar or may occur in corresponding regions in the Atlantic, Pacific, and Indian Oceans. Because the volume of water in the oceans is so vast in comparison with the surface presented at the bottom-water interface, the water dictates the conditions of life, except near the shore, where bottom, shore, and drainage from land play a varying part. For this reason, there is a neritic as well as an oceanic flora and fauna to be distinguished, and neritic forms may differ from estuarine forms, in which fresh water affects the environment more strongly. At the mouths of big rivers such as the Amazon, and the Congo, fresh water characters and communities extend beyond the estuary into the oceans.

The movement of organisms which cannot swim rapidly, i.e. plankton, including the planktonic larvae of sedentary forms, is controlled by ocean currents which vary in their courses from time to time, and in some areas, e.g. Torres Strait, may be seasonally reversed. Variations in the course or intensity of currents cause variations in the growth and movement of plants and animals and ultimately of fish. Divergences, convergences, and upwellings have considerable biological effect. Water moving downwards takes with it photosynthetic organisms from the photic zone. It was formerly assumed that these perished rapidly, but there is increasing evidence that they may persist either in the vegetative form or as spores, and may be associated with the same body of water below the photic zone for a very long period. The finding of Antarctic diatoms in regions of upwelling off the east coast of Australia is evidence of this. These organisms must have been below the photic zone for a number of years, as the Antarctic water passes under the tropical water off the east Tasmanian coast as it moves across the Tasman Sea to New Zealand. Water moving upward brings spores and vegetative forms of phytoplankton, which may form blooms under favourable conditions. It is not unusual for a water mass to disappear under another water mass of lower density and reappear on the far side of it, in which case it may still contain the same plant community, though separated by a distinct community associated with the second water mass. As an example may be cited the disappearance of certain diatoms and dinoflagellates of the East Australian Current between Cape Howe and St Helens in Tasmania and their reappearance off the east coast of Tasmania which were recorded by Crosby and Wood [1]. Phytoplankton associated with a given water mass may remain with its characteristics unaltered for many thousands of miles and through a considerable range of temperature: for instance, diatom and dinoflagellate species occurring in the tropical waters of the Coral Sea will remain in the surface current flowing south along the coast of eastern Australia and still be found in the water when it reaches the vicinity of New Zealand, some 3,000 miles from its source, although the temperature is considerably lower (30° to about 15°C). The more stenothermal species have disappeared, and it is by a study of such differences in the behaviour of plankton species that the ecology of the region becomes intelligible. A difficulty in associating hydrological concepts of water mass with biological communities is that the latter may continue for a time after conditions have ceased to be favourable, i.e. may extend from one water mass into another; at other times, and with other communities, the physico-chemical environment is strictly limiting. An example of the first community is the west Tasmanian facies of the south-west Australian community of Wood [2] which is similar to, and obviously derived from, the tropical Indian Ocean community though now separated by other facies. There is evidence that it may still be reinforced from time to time from the original source. An example of the second type of community is the appearance of the high temperature–low salinity diatom–dinoflagellate community of the Arafura Sea on occasion on the east coast of Australia. The community is marked by such species as *Ceratium dens* and *Chaetoceros messanense*, and occurs as pockets of low salinity water in the high-salinity–high-temperature water of the East Australian Current. For the above reasons, I have referred to communities rather than ecosystems in the papers quoted, though more consistent data may enable us to get a unified conception of the planktonic communities and their habitats.

Because of the high dilution of the majority of elements in the ocean, the depletion of one or more of them by biological utilization, chemical precipitation, or a valence change may have a profound effect on the population, especially the plant population in the area, which effect may be transient, e.g. a protoplankton bloom, or of long duration, e.g. long-term fluctuations in fish movements, many of which are considered to be cyclic. Although one can frequently delimit the distribution of a species of protoplankton by the salinity–temperature data, the cause of the distribution patterns of many species may well be due to the availability of minor elements, e.g. sulphur, iron, and silica or perhaps even less obvious ones, or to the presence of organic exocrines. Because of the diffusibility of ions in sea water, and of the continuity of movement, it would seem on theoretical grounds that critical depletion of ions, even of trace elements, would occur only on rare occasions. Most organisms concentrate chemical elements, so that plankton swarms as they decay would tend to release them and thus regenerate the conditions for growth. One might assume that the limiting factors for the standing crop of microbial plankton could be growth factors and the grazing rate of non-photosynthetic organisms, and innate rhythms may also play a part. Growth factors and antibiotics are both produced during red tides, as has been discussed in Chapter 6. Protoplankton blooms in east Australian waters usually consist of a succession of peaks by different species, one species declining as the other increases. The main peak of each species is usually followed by a smaller, somewhat ineffectual peak. The failure of a species to maintain its superiority in the community is not due to its disappearance from the community; it could be due to a diminishing wave of biological activity intrinsic in the organism, or to pressure from other members of the community.

## Bacteria in the Oceans

The functions ascribed to marine bacteria have already been discussed. Adsorption, already considered at some length, is nowhere more important than in sea water, microscopic examination of which shows that nearly all the bacteria are adsorbed on particles, and that the distribution is more even than in the sediments. Viable and direct counts approximate more closely to each other with decreasing numbers (Wood [3]), and it can be shown that the number of viable bacteria increases roughly in proportion to the number of particles. The numbers of bacteria in ocean waters have been estimated by viable counts, but more recently by counts on molecular filters and by slide counts. Such methods are of use primarily to give an idea of the relative numbers of bacteria in given regions or at given depths, and are of little use in assessing the biomass of bacteria in the oceans. The counts do tell us that, in the open sea, apart from plankton swarms, the numbers of bacteria are far lower than one would expect from their potential activity. On the other hand, it would seem that there is always a small nucleus population which is capable of rapid development in order to deal with any situation which may arise. Thus, as soon as a plankton bloom occurs, there are sufficient bacteria in the ecosystem to cope with dead or dying organisms and excreted products, as an example of which we may cite the rapid regeneration of phosphorus in the vicinity of plankton blooms, minutes and hours rather than days being involved in the recycling. I am not willing to admit that 'everything is everywhere' in the microbial world, but have to agree that everything is in most places, ready to play its part in the ecosystem when conditions are right. Even the strictly anaerobic purple and green sulphur bacteria have been cultivated from sea water, and it is possible that they play a part in the devastating anaerobiosis caused by some red tides, e.g. in Walvis Bay.

Hydrologists have questioned whether there are enough bacteria in the sea to carry out the transformations that are attributed to them. Harvey [4] has quoted Kreps [5] and Keys et al. [6] in support of the idea that, in addition to the living bacteria, there are free enzymes or catalysts, and it may be that enzymes of microbial origin are to be numbered among the extracellular substances excreted by micro-organisms in the sea. Adsorption of both catalyst and substrate would greatly facilitate the reactivity of the catalysts. I do not know whether such enzymes have ever been isolated from sea water, or even whether they have been looked for to any extent, but I do know that enzymes such as urease can be demonstrated in filtered suspensions of bacteria in sea water, and Holmes [8] has shown that phytoplankton filtered through a millepore HA filter can assimilate carbon dioxide from the filtrate.

ZoBell [9] discussed the assessment of bacterial populations in the sea up to 1946. The figures from Scripps Institution in southern California lie between 43 and 750 bacteria per ml, while those made from four stations off the south-east coast of Australia range from 4 to 500 per ml except in the vicinity of plankton swarms and after flood rains when they are much higher. The figures from Australia (fig. 12) are of the same order as those

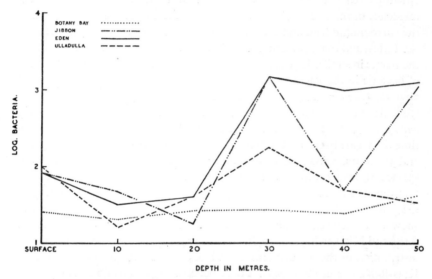

FIG. 12. Viable counts·of bacteria 20 miles off the Australian coast, i.e. east of the continental shelf, except for the Botany Bay station which is on the shelf. The other three stations show a minimum between 10 and 20 m and maxima at or below 30 m.

from California, but rather higher than those of Waksman *et al.* [10] from the Gulf of Maine which lie between 0 and 380. These authors gave figures of 890 to 37,500 bacteria per ml of plankton tows, but as these were net hauls, the results are not applicable to bacterial populations in plankton swarms. Their conclusion that bacteria are rarely free in the water but are attached to plankton, I heartily agree with; and it has in fact been confirmed by Jones [11]. Velankar [12] estimated viable bacterial populations as between 150 and 620 organisms per ml in Palk Bay and 100 to 860 per ml in the Gulf of Manaar (India), but Cviic [13, 14] found somewhat higher viable counts than most authors, these ranging from 45 to 10,599 per ml in

M

the Adriatic Sea, the highest counts occurring near the shore. Direct bacterial counts made by Cviic [14] ranged from 2,700 to 320,000 bacteria per ml for the same stations at which he made his viable counts (table III). This table compares the bacterial counts made by several authors in different parts of the world.

Kriss et al. [15, 16] have made a comparative study of bacterial populations in the oceans by culturing filter discs through which 35 to 50 ml of sea water had been filtered. They found that the highest concentrations of bacteria occurred in tropical waters near the equator in the Pacific and Atlantic Oceans, and north of the equator in the Indian Oceans. The high incidence in the Indian Ocean between 10° and 21° N may be ascribed to the surrounding land and the existence of such large rivers as the Ganges, the Indus, and the Irrawaddy. The Southern Ocean has more bacteria than the Arctic in similar latitudes. Kriss and Rukina [17] estimated the biomass of bacteria in the Pacific Ocean as reaching 1 g per m³ between 25 m and 30 m depth, i.e. in the region of maximum plankton population in the area studied; at 0·01 g per m³ between 35 m and 100 m, and less than 0·01 g per m³ from 100 to 500 m. These authors also believe that the generation time of marine bacteria attached to and growing on slides was between 2·0 and 3·4 hours. Kriss [18] has also given evidence that bacterial numbers in surface waters tend to be a maximum in the region of the thermocline, i.e. that they are associated with discontinuity. This is also frequently true of the protoplankton. Kriss and co-workers [15, 16] have also attempted to show that bacterial numbers are associated with distinct water masses. Kriss and Mitzkewich [19, 20] have tried to get quantitative evidence of the distribution of the 'filamentous cluster organisms' which they have called Krassilnikoviae in the oceans. These peculiar organisms do not appear on membrane filters or in culture, but attach on glass slides left in situ in the ocean for 30 minutes or more. They occurred on slides to 1,000 m depth in the Atlantic and to 500 m in the Pacific Ocean, maximum numbers usually occurring between 50 m and 100 m depth. Numbers ranged from 0 to 13,150. Their position in the microbial world is doubtful.

Bacterial populations close inshore, especially where land drainage is considerable, or in the immediate vicinity of sewer outfalls, may reach astronomical figures, but such populations are rapidly reduced. This reduction of bacterial populations in the sea has produced considerable speculation. ZoBell [9, 21] has shown that there is a bactericidal principle in the sea, and Waksman and Hotchkiss [22] have shown that it affects both marine and terrestrial bacteria. Taylor [23] considers that coliform and similar terrestrial bacteria diminish more rapidly in fresh water than dilution and natural mortality can account for, and presumes an inhibitory

## Table III
### *Vertical distribution of bacteria in different regions*

| Place and observers | Bacteria per ml at depth in meters | | | | | | | | | | | | |
|---|---|---|---|---|---|---|---|---|---|---|---|---|---|
| | S | 5 | 10 | 20 | 30 | 40 | 50 | 75 | 100 | 200 | 300 | 400 | 500 |
| Canary Is. Otto and Neumann, 1904 | | 120 | | | | | 76 | | 120 | 1 | | | |
| C. Verde. O. and N., 1904 | | 58 | | | | | 16 | | 64 | 6 | | | |
| St Paul I. O. and N., 1904 | | 20 | | | | | | | 54 | 4 | | | |
| Pernambuco. O. and N., 1904 | | 48 | | | | | 168 | | 83 | 14 | 36 | | |
| Nr. Monaco. Bertol, 1912 | 1 | | | 7 | | | 16 | | 24 | 38 | | | |
| Andros I. Drew, 1914 | | very many | | | too many | 23 | | | | | | 160 | falling |
| Clyde Sea. Lloyd, 1930 | 100 | | | 9 | | | 19 | 4 | 5 | | | | |
| Pacific Ocean. | 344 | 400 | 224 | 528 | | | 620 | | 17 | 2 | 0 | 1 | 0 |
| ZoBell and Feltham, 1932–1934 | 147 | 126 | 238 | 292 | | | 86 | | 14 | 3 | 6 | 0 | 2 |
| North Polar Sea. Butkewich, 1932 | | | 63 | 0·6 | | | 35 | | 105 | 214 | 0·1 | | |
| Adriatic. Cviic, 1948 | 76 | | | 1,457 | 1,684 | | 2,541 | 1,325 | 230 | | | | |
| Adriatic. Cviic, 1951 | 33 | | | 2,272 | 6,780 | | 1,643 | 1,202 | 639 | | | | |
| Adriatic. Cviic, 1960 (average) | 39 | | 85 | 408 | 1,070 | | 208 | | 110 | 200 | 2,600 | 1,580 | 97 |

*Direct counts at this time ranged from 2,700 to 320,000 on the same occasions*

| | S | 5 | 10 | 20 | 30 | 40 | 50 | 75 | 100 | 200 | 300 | 400 | 500 |
|---|---|---|---|---|---|---|---|---|---|---|---|---|---|
| Australia, Wood 1953 *et seq.* | 100 | | 70 | 60 | 2,000 | 300 | 1,200 | | | | | | |

substance for fresh water. Sea water filtered through bacterial filters or autoclaved has no bactericidal properties, as has been discussed elsewhere. Apparently, bacteria living in the environment are immune or nearly so to the bactericidal property and can increase during storage of the sample or in plankton swarms, yet the same bacteria lose their immunity on subculture on artificial media followed by re-exposure to sea water.

The destruction of bacteria derived from terrestrial pollution such as coliform bacteria has been studied by Ketchum [24]. He made a mathematical model for assessing the relative effects of dilution, bactericidal action of sea water and predation in reducing the population of coliform bacteria in the tidal estuary of the Raritan River, and gave the following equation:

$$C_n = (C_0)_n r_n - \frac{1}{1 - (1 - r_n)_e - k + wp}$$

where $C_0$ = original count
$C_n$ = steady state population
$r_n$ = exchange ratio
$w$ = volume of water filtered
$k$ = coefficient of death rate
$p$ = number of predators per unit volume.

Ketchum shows that these processes account for at least 99% of the decrease of coliforms, and that bactericidal action is the most important factor, followed by predation and dilution. Bacteriophages do not seem to be very numerous or widely distributed in the oceans, and phages for terrestrial organisms must be of terrestrial origin. Charlton [25] recorded the inhibition of bacterial growth due to competition for gaseous nutrients in the medium. Jones [26] suggests the ionic balance of heavy metals as the cause of death of terrestrial bacteria in sea water. The final solution of the problem is still to be found. Although there are a great number of transformations in the sea which must be biological, and therefore, presumably microbiological, the apparent scarcity of bacteria in many marine environments, and the apparent inactivity of many marine bacteria in culture, make it difficult to explain how these transformations are brought about. The first difficulty would be partly met by the free catalyst theory of Harvey, or by the rapid development of local populations of bacteria to meet immediate needs, a development which can be shown to occur, for example in spoilage. The second difficulty can possibly be explained by the differences in microbial behaviour in the laboratory and in the sea. We are in fact short of suitable methods for studying the activities of bacteria under natural conditions. We cannot even wall off part of the sea by putting a glass or plastic vessel around it. If we do, we get, as ZoBell [9] points out, an unnatural increase in the number of bacteria which does not occur in the sea around it. Moreover, storing bacteria in sea water will alter the ratio of different forms to one another; so the most usual bacteriological techniques have serious objections. What then will be the effect of growing marine organisms on nutrient agar or even on the special media devised by ZoBell and Feltham [27] and others ? I do know that, while there is a number of agar digesters which are not inhibited by the presence of other carbon sources, the majority of strains will not digest agar if such alternate sources are present. I have obtained up to 100 times as many agar digesting colonies on non-nutrient, washed agar as on nutrient agar. Cellulose digest-ing bacteria also prefer carbon sources which are easier to attack. Just how often this behaviour occurs with other organic substances I do not pretend to know, but it does explain the apparent lack of cellulose or agar digesters in certain environments when standard methods are used. Gelatin liquefac-tion seems to be another reaction which can give equivocal results. Many marine organisms give only a slight hollowing of the medium and even that depends on its constitution. About 99% of the strains tested gave liquefac-tion only if peptone or meat extract were present, and not in non-nutrient gelatin. In sugars, the marine bacteria are not as a rule fermentative, forming neither acid nor gas. Galactose and mannitol are fermented by as many strains as glucose, and are preferred by some strains, due no doubt to the fact that agar is a galactosan and alginic acid breaks down to give mannuronic acid.

While there is considerable uniformity in the biochemical reactions of a number of strains taken from a single water sample, there is considerable variation in the reactions of strains taken from a series of samples either in the same locality or at different stations at different times. When one studies strains from different stations over a period of time, one finds that the reactivity varies so as to give a spectrum, the continuity of which increases with the number of samples. Taking marine bacteria as a group, they are equipped to break down almost any organic matter that occurs in the sea, and the variability they show is necessary in order that they shall be able to adapt themselves readily to different substrates.

So far there has been little work done on the bacteriology of plankton swarms, apart from some counts by Waksman and his school, and his observation that agar digesters were associated with phytoplankton blooms but not with zooplankton. There has also been some work done on chitin digestion in the sea with the object of explaining the degradation of crusta-cean remains (Benton [28], Hess [29], Hock [30, 31], ZoBell and Rittenberg [32]). There is little information, however, on the actual activity of each bacterial group, or on the interaction between them, except for some studies on fish spoilage. The chief reason for this is the lack of adequate techniques, the expense of suitably equipped expeditions, and the limits imposed on the experimenter by the need for working at sea.

## The Protoplankton

Wood, in a recent series, has studied the distribution of protoplankton in the south Pacific and Indian Oceans, in the Australasian region. He showed that, in the Coral Sea, the extinction coefficient of the water at the surface was related to the number of particles in the water, irrespective of their nature, but between 50 m and 100 m, it was related to the numbers of protoplankton. He also showed that, in the Coral Sea, the protoplankton maximum occurred in most cases below the thermocline. However, in the vicinity of upwelling, the maximum occurred at the surface. In temperate Indian Ocean waters, where there is no recognizable thermocline, two maxima occurred, one at the surface and one at 75 m. In the sub-tropical convergence, there was a surface maximum, and in sub-Antarctic water the maximum occurred at the surface or at 50 m. The microplankton is usually an order of magnitude higher than the net-protoplankton, and the total particulate matter still another order of magnitude higher. Wood shows too that in the Indian Ocean between 10° and 30° S there is a 'species desert', much of which also contains only few individuals. The same phenomenon occurs in the west central south Pacific water mass between 25° and 35° S in the Coral–Tasman Sea area. He also selected a series of stations on the basis of species distribution and found that they occurred in two geographical areas, both derived from the low-salinity–high-temperature water of the Arafura and Banda Seas. The protoplankton distribution was quantitatively very similar in both, with maxima at 50 m to 75 m and 100 m to 150 m. The correlation with $C^{14}$ assimilation measured by the Jitts method was poor. However, in a series of stations from North Cape, New Zealand to Cape Howe, Australia, the protoplankton distribution corresponded very well with the curves for $C^{14}$ assimilation at depths to 150 m (fig. 13). This was in a uniform water mass derived from the East Australian Current with uniform species distribution. Studies of the regression between $C^{14}$ assimilation and protoplankton numbers at different depths on the same station suggested either shade adaptation of species or the predominance of shade species at increasing depths.

The horizontal distribution of protoplankton in a given water type has been shown by Wood [34] to be uniform except for diurnal variation. This was confirmed from the Coral and Arafura seas and even included the less important species. In shallow seas, turbulence of the water was demonstra-

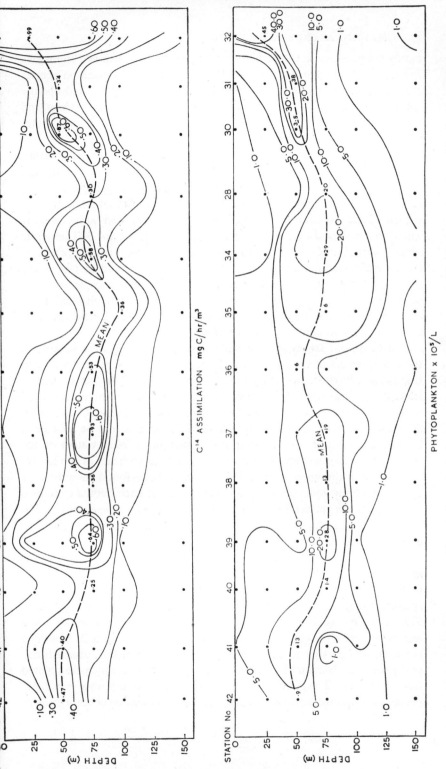

FIG. 13. Carbon[14] assimilation (upper graph) and phytoplankton count (lower graph) from profiles in a section from North Cape, New Zealand, to Cape Howe, Australia, in the East Australian current.

ted by the presence in the plankton of benthic species such as *Pleurosigma* and *Coscinodiscus gigas*. In Florida Straits, oceanic protoplankton species are intermixed at about 100 m with living and dead benthic and epontic species such as *Navicula lyra*, *N. hennedyi*, *Mastogloia* spp., *Amphora*, and *Climacosphenia moniligera*, showing a continued admixture of oceanic water with water from the shelf.

It would appear both from quantitative studies and from species distribution that in the area studied by Wood [3], the protoplankton populations are derived from a sub-equatorial community which extends its influence to the south in water derived from the tropics and from an Antarctic and sub-Antarctic community derived from Antarctic and sub-Antarctic water, the north and south components meeting at about 40° S. Temperate species were almost entirely of estuarine or neritic origin and there was no evidence of an oceanic temperate flora. Communities could best be established by the absence of certain more stenothermal species as one proceeded from the tropics south or from the Antarctic north, although there are certain species which are confined to the sub-Antarctic, such as *Ceratium lineatum* and *Synedra reinboldii*.

THE DIATOMS. It has already been stated that diatoms are oceanic in the colder waters of the Arctic and Antarctic and estuarine and neritic in tropical and warm-temperate waters of the Pacific and Indian Oceans at least. In the areas where they are most abundant, i.e. the Antarctic, coastal waters, and the tropical island waters of the Pacific and Indian Oceans, they are growing in water of relatively low salinity, and this may be a factor in their distribution. Lohmann [35] stated that the coastal waters of the Northern Hemisphere are on the whole more than 50 times as productive of diatoms as the open waters. Diatoms have been found in waters far below the photic zone, i.e. to 4,000 m and some at such depths contained chlorophyll; the species included *Nitzschia*, *Navicula*, *Amphora*, *Coscinodiscus*, and *Striatella*, and these have also been recorded from the surface of deep sediments (see Chapter 3).

THE BLUE-GREEN ALGAE. Like the diatoms, these are largely planktonic in the ocean; they have been discussed in some detail in Chapter 3. The pattern of their distribution is not easy to follow, as they are rarely conspicuous unless they are in bloom proportions. Apart from one species of *Trichodesmium*, such blooms are tropical or sub-tropical, and in such waters they are characteristically present, but the pattern of their blooming is not known, partly because warmer waters have been little studied, and partly because the main blooms are oceanic and not in the much-frequented steamship lanes. The suddenness of their appearance implies a very rapid proliferation in forming blooms. Their ecological effects on other organisms is also unknown, but must be considerable, if only from their consumption of nutrients.

THE PROTOZOA AND PROTOPHYTA. Like the diatoms, these are largely planktonic in the ocean, though many ciliates and Sarcodina do live in the sediments.

*Flagellates.* Of these, several groups are highly significant in oceanic plankton, the dinoflagellates, chrysomonads, and coccolithophores being the most important.

*Dinoflagellates.* This group of organisms provides the most useful series of indicator species of any protoplankton. The genera *Amphisolenia, Triposolenia, Ornithocercus, Histioneis, Parahistioneis,* and *Citharistes* are confined to waters of tropical origin and the genus *Heterodinium* is normally found in or derived from the aphotic zone in the warmer waters. *Ceratium* has the widest oceanic distribution, and though it occurs from the Arctic to the Antarctic, has species which are of the greatest use in indicating the origin of the community. Wood [3] shows that *Ceratium dens* is practically confined to the tropical Indian Ocean in the Australasian region, *C. gravidum, C. gibberum, C. cephalotum* are confined to the warmer tropical oceanic waters, while such species as *C. carriense, C. massiliense, C. karsteni,* and *C. kofoidi* while derived from tropical oceanic water, occur in warm currents as they lose their heat in temperate regions, even to the southern edge of the sub-tropical convergence. Thus, such species allow us to demarcate regions in tropical and sub-tropical waters. In the Antarctic, *C. pentagonum* occurs in a population which is distinct from the populations of tropical origin, and *C. lineatum* is, as has been said, an indicator of sub-Antarctic water. *Ceratium furca* and *C. fusus* occur from the equator to the Antarctic convergence and *C. tripos* has almost as wide a distribution. Many Antarctic species chiefly of *Dinophysis* and *Peridinium* have counterparts in the estuaries of warmer climates, e.g. *D. ovum, P. piriforme, P. granii, P. ovatum,* and *P. depressum.* I prefer to regard these as separate populations of species rather than as distinct species, as it is impossible to find sufficient distinguishing characters, and, if the species are common to both environments, they explain the otherwise bipolar distribution by their restriction in less favourable environments. One can envisage a general distribution of these species following ice ages and the shrinking of the distribution in tropical waters as temperatures increased, to areas of lower salinity, i.e. the estuaries.

When I began the study of living protoplankton at sea, I was struck by the importance of the naked flagellates in the biomass of tropical waters. The most numerous and ubiquitous are *Gymnodinium simplex, G. gelbum, G. nudum, G. marinum* and other species about 5 μ in diameter. The small gymnodiniums vary considerably in shape in a given sample, and probably most of them belong to a single species. Less numerous, but often quite important are the larger *G. mirabile* complex, *Gyrodinium, Amphidinium*, and the usually colourless *Cochlodinium, Nematodinium*, and *Warnowia* (*Pouchetia* of Kofoid). *Gymnodinium* species also occur in deep water between 500 m and 3,000 m, some containing chlorophyll. Most of these forms are delicate and are not identifiable in preserved plankton, which is why their importance has not been generally recognized.

*Chrysomonads.* The chrysomonads have been reported by Parke [36–39] and her colleagues (see Chapter 3) to be important in the waters of the English Channel and the Irish Sea; Wood and Davis [40] found them in quantity in coastal waters of New South Wales, and they are present in varying quantities, sometimes quite abundant, in the south-west Pacific, the Atlantic and north-east Indian Oceans. They also occur in the aphotic zone and have been cultivated from 4,000 m. The cells are not easily preserved, and they are probably much more significant in the protoplankton than has been generally recognized.

*Coccolithophores.* The biology and cytology of this group has been studied by Braarud and his group at Oslo, and the ecology by Bernard [41]. This author recorded up to 30,000 cells per litre in the tropical Atlantic and I have seen catches of this order in the Timor Sea. They form 40% of the protoplankton in the equatorial Indian Ocean, 45% at 39° S and 5% at 55° S, and are frequently attached to copepods and other animals, while in the upper waters they are often epiphytic on diatoms and other planktonic algae. They are also recorded by Bernard in the aphotic environment as the most important part of his catches, and I have also seen them in this zone, but their actual importance is not yet known.

Other flagellate groups such as the silicoflagellates and eugleinids are usually present in plankton catches, but except for the colourless ones and for some tiny phytomonads, including the ubiquitous and often dominant *Phaeocystis*, are not numerous enough to be significant.

## The Sediment Ecosystem

We have already considered the oceanic sediments as an environment, and although there is interchange of nutrients and to an extent of organisms between it and the water above, it can be considered a semi-independent ecosystem. It is only since ZoBell stressed the possibility of bacterial life in the ocean deeps that we have learned anything of importance about the biology of this part of the world. When on the Danish research ship *Galathea*, ZoBell [42] proved beyond all doubt that bacteria can and do live at the greatest ocean depths. From these depths he cultivated 'barophilic' bacteria which belong to the usual marine groups, but which do not grow at atmospheric pressure at all, or not until they have been trained to do so by a staging process. The occurrence of diatoms in this environment has also been mentioned in previous Chapters. I have since studied a number of core samples taken in the Coral Sea, and nearly all these contained diatoms (usually *Coscinodiscus*, *Navicula*, or *Diploneis*) in the surface layers. Only in three stations on coral bottom at 20 to 40 m depth off Port Moresby, New Guinea, were traces of planktonic diatoms found, and these consisted of a few valves of *Rhizosolenia* and the thickened distal ends of the setae of *Chaetoceros messanense*. If this was all that remained of the planktonic flora at 40 m, there is little chance of frustules of such a flora occurring in the ocean deeps. Wiseman and Hendey [43] described a large deposit of *Ethmodiscus rex* from the Challenger Deep, and pointed out that the species was not collected in the phytoplankton. It seems unlikely that a deposit such as they describe could have rained quantitatively into an abyss, especially as the species is rare or uncommon in the upper waters. McHugh [44] found *E. rex* in phytoplankton off the Californian coast, but here are many submarine canyons and considerable upwelling which could have transported the diatoms into the photic zone. I have found *E. rex* on rare occasions (less than six samples out of several thousands) in the Pacific and Indians Oceans, and then only dead cells in regions of upwelling along the continental shelf. I therefore believe that the Challenger Deep deposits are autochthonous and have occurred over a very long period.

Kolbe [45] found that the diatoms from marine cores in the Atlantic were predominantly fresh water forms. He gave three theories for this: (1) that they originated in the African lakes and swamps and were washed down into their present location, (2) that they were blown into the Atlantic after the desiccation of the swamps, and (3) that they originated in lakes on the Atlantic continent. In fact, the benthic flora has a great deal in common from the shallowest estuary to the greatest depth, and as I have already implied, the most probable theory seems to me that the diatoms observed by Kolbe were autochthonous, though in some cases they could descend to a considerable depth attached to *Thalassia* or *Zostera*, where deeps occur close to shallow banks. The benthic collections from the Albatross identified by Mann [46] also contain bottom forms rather than planktonic.

Cooper (verbal communication) believes that in deep ocean waters there is a decreasing phosphate gradient, due to living matter, especially as the phosphate is concentrated in the sediments, in other words, the organisms of the sediments are taking phosphate from the water above. There is also a continuous increase in the dissolved silica content of the water from the top of the sub-photic zone to the deeps, but sea water is at no time saturated with silica, which is quite soluble at the pH of sea water. We may conclude that the tests of diatoms sinking from the photic zone would be dissolved before reaching the bottom of deeper waters, the evidence from Port Moresby confirming this. All available evidence suggests that there is a distinct ecosystem at and near the bottom in the ocean depths, consisting essentially of sponges, diatoms (including epiphytes), foraminifera, bacteria, and possibly pteropods and copepods. Whether ciliates and flagellates are present is not certain. This ecosystem probably derives energy from chemoautotrophic processes, including sulphate reduction, and presumably sulphur oxidation, nitrification, and maybe methane and hydrogen oxidation. It must also be fed continuously from above or from the sides by dissolved or particulate organic matter, not by a continuous rain of dead plankton organisms from the photic zone to the depths, though there is evidence that organisms may descend alive in sinking Antarctic waters.

Studies on the bacteriology of marine sediments have been made by a number of workers, but mainly in shallow waters. Such papers include studies by Lloyd [47], Duggeli [48], Issatchenko [49], Rittenberg [50], Rubentschik and Goichermann [51], Stone [52], Thiel [53, 54], Waksman [55], Zelinski [56], ZoBell [57–61, 9, 42], ZoBell and Anderson [62].

It would be difficult to calculate precisely the relative activity of bacteria in sea water and marine sediments, but the work of Waksman and his school [55] shows that the sediments are much more active bacteriologically than the water above, and chitin digestion, decomposition of algae such as *Fucus* or *Laminaria*, nitrification, reduction of nitrate, and nitrogen fixation by bacteria are concentrated at the bottom of the ocean; the same applies to sulphate reduction.

The milieu of the sediments has been delimited by ZoBell [60]. He gives the Eh limits as from $+$ 350 mV to $-$ 500 mV, and the pH limits as from 6·4 to 9·5, and states that 'bottom deposits are rich in organic matter, and bacteria are generally reducing'. Negative Eh values or reducing conditions are also the property of fine sediments, coarser sediments being less reducing. As a general rule, the Eh decreases with core depth, while the pH increases. ZoBell [60] and Emery and Rittenberg [63] give a series of interesting profiles of deep sediment cores and show close correlation of negative Eh with the presence of hydrogen sulphide. This suggests the dominance of *Desulphovibrio* in marine sediments of low Eh, similar to that found by Baas Becking and Wood in estuarine sediments (see Chapters 5 and 8). ZoBell, ZoBell and Anderson, ZoBell and Anderson and Rittenberg have made counts of bacteria in long cores of marine sediments, and have shown that in general the number of heterotrophic bacteria decreases with depth, rapidly at first and then more slowly, but Rittenberg still records 15,000 bacteria per gm from 355 cm at the bottom of his longest core taken at a depth of 566 m. At 3,000 m of water depth, there were 200 bacteria per gm below 226 cm of sediment. Rittenberg comments on the scarcity of anaerobes, which is in accord with the findings of ZoBell and of Wood. The low count at 3,000 m may show a real diminution of bacterial numbers as the water deepens, but the pressure at this depth (*circa* 300 atmospheres) may have had an effect on the count made at atmospheric pressure. In two of his cores, Rittenberg found a departure from the continued decrease in

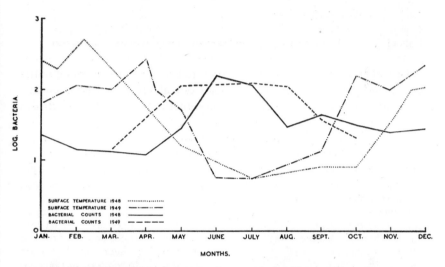

FIG. 14. Viable bacterial counts in the waters of Botany Bay, showing an inverse correlation with temperature.

numbers with depth. These coincided with discontinuous changes in the water content of the strata. Similar discontinuities in bacterial numbers and sediment characteristics have been found during estuarine studies in Botany Bay, New South Wales.

ZoBell [53] gives an interesting table showing the relationship between bacterial population and type of sediment (table IV). He also lists the number of different physiological types of bacteria found in the topmost 3 cm to 5 cm of sediment. His table represents only three samples, but the information is of value despite its limitations (table V).

The absence of nitrogen fixation is commented upon by ZoBell. However, as Sisler and ZoBell [64] have since shown, sulphate-reducing bacteria, which ZoBell records, are capable of fixing nitrogen, and from recent work on the subject other organisms with a hydrogenase may be suspected of the ability to fix nitrogen. This would mean that the nitrogen lost by denitrification, which is relatively unimportant in ocean bottoms, may be more than made up by fixation by anaerobes.

Table IV

Bacterial population in different types of sediment (from ZoBell, 1938)

| Deposit | Median diam. of particles in μ | Nitrogen p.p. 10,000 | Water content per cent | Bacteria per gram |
|---|---|---|---|---|
| Sand | 50–1,000 | 9 | 33 | 22,000 |
| Silt | 5–50 | 19 | 56 | 78,000 |
| Clay | 1–5 | 37 | 82 | 390,000 |
| Colloid | less than 1 | more than 100 | more than 98 | 1,510,000 |

Rittenberg, Emery, and Orr [65] have studied the regeneration of nutrients in sediments of basins off the coast of California, and have reached some important conclusions. They found that organic nitrogen decreases

Table V

Microbial populations of sediments and their functions

| Depth of overlying water | 780 m | 505 m | 1,322 m |
|---|---|---|---|
| Total aerobes (plate count) | 930,000 | 31,000,000 | 8,800,000 |
| Total anaerobes (oval tube) includes facultative | 190,000 | 2,600,000 | 1,070,000 |
| Ammonification (peptone NH₄) | 100,000 | 1,000,000 | 1,000,000 |
| Ammonification (nutrose -NH₄) | 10,000 | 1,000,000 | 100,000 |
| Urea fermentation | 100 | present | 1,000 |
| Gelatin liquefaction | 100,000 | 10,000,000 | 1,000,000 |
| H₂S from peptone | 10,000 | 1,000,000 | 100,000 |
| Denitrification (to N₂) | 100 | 1,000 | 10,000 |
| Nitrate reduction (to NO₂) | 100,000 | 10,000,000 | 10,000 |
| Nitrogen fixation | 0 | 0 | 0 |
| Nitrification | 0 | 0 | 0 |
| Sulphate reduction | 1,000 | 1,000 | 10,000 |
| Starch hydrolysis | 10,000 | 100,000 | 1,000 |
| Glucose fermentation | 10,000 | 100,000 | 10,000 |
| Xylose fermentation | 10,000 | present | 10,000 |
| Cellulose decomposition | 1,000 | present | 1,000 |
| Fat hydrolysis | 1,000 | present | present |
| Chitin digestion | 100 | present | present |

with depth, but ammonia nitrogen increases to 3,000 times that of sea water, and the reduction of other forms of nitrogen is ascribed to bacterial activity. In sediments with an oxidized surface, nitrate and nitrite will occur and enter the water along with the ammonia. The inorganic nitrogen accumulating does not balance the organic nitrogen being broken down, which means that some of this is being returned to the overlying water. Phosphorus is concentrated in sediments of low Eh as Baas Becking and his co-workers found. If the Eh is positive and the pH low, phosphate shows little change with depth. Silicate distribution is probably indirectly controlled by bacterial modification of the environment. On the whole, there is a concentration gradient between the upper sediment and the overlying water, with a resultant enrichment of the latter by diffusing and mixing.

### The Aphotic Zone as an Ecosystem

A certain amount is known about the aphotic zone, which extends from the photic zone to the sediments, and chemically has much in common with the photic zone from which it is derived. We know that there are movements of large water masses at various levels, that temperatures are relatively low and pressure is increasing with depth, thus affecting the equilibria but not the nature of chemical reactions.

Biologically, that part of the zone just below the photic zone has much in common with the photic zone. Planktonic animals live in this area and migrate upwards for food, so there is a strong vertical movement of the plankton. Some of the protoplankton also strays into this and probably lives for a time by alternative means of nutrition. Bernard has shown that, in many cases, the protoplankton below the photic zone outnumbers that above. His record catch was 4,200 cells per ml at 400 m off western Algeria, but he also found considerable protoplankton from 300 m to 1,000 m in the central Indian Ocean, and to 2,500 m off Sardinia and Libya. In these places he found the palmelloid *Cyclococcolithus, Exuviaella*, and *Nostoc*, with small naked flagellates including *Gymnodinium* species. Bernard found that the rich protoplankton of the aphotic zone is related to fast-moving sub-surface currents, and to a rich seston content from which he concludes it derives its dissolved or particulate nutriment. It is reasonable to believe that, as mentioned above, equilibria in deeper water will differ from those at or near the surface and that reaction rates will also differ. Bernard's work is especially important in calling the attention of microbiologists to this region of the oceans as a separate ecosystem requiring study.

### The Estuarine Ecosystem

In considering the estuaries as a single ecosystem instead of dividing it into its benthic and planktonic components, I have followed tradition and also convenience, as the sediments and their biological activity play such an important part in the overall ecology of the estuary. In discussing the estuarine environment, I stressed the part played by the sea-grasses in providing a characteristic habitat and in their effect on the sediments. The habitat is largely conditioned by the epontic organisms which even contribute noticeably to the biomass.

The epiphytic flora and fauna of *Posidonia* usually contains far more bryozoa, *Spirorbis*, larger red algae such as *Laurencia*, *Grateloupia*, *Gracilaria*, *Porphyra*, *Gigartina*, *Dictyota* and filamentous algae such as *Enteromorpha* and *Vaucheria* than the *Zostera* and *Thalassia* communities, which support diatoms, blue-green algae, *Polysiphonia*, *Ceramium*, *Ectocarpus*, *Chaetomorpha*, *Cladophora*, etc. *Ruppia* has few diatoms and more blue-green algae, and so far as has been observed, less of the filamentous red and brown algae. The brown algae such as *Fucus*, *Sargassum*, and *Hormosira* and the kelps *Laminaria*, *Ecklonia*, and *Macrocystis* have few epiphytes, possibly because they produce antibiotics.

The surface of the sand flats contains diatoms, largely naviculoids, *Nitzschia*, *Mastogloia*, *Navicula* (e.g. *N. grevillei*), *Diploneis*, blue-green algae (often tapetic or encrusting forms), bacteria, protozoa (mainly flagellates including Chrysophyceae, dinoflagellates, and colourless monads), while the mud surface contains more ciliates, some euglenids, especially those forms which can exist anaerobically (e.g. *Euglena*, *Eutreptia*, *Astasia*). The muds contain facultatively anaerobic bacteria and obligate anaerobes, e.g. *Desulphovibrio*, heterotrophic or photoreducing algae and bacteria (diatoms, blue-green algae, and purple and green bacteria), ciliates, nematodes, flagellates and certain burrowing mollusca and worms which, no doubt, feed on micro-organisms and turn over and aerate considerable quantities of mud, thus modifying the microbial flora by changing the physico-chemical conditions. For example, in a reduced sediment, one frequently finds worm or gasteropod burrows which are highly oxidized as can be seen by the fact that such tubes are lined with ferric hydroxide, giving a brown colouration in a grey sediment. Mangrove roots have the same oxidizing effect.

We presume that the diatoms which occur in the sediments down to 12 cm (Oppenheimer and Wood [66]) are feeding heterotrophically (see Lewin [67], Lewin and Lewin [68]). According to Aleem [69] and Callame and Debyser [70], these diatoms migrate into the mud as the tidal edge approaches on the outgoing tide and reappear just after it has passed as the tide comes in, if the light intensity is sufficient. On the other hand, *Hantzschia* comes to the mud surface after the tide has left it and retreats below the surface with the incoming tide. This brown *Hantzschia* film is particularly noticeable at Barnstaple, Massachusetts, and in the inter-tidal muds of Sapelo Island, Georgia.

Most of the organisms found in the estuarine environment are euryhaline, though some are more sensitive to salinity changes than others. They are also very tolerant of changes in temperature and nutrient concentrations, and I have found both in the east coast estuaries of Australia and in the Texas Bays that geographical boundaries are often more important than physico-chemical differences in delimiting the estuarine community. In the estuarine environment, the sediment dominates the shallow water, and even in fairly deep estuaries (say up to 50 feet) is the controlling factor of the ecosystem. If a plant community is established in an estuary, the interplay between it and the sediment community is more even, but once that plant community is removed, the sediment determines what cover will replace it, if any.

*Bacteria in the Estuarine Environment*

The sediments are of two types: inorganic and organic, or peaty, though many muds are a mixture of the two. Unless there is a great preponderance of organic matter, e.g. in a mangrove swamp, the sulphur cycle appears to control the situation both chemically and biologically (Baas Becking and Wood [71]). This has already been discussed in some detail. The organic matter required for initiation of sulphate reduction is provided by seagrasses or algae and if these are prevented from accumulating in the area, e.g. by increased currents, the sediment soon becomes oxidized, at least on the surface. Because plants cannot survive the currents and heavy surges, river mouths and the seaward reaches of estuaries and channels are usually sandy and are in the oxidized state with Eh values above $+ 250$ mV. Further, if the weeds are thoroughly cleaned from a bank, it usually changes from a mud to a sand, unless there is a large amount of organic matter present, such as an old mangrove swamp. The removal of the weed allows the oxidation of the mud, and water movement gradually removes the clay and silt mechanically. This process can be demonstrated in the laboratory by placing *Zostera* or *Fucus* in a sealed jar with clean beach sand and sea water. As soon as the weed decays, black iron sulphide is formed and the sand becomes black and thixotropic. If the jar is then exposed to light, the sulphide is oxidized and the sand bleaches.

True sulphide muds are rare; they occur naturally in places like Killarney in Georges Basin and in Coila Lake in New South Wales, and in newly formed sand-banks where there is sufficient organic matter to start sulphate reduction. They are characterized by a very low Eh which may be $- 270$ mV to $- 300$ mV. A method of comparing the amount of

N

'humus' to inorganic sulphide is due to Baas Becking. The sediment is placed in a petri dish and a glass microscope slide is pressed into it. The aerobic area will bleach in about 4 hours in a sulphide sediment, while the anaerobic area under the slide will remain black. A series of arbitrary colour standards can be made by mixing lamp-black, zinc white, and yellow ochre in varying proportions, so as to correspond with varying concentrations of iron oxide, sulphide, organic material, and sand. If the redox potential of a sulphide mud is recorded and the mud aerated, the potential will drop by as much as 200 mV, and then rise steadily as the $H_2S$ leaves the mud. If distilled water is added to the mud to allow the insertion of the electrodes, the pH of the mud will drop by as much as 0·6 pH. To avoid this, it is advisable either to agitate the mud with a glass rod to make it thixotropic or to add water from the locality from which the mud is taken, when determining the pH and Eh of muds.

The normal sequence of events in this environment is the rapid growth of algae, e.g. *Enteromorpha*, or *Ectocarpus* in the early spring. As soon as the algal blooms begin to die off, sulphate reduction increases rapidly until a stage is reached where apparently the night deoxidation is sufficient to allow the growth of the purple sulphur bacteria on top of the mud or of the partly rotting or sulphide-producing algae. Sometimes the purple sulphur bacteria occur below the algal mats, and may even form a band 1 cm thick below 1 mm to 2 mm of algae. This is possible because the wave-lengths of light required by them for photosynthesis are complementary to those absorbed by the algal pigments. The green sulphur bacteria are also often present but are rarely obvious as they require a lower electrode potential and a higher sulphide tension than the purples. It seems probable from studies in Lake Macquarie, Woods Hole, and Sapelo Island that the green sulphur bacteria are relatively numerous in estuarine sediments. Their presence, as well as that of the purple sulphur bacteria, diatoms, and algae can be demonstrated by Winogradsky columns (see Chapter 9). In places where the concentration of organic matter and sulphide is high, e.g. in polluted areas or areas of piled driftweed, *Beggiatoa*, *Thiothrix*, and *Thiovulum* may occur. The purple bacteria are followed by a copious bloom of blue-green algae, *Lyngbya*, *Rivularia*, *Microcoleus*, *Phormidium*, *Synechococcus*, and slightly later by a diatom bloom of *Pinnularia*, *Navicula*, *Nitzschia*, *Hantzschia*, etc. This succession may well be controlled by the concentration of hydrogen sulphide, as most or all of these organisms are capable of photoreduction to varying extents. The environment at this stage also abounds in flagellates, ciliates, and bacteria, which, judging by the number of small fish usually present in these locations, would appear to serve as a source of food. The question that arises in one's mind is whether these algal blooms are necessary to provide the minute organisms required as food by the young fish. Large algal blooms which deoxygenate whole lagoons are of course deleterious, but the blooms localized on the flats may be required to produce the metabiotic activity necessary to provide the food though they may not themselves serve as food (see Wood [72]). The presence and extent of the organic matter complicates this system, and we have little information on this factor. We do know that the redox potential below the surface is higher in organic than in sulphide sediments, as shown in table VI, and

Table VI

*The pH and redox potential of typical organic and organo-sulphide sediments*

| Depth | Organic | | Organic-sulphide | |
|---|---|---|---|---|
| | pH | Redox | pH | Redox |
| Surface | 7·61 | +200 | 7·81 | + 65 |
| 5 cm | 7·32 | +240 | 7·12 | − 10 |
| 10 cm | 7·54 | +195 | 6·50 | − 55 |
| 15 cm | 7·60 | +180 | 6·11 | + 40 |
| 20 cm | 7·53 | +185 | 6·80 | +155 |
| 25 cm | 7·60 | +193 | — | — |

the sulphur cycle seems less important in such organic sediments. In some cases, the iron bacteria will form a surface film on such organic sediments; they have no effect on the redox potential as they are aerobic, but are affected by it as they need a redox gradient. The bacteria in organic sediments are mainly heterotrophic, but the microbial ecology has still to be worked out. No attempt has yet been made to estimate the lignin or chitin content of estuarine sediments, though Erikson [73] has shown the presence of chitin- and lignin-digesting actinomycetes, and I also found them abundant in the water and sediments of Lake Macquarie, especially in the organic ones (Wood [72]).

Heterotrophic bacterial populations have been estimated in estuarine environments by Wood [72, 74], Velankar [75], and Oppenheimer [76]. Velankar, working in the Gulf of Manaar, India, has recorded bacterial populations at the surface of the water and close to the bottom. He found that the viable count ranges from less than 100 to 850 per ml at the water surface, but was usually of the order of 200 to 300 per ml. In looking at Velankar's graphs, one sees a series of somewhat rhythmic peaks and troughs suggesting a possible periodicity similar to that recorded by Dew and Wood [77] for barnacle and other larvae on test panels in Sydney Harbour. Wood found an irregular seasonal distribution of bacteria in the water of Lake Macquarie, giving a maximum viable count in June–July (winter), and the numbers were of the same order as those of Velankar; the surface counts were also slightly higher on the average than those from close to the bottom (fig. 15). The range of counts was from 5 to 13,000, much greater than that found by Velankar, due no doubt to the nutrients brought down by flash floods. In this lake, the level and salinity are controlled by the inflow of sea water at king tides in the summer, and by the inflow of fresh water from the land after heavy rains, usually in winter or late summer. This causes complex, and often unpredictable situations which affect the microbial populations in the water, and the relation of

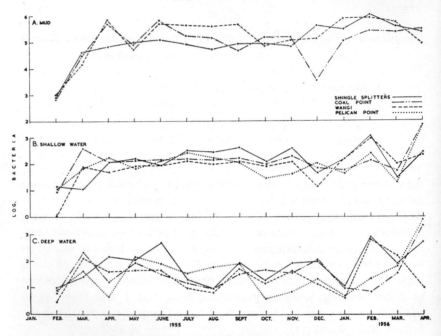

FIG. 15. Viable counts of bacteria from A. sediment, B. surface water, and C. water 1 m from bottom in Lake Macquarie.

different forms to each other. This lake is frequently stratified in the summer. Microbial populations of estuarine sediments have been studied by Wood in Lake Macquarie and by Oppenheimer in the Texas Bays by means of viable counts. Oppenheimer found that the aerobic bacteria from the sediment surface ranged from $5 \times 10^5$ to $5 \times 10^6$ and Wood recorded from $3 \times 10^5$ to $6 \cdot 5 \times 10^6$. It seems surprising that the order of magnitude of these figures should be so close seeing that they were derived from different hemispheres and from lagoon evaporites and a drowned valley respectively. Oppenheimer found a rapid diminution in numbers from surface to 40 cm, and a slower diminution or at times an increase from 40 cm to 100 cm.

In studies of Botany Bay and Port Hacking, two estuaries near Sydney, Australia, using the Jones and Mollison technique (see Chapter 6), I have obtained direct bacterial counts from $5 \times 10^6$ to $5 \times 10^7$ for the water at the surface and the tidal edge and $5 \times 10^7$ to $3 \times 10^9$ for the sediments, there being little significant difference between the population of the exposed sediments at low tide and those covered by 3 feet of water. In Botany Bay, direct counts of the sediments decreased from about $10^7$ at the surface to $10^6$ at 3 feet, but in Port Hacking, in a newly formed sediment produced by the diversion of a swift channel, the count rose from $5 \times 10^7$ at the surface to $8 \cdot 5 \times 10^7$ at a depth of 1 foot in the region of lowest Eh ($-270$ mV) and highest sulphide production. From here to 3 feet the direct count fell to $4 \times 10^7$ bacteria per ml. Of these two estuaries, Port Hacking samples were taken from a sandy flat with strong tidal influence and considerable land drainage in winter rains; Botany Bay from an ancient mangrove flat at the head of a bay and used for oyster cultivation. The Port Hacking sediments are not as stable as the Botany Bay ones in which the Eh of aerated sediments remained almost constant during an hour's aeration, while the Port Hacking sediments dropped 100 mV in the first 30 minutes; these differences were reflected in the relative constancy of the bacterial counts (fig. 16).

The hydrological evidence points to vertical water movements in these tidal flats, and the evidence of the gradual change in the bacterial counts

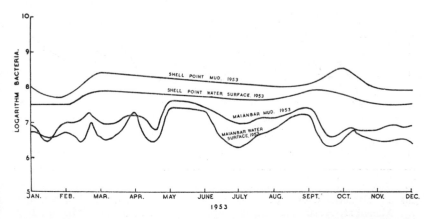

FIG. 16. Direct counts of bacteria from sediment and surface of intertidal water. Note the comparative stability of the oyster culture area at Shell Point and the instability of a newly formed sediment at Port Hacking (Maianbar).

with depth tends to confirm this. The increase of the counts in March was accompanied by heavy rains and a corresponding increase in the bacteria of the overlying water.

ZoBell and Feltham [78] have given heterotrophic aerobic and anaerobic (facultative) counts of bacteria in cores 90 cm long from sediments in Mission Bay, California, correlated with redox potential. They showed that, assuming an average plate count of $10 \times 10^6$ bacteria per ml of dry sediment, there will be 1·1 gm dry weight of bacteria per cu ft of sediment. Wood's figures for direct counts in Botany Bay (No. 1) are of the expected order (1,000 times ZoBell and Feltham's plate counts), and suggest that the higher count of sediment No. 1 (Eh + 240 mV) may be due to the oxygen content, as the second sediment had a lower count and a lower oxygen content (Eh + 160 mV) (fig. 17).

*Azotobacter*-like bacteria have been isolated from these sediments and Velankar also reported such cells. Whether they are autochthonous and are nitrogen fixers was not proven in either case. No *Azotobacter*-like organisms were found in the Lake Macquarie survey though they were sought for. In the east Australian estuaries, thiobacilli were frequent at the surface of the sediments and included *T. denitrificans*, the commonest being *T. thioparus* and forms (probably *T. boveri*) intermediate between it and *T. thiooxidans* which was very rare. The sulphate reducers in Port Hacking did not possess hydrogenase, but those in Botany Bay and Lake Macquarie did so. Wood found the green sulphur bacterium *Chlorobium* in sediments below 15 to 20 feet of turbid water in Lake Macquarie.

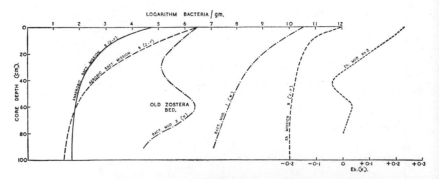

FIG. 17. Bacterial counts of mud profiles in Mission Bay, California, and Maianbar, Australia, and also Eh changes. In the 'old' Mission Bay mud, the bacteria and Eh fall rapidly to constant level, while in the 'new' Port Hacking (Maianbar) mud, there is a rapid increase between 40 and 80 cm with a corresponding rise in Eh where a partly rotted *Zostera* bed had been covered with sand.

In the water, the bacteria are largely heterotrophic. It is from this milieu that Wood [79] isolated many of the gram-negative pleomorphic rods which grew on low-phosphate media. Bacterial counts are highest just above the sediment surface unless there is a great deal of turbulence, when the counts are higher in the upper layers. The bacterial counts of water in Port Hacking and Botany Bay previously referred to, show peaks and troughs corresponding to those of the sediments suggesting that the same influences are at work and considerable mixing occurs.

Wood [80] found that proteolytic bacteria formed a greater percentage of the whole flora in the sediments than in the water, in which they were most numerous close to the sediment. Chitin digestion occurred both in sediments and water, especially in autumn and spring. Cellulose and agar digestion were unaccountably rare in Lake Macquarie, though they were common in Port Hacking. Lignin-digesting bacteria (Actinomycetes) and fungi were very numerous in late summer, and were present all the year in sediment, deep water, and surface samples. Table VIII shows the pre-

## Table VII

*Occurrence of bacteria in various estuarine environments (percentage of species)*

| Species | Water | | | Sea-grass community |
|---|---|---|---|---|
| | Bottom | 1 m from bottom | Surface | |
| *Bacillus subtilis* | 45 | 39·5 | 22 | 10–25 |
| *B. megaterium* | 18 | 7 | 5·5 | 0 |
| *B. sphaericus* | 0 | 7·5 | 0 | 0 |
| *Corynebacterium globiforme* | 0 | 7·0 | 0 | 0 |
| *C. flavum* | 0 | 0 | 0 | 10 |
| *C. miltinum* | 0 | 0 | 0 | 5 |
| *Actinomyces* spp. | 18 | 0 | 5·5 | 10–25 |
| *Staphylococcus candidus* | 0 | 8 | 8 | 0 |
| *S. roseus* | 0 | 8 | 0 | 0 |
| *Mycoplana dimorpha* | 19 | 23 | 54 | 40 |
| *M. citrea* | 0 | 0 | 0 | 5 |
| *Sarcina lutea* | 0 | 0 | 5·5 | 0 |
| Pigmented strains | 20 | 38 | 27·5 | 50 |
| Ratio gram pos./gram neg. strains | 1·9 | 2·0 | 0·7 | 0·9 |

dominant bacterial species from the water at the surface and 1 m from the bottom, from the surface of the sediment and from the sea-grass community. The gram-negative rods predominated in the water at the surface, gram-positive sporers and Actinomycetes on the surface of the sediments, while the water above the sediments had an intermediate flora. The sea-grass flora varied considerably, but had characteristics of its own. Coliform organisms have not been found in uncontaminated estuaries, and do not persist for long in estuarine waters; their presence indicated recent contamination.

*Protoplankton in Estuaries*

Wood [81] has divided the protoplankton found in estuaries into oceanic, neritic, and estuarine species on the basis of their minimum salinity requirements, and correlated these divisions with the ability of a species to reproduce in the several parts of the estuary.

Oceanic species should:
Proliferate only in oceanic environments
Be stenohaline, requiring salinities close to that of sea water
Exist in low nutrient ranges
Be found only occasionally in estuaries and then be traceable to onshore movements of oceanic currents.
Estuarine species or strains should:
Proliferate only within the estuary
Be tolerant of low or moderate salinities and/or rapid changes of temperature
Require high nutrient concentrations
Occur on nearly all occasions in estuarine samples and rarely outside.
Neritic species or strains should:
Proliferate within the marine-dominated part of the estuary or outside
Require moderate or high salinities and moderately constant temperatures
Have a wide range of nutrient requirements
Occur frequently in estuaries, particularly the marine-dominated parts and equally or more often outside.

In practice, the planktonic diatoms and dinoflagellates do allow of separation on these grounds. Oceanic species, i.e. those which occur widely in waters that are geographically oceanic such as *Climacodium frauenfeldianum* or *Ceratium candelabrum*, do not reproduce in estuaries, even in the mouths, do not occur in water with salinities below 30% and are found in estuaries only during invasions by oceanic waters. Neritic species bloom, usually outside the estuary, and the bloom may invade the estuary or occur in the marine-dominated part, sometimes extending upstream, apparently governed by salinity limits. Estuarine species usually bloom in the upper or middle sections and extend downstream. Records from Port Hacking show these developments very clearly in the case of neritic species such as *Schroederella delicatula*, *Asterionella japonica*, and *Nitzschia seriata*. Estuarine species such as *Peridinium ovatum*, *P. subinerme*, *Coscinodiscus granii*, or *Rhizosolenia robusta* appeared first in the upper tidal waters, spreading through the middle reaches to the entrance, and in some cases failed to reach the entrance. Species such as *Ceratium buceros* and *C. furca* which are endemic in many estuaries of eastern Australia seem to have estuarine clones which may have morphological differences from the neritic and oceanic clones, and the blooms of neritic and estuarine clones do not always coincide. There is evidence that estuarine and neritic species remain in the hypolimnion of stratified estuaries when they are not in bloom and that the epilimnion is fed from this source. Diatoms and dinoflagellates which form spores such as *Skeletonema costatum, Chaetoceros,* and *Goniaulax* tend to sink to the sediments in the spore stage, as I have found by culturing them from surface sediments, and from their progress upwards from the sediment during the development of blooms. Wood differentiates two groups of oceanic species one of which does not penetrate the estuaries at all and includes *Ceratium gravidum, C. euarcuatum,* and *C. concilians,* the other being able to live but not reproduce in oceanic water which has penetrated into an estuary, and represented by *C. candelabrum, C. carriense,* and *Goniodoma polyedricum.*

In a study of different estuaries, even those adjacent to each other such as Port Jackson and Port Hacking, many differences will be observed in the protoplankton. Wood endeavoured to express this by listing the species of each estuary according to the percentage of samples in which they occur. This gives a general picture in terms of the frequency with which one is likely to observe a given species or group of species, but does not depict the relative numbers of each species that one is likely to encounter. Some species, e.g. *Melosira sulcata* or *Peridinium roseum,* are almost always present in an estuary, but never dominant or sub-dominant, while others such as *Coscinodiscus granii* are abundant and dominant in Australian estuaries at certain times of the year (winter), but are rarely seen between blooms.

Protoplankton communities in different estuaries reflect the nature of the estuary. Moreton Bay is a very large, shallow estuary open to the northeast, with Coral Sea water moving usually south across the mouth. Consequently, there is a quasi-endemic population of oceanic species such as *Ceratium karsteni, C. carriense, C. massiliense,* and *Guinardia flaccida* which appears to be renewed from time to time by oceanic waters. In the shallow water with numerous sandbanks there is considerable current activity and strong wind action. We therefore get a large infusion of detached stipitate diatoms from the periphyton, e.g. *Climacosphenia moniligera* and *Thalassiothrix nitzschioides* into the protoplankton, and at times *Climacosphenia* may become dominant. Port Hacking is a much smaller estuary, but has also an open entrance and onshore oceanic current movements and once again oceanic characters are frequently obvious in the protoplankton, and because of fast-moving water over the sea-grass banks, *Climacosphenia* and *Licmophora* forsake their epontic community for the plankton, and may dominate the latter community. In such estuaries, too, turbulence results in the presence of benthic species in the plankton, e.g. *Pleurosigma*, *Mastogloia*, and *Diploneis*. Port Hacking, being a drowned valley type, has deep holes at the heads of each valley and the hypolimnion of the upper reaches serves as a reservoir of estuarine species which invade the lower reaches during wet weather as these are diluted by fresh water. In Moreton Bay, which is an old river delta, the estuarine species are confined to the upper parts except on rare occasions, as there are no reservoirs for resting populations.

Port Jackson, which is a drowned valley with little dilution from rivers, and has a deep entrance extending inland for several miles, contains a mixture of estuarine and neritic species both of which appear to be endemic. The protoplankton of Port Jackson is different in most of its essentials from that of Port Hacking some 15 miles south, and the difference can only be attributed to differences in the structure of the estuaries. In Lake Macquarie, a drowned valley cut off from the ocean by a sand-bar, and like the last two ports with little run-off, there is little oceanic influence. When oceanic waters do pass through the narrow channel connecting the lake with the sea, they spread out on the surface for a mile or so from the entrance or sink to the bottom just over the sill, depending on the salinity of the surface water of the lake at the time. Such invasions of oceanic species are very localized and short-lived. In this lake, however, there is a residual oceanic protoplankton comprising the diatoms *Chaetoceros peruvianum* and *Ch. lorenzianum* and the dinoflagellates *Peridinium depressum* and *Pyrophacus horologicum*. The two diatoms have developed clones which are smaller than their oceanic counterparts. None of these species occurs in estuarine or neritic habitats in any other estuary. There is evidence that Lake Macquarie represents an ancient relic of oceanic water, and the explanation could be that it was cut off by the sand-bar while a bloom of oceanic plankton was occurring. Oceanic conditions prevailed long enough for the population to become established and it is still associated with the old water, the oceanic character of which is maintained by infusion from outside, while the inflowing fresh and brackish water from the small watershed forms the epilimnion and escapes through the channel to the open sea.

Port Phillip, which is part of a large flood plain, has also a small entrance and is shallow throughout. The endemic species include *Coscinodiscus granii*, *Nitzschia seriata*, and *Rhizosolenia setigera*, and the dinoflagellate *Ceratium tripos*. This flora does not extend more than a few miles out from the entrance and has nothing in common with the sparse protoplankton population of Bass Strait, viz. *Rhizosolenia hebetata* v. *hiemalis*, *Chaetoceros convolutum*, and *Ceratium horridum*. In Port Hacking and Port Jackson, but not in Port Phillip, the diatoms *Coscinodiscus granii* and *Rhiz. olenia robusta* or *Asterionella japonica* and *Chaetoceros secundum* usually ap ar as co-dominants in plankton blooms. Their growth curves have appeared identical when observed, and the pairs of species give evidence of occupying the same ecological niche. One would conclude that the species were mutually dependent for growth factors and vitamins except that in other communities and habitats the pairs are not associated.

In the Southern Hemisphere estuaries which I have studied, the maximum diversity of species of diatoms and dinoflagellates occurs in early August (early spring), decreasing sharply in September and rising in October through December, with at times an increased diversity in March. Protoplankton blooms usually occur in autumn (April–May) and spring (late August through to November), but the maxima were very irregular in their occurrence. Some species, e.g. *Coscinodiscus granii* and *Rhizosolenia robusta*, are winter forms with maxima in June–July. There is much less regularity in the Australian region than in the Northern Hemisphere where the spring and autumn peaks are in general predictable (fig. 18, page 212).

The nanoplankton of the estuaries has not been studied in any detail, but it is in general much more numerous than the larger protoplankton, usually by at least one order of magnitude. Estuarine waters also contain large numbers of colourless flagellates, especially after the flowering of the sea-grasses and their subsequent decay.

The form-variation of some estuarine species, such as *Ceratium buceros* and *Chaetoceros peruvianum*, which have oceanic counterparts, has been mentioned. Other estuarine–neritic species, especially dinoflagellates, have form-variations which can be used to identify the form with the estuary. In Port Stephens, the predominant *Dinophysis* is a rounded form of *D. caudata*; in Port Jackson, *D. caudata* and the closely associated *D. tripos* are almost equal in occurrence with the intermediate *D. diegensis* also present. In Port Hacking, a rounded *D. tripos* is more common than *D. caudata*, and in more southerly estuaries, *D. caudata* is rarely found. In Tasmanian waters, *D. tripos* becomes more rugose and papillate; and *D. caudata* is more irregular in shape as we go farther into the tropics, the forms found in the Solomon Islands being almost square.

*Epontic Communities (The Periphyton)*

I have mentioned the importance of the sea-grasses in the estuarine community and their association with the epiphytic diatoms, blue-green and other algae to form an important sub-community. In this sub-community, the larger forms such as *Dictyota, Laurencia, Gracilaria,* and *Gigartina* form a bulk of epiphytes in the spring and summer which may be of the same order of magnitude as the sea-grasses themselves, and the smaller algae *Ectocarpus,* followed by *Ceramium, Polysiphonia, Antithamnion,* grow out to form a mat which often becomes interlaced with *Enteromorpha* to form a blanket of comparable mass. Such mats or blankets may cover the whole sea-grass community and produce so much oxygen by photosynthesis that the mat floats off in large rafts until it is broken up by wave and wind action. The mat will carry off with it any attached pebbles or shells (often littorinids) which it may transport for several miles and thus be a factor in distributing various molluscs. These mats cause a low redox potential in the sea-grass community at night when available oxygen is used up in respiration.

The epiphytic diatoms are very important in this habitat as has been shown by Wood [81]. They loom large not only in actual bulk, but, as has been said, are an important source of food for phytophagous fish. Quantitative estimates have been made, but these do not allow for the quantity grazed or for those breaking away into the plankton or the benthos. The seasonal peaks occur in spring–summer, and at times in autumn. The spring–summer maximum may consist of two peaks, often of different species and the autumn maximum may be large or small or may not occur in some seasons. Monospecific blooms of epiphytic diatoms are rare, only one (of *Nitzschia sigma*) being recorded during several years' observation. The distribution of epontic diatoms over an area of sea-grass flat is usually reasonably uniform though anomalies do occur. Differences in the diatom associations on flats in the same estuarine system can be small or great and are usually sufficient to allow an observer to determine by examination of these associations and of fish stomachs just where in the estuary the fish have been feeding.

I have earlier given a short list of epiphytic diatoms from estuarine situations. In addition, there is a flora of unattached species, such as *Coscinodiscus centralis, C. asteromphalus, C. argus,* the cyclotellas and some biddulphias, which appear to be an integral part of the association. There is also a relatively static community of animals, particularly crustaceans and tube-worms which no doubt feed in part at least on the plant community. I have already discussed the effect of this intense plant and animal life on certain parameters of the estuarine environment such as the pH, Eh, and oxygen tension.

The dissemination of these species was found to be by transportation on the surface of the water in the tidal zone, the organisms being held there by surface tension. Epontic diatoms are relatively rare in the plankton as was found during an 18 months' study of this environment in connexion with oyster farming. Experiments in fertilizing intertidal flats showed that the fertilizer originally added to the sediments in certain areas, quickly became disseminated over the whole flat area, and the tidal movement was found by fluorescein studies to be somewhat circular in a horizontal plane, which would account for the fertilizer distribution and for the uniformity of the periphyton. The epontic species appear to vary in their sensitivity to salinity changes, so that the floral associations in the estuary will vary, as has been shown. Each estuary has its own epontic flora as well as its planktonic one, for example, *Licmophora flabellata*, which is abundant in the central reaches of Port Hacking, is relatively unimportant in Lake Macquarie. The flora which is normally epontic on rocks, timber, and other features of the estuarine environment differs considerably from that on the sea-grasses, first by the greater importance of the blue-green algae, and second by the more frequent appearance of the sessile forms of diatoms such as *Synedra*, *Cocconeis*, and *Fragilaria* rather than *Achnanthes*, *Licmophora*, and *Climacosphenia*. The difference in flora would seem to be accompanied by a difference in the grazing population, though observations on this have been somewhat superficial. I have mentioned that it is possible to tell from examinations of fish stomachs in what estuary they have been feeding, and often in what part of the estuary as well as whether they have been in the sea-grass association or working along the rocky reefs. I have stated that planktonic diatoms are rarely used as food by estuarine animals, as far as I have been able to observe. If this is universally true it makes very difficult the assessment of organic production in estuaries by pigment estimation or assimilation studies *in vitro*.

*The Benthic Protist Community*
The benthic environment and the interaction between it and the bacterial inhabitants in the estuaries has already been discussed. I have pointed out that the estuarine, continental shelf, and abyssal sediments have a great deal in common, far more than the sediments have with the water immediately above. The numbers and types of organisms and rates of change seem from the evidence available to diminish as the depth increases.

THE ROCK FACIES. This is related to the epontic community in that a number of species are attached to the rocks as stated above. However, the majority form a felt over the rock surface, and this tapetic flora consists largely of blue-green algae intermingled with such species as *Nitzschia closterium*, *N. martiana*, *Navicula grevillei*, and *Amphipleura micans*, all of which are active felt formers. They are not usually attached to the rock, but have a thin layer of reduced organic matter containing sulphate-reducing bacteria, purple and green sulphur bacteria and many heterotrophs and composed largely of decomposing blue-green algae such as *Oscillatoria*, *Lyngbya*, *Microcoleus*, and members of the Nostocaceae. Associated with and often attached to the felts are such diatoms as *Synedra*, *Melosira*, *Grammatophora*, *Plagiogramma*, *Striatella*, *Bacillaria*, *Triceratium*, and *Amphora*, and mingling with these many coloured and colourless euglenids, monads, sarcodina, and ciliates. This rock facies has its maximum development in the spring, especially in sheltered areas where it cannot be removed by current and wave action.

THE SEA-GRASS FACIES. The sea-grass facies occurs in sediments with an oxidized layer overlying a reduced sediment, usually with a high content of organic matter derived from above. The rate of turnover of organic matter in this facies is very rapid as is shown by the change in pH from about 5·8 at night to up to 9·4 in daylight. The planktonic species from the water above disappear from the sediment very rapidly and their skeletons are rarely seen even on the surface of the sediments. It would appear that the settling out of protoplankton is negligible and that the degeneration of planktonic material occurs mainly in the water. Epontic species which settle out, such as *Licmophora* and *Amphora*, do appear in sediment samples, but even these do not usually make up an important part of the sediment facies except for *Amphora* in some of the Texas Bays. The micro-organisms of the sea-grass benthic facies are therefore largely true benthic species. Of the flagellates, *Astasia*, *Eutreptia*, *Euglena*, *Gymnodinium*, *Amphidinium*, *Gyrodinium*, *Murayella*, *Cochlodinium*, *Massartia*, and *Warnowia* are frequent and abundant. Ciliates and amoebae occur throughout the upper sediments, even in anaerobic areas. Diatoms include the genera *Pleurosigma*, *Navicula*, *Pinnularia*, *Neidium*, *Trachyneis*, *Anomoeoneis*, *Mastogloia*, *Cyclotella*, *Caloneis*, *Auliscus*, *Coscinodiscus*, *Surirella*, *Campylodiscus*, *Nitzschia*, and *Hantzschia*.

THE BARE SEDIMENT FACIES. By bare sediment I mean those sediments without a cover of sea-grasses or tapetic species. Microscopic algae, especially blue-greens, occur in clear sands in many estuaries, often to considerable depths as at Lake Conjola in New South Wales and Port St Joes in Florida, where the blue-green coloration was visible to a depth of $2\frac{1}{2}$ inches. The algae in these cases were species of *Microcoleus*, but other blue-green and green algae may be involved. In Botany Bay, the oyster-growing flats are covered in the spring with the alga *Vaucheria* which gives a dark green colour to the whole flat and is accompanied by the diatom genera which I have listed above. The sediment smells of hydrogen sulphide. It is no doubt significant that these species are nearly all facultative heterotrophs and some may be capable of photoreduction of carbon dioxide. In brackish water of Australian and Texas estuaries, reduced sediments are covered in winter with a heavy felt of *Enteromorpha intestinalis*, and as this decays, a purple layer of sulphur bacteria (*Chromatium*) appears below which are the green sulphur bacteria and *Desulphovibrio*. There is intense growth and activity of flagellates under this material and small fish will usually be seen grazing in the immediate vicinity. If the bare sediments are clayey, they usually incorporate a great deal of organic matter, much of which is resistant to oxidation, especially degraded pigments such as carotenoids (Fox et al. [82]). Such sediments will be blue, green, or black and have a low content of micro-organisms. Diatoms are usually few and the main genera are *Navicula* and *Diploneis*.

Grøntved [83, 84] studied production by the microbenthos in some Danish fjords, estimating assimilation by the $C^{14}$ method and by the diatom cover in terms of cell volume and thickness of cover. He showed a maximum production in summer, i.e. June through August, closely related to temperature. He assumed in his first paper that organo-production was due to diatoms and that other organisms were unimportant. In his second paper he recorded production figures for the tidal flats of the Wadden Sea where microbenthic photosynthesis was about 4 times as active as that in the fjords. Maximum production occurred from September through October in 1960 and from June through August in 1961. He found that there is considerable stirring of the sediments in the intertidal flats so that the effective photosynthetic region is about 4 cm deep in contrast to 1 cm in the sub-tidal sediments. He found that the flagellates, including monads, were usually one order of magnitude greater than the diatoms. Among the diatom species, recorded from the sediments, he lists *Asterionella japonica*, *Cerataulina bergonii*, *Chaetoceros* spp., *Guinardia flaccida*, *Thalassiosira decipiens*, *T. rotula*, and *Rhizosolenia* spp., planktonic species which were not found in Australian or Texas sediments. In addition to these he found *Aulacodiscus argus*, *Auliscus sculptus* (common at times in Port Hacking sediments), *Cyclotella caspia*, *Melosira moniliformis*, *M. sulcata*, *Biddulphia aurita*, *B. rhombus*, *Triceratium alternans*, and *Skeletonema costatum*, all common species in the benthic communities in both hemispheres. Grøntved observed that there is little settlement of planktonic species on the sediments of the tidal flats. It is difficult to understand the absence from his area of the pennate diatoms so characteristic of shallow water and intertidal flats in other regions.

He found that the dark uptake of $C^{14}$ was up to $37 \cdot 5\%$ of the total in the suspendible fraction on the tidal flats, but only $4\%$ in the sand fraction, another example of the greater biological activity of the finer materials of the sediments.

Grøntved's estimations of annual productivity of the areas may be taken with reserve as he did not include the sea-grass areas, although he mentioned their existence, nor did he allow for introduced detritus which would be expected to provide a large bulk of food for the bacteria and the phagotrophic protista. Further, monthly examinations are hardly frequent enough for accurate estimates, in warmer waters at least, as I have found that blooms tend to last 1 to 2 weeks on the average.

## REFERENCES

[1] CROSBY, L. H. and WOOD, E. J. F. (1958), 'Studies on Australian and New Zealand diatoms, I', Trans. Roy. Soc. N.Z., 85, 483–530.

[2] WOOD, E. J. F. (1953), 'Heterotrophic bacteria in marine environments of eastern Australia', Aust. J. Mar. Freshw. Res., 4, 160–200.

[3] WOOD, E. J. F. (1964), 'Studies in microbial ecology of the Australasian region. I–III', Nova Hedwigia, 7, 6–54.

[4] HARVEY, H. W. (1955), Chemistry and Fertility of Sea Water, Cambridge University Press, 224 pp.

[5] KREPS, E. (1934), 'Organic catalysts or enzymes in sea water', James Johnstone Memorial Volume, Liverpool, 193 pp.

[6] KEYS, A., CHRISTENSEN, E. H., and KROGH, A. (1935), 'Organic metabolism in sea water', J. Mar. Biol. Ass. U.K., 20, 181.

[7] HOLMES, R. W. (1958), 'Size fractionation of photosynthesizing phytoplankton', U.S. Fish. Wildl. Serv. Spec. Sci. Rept. Fish., 279, 69–71.

[8] HOLMES, R. W. and ANDERSON, G. C. (1963), 'Size fractionation of $C^{14}$ labelled natural phytoplankton communities', Symp. Marine Microbiol., Ch. 25, C. H. Oppenheimer, ed. Thomas, Springfield, Ill.

[9] ZOBELL, C. E. (1946), Marine Microbiology. Chronica Botanica Co., Waltham, Mass.

[10] WAKSMAN, S. A., REUSZER, H. S. R., CAREY, C. L., HOTCHKISS, M., and RENN, C. E. (1933), 'Studies on the biology and chemistry of the Gulf of Maine, III', Biol. Bull., 64, 183–205.

[11] JONES, G. E. (1958), 'Attachment of bacteria to zooplankton', U.S. Fish. Wildl. Serv. Spec. Sci. Rept. Fish., 279, 77–78.

[12] VELANKAR, N. K. (1955), 'Bacteria in the inshore environment at Mandapam Camp', Ind. J. Fish., 2, 96–112.

[13] CVIIC, V. (1955), 'Distribution of bacteria in the waters of the Mid-Adriatic Sea', Repts. M.V. Hvar cruises, 4 (1), 1–41.

[14] CVIIC, V. (1960), 'Méthodes de détermination directe et indirecte du nombre des bactéries dans l'eau de mer et cértaines données de leur

distribution verticale dans la partie meridionale de l'Adriatique', *Rapp. et Proc. Verb. Cons., Expl. Med.*, 38–43.
[15] KRISS, A. E., LEBEDEVA, M. N., and MITZKEWICH, I. N. (1960), 'Microorganisms as indicators of hydrological phenomena in seas and oceans, III', *Deep Sea Res.*, **6**, 175–83.
[16] KRISS, A. E., ABYZOV, S. S., and MITZKEWICH, I. N. (1960), 'Microorganisms as indicators of hydrological phenomena in seas and oceans, III', *Deep Sea Res.*, **6**, 335–45.
[17] KRISS, A. E. and RUKINA, E. A. (1952), 'Biomass of micro-organisms and their proliferation rates in ocean depths', *Zhur. Obschei Biol.*, **13**, 346–62.
[18] KRISS, A. E. (1960), 'Micro-organisms as indicators of hydrological phenomena in seas and oceans, I', *Deep Sea Res.*, **6**, 88–94.
[19] KRISS, A. E. and MITZKEWICH, I. N. (1959), 'Krassilnikoviae; a new class of micro-organisms', *J. Gen. Microbiol.*, **20**, 1–12.
[20] KRISS, A. E. and MITZKEWICH, I. N. (1960), 'On distribution of filamentous-cluster organisms (Krassilnikoviae) in sea and ocean depths', *J. Gen. Microbiol.*, **23**, 441–43.
[21] ZOBELL, C. E. (1936), 'Bactericidal action of sea water', *Proc. Soc. Exp. Biol. Med.*, **34**, 113–16.
[22] WAKSMAN, S. A. and HOTCHKISS, M. (1938), 'On the oxidation of organic matter in marine sediments', *J. Mar. Res.*, **1**, 101–18.
[23] TAYLOR, C. B. (1942), 'Biology of fresh water, III', *J. Hyg.*, **42**, 284–96.
[24] KETCHUM, B. H. (1952), 'Processes contributing to the decrease of coliform bacteria in a tidal estuary', *Ecology*, **33**, 247–58.
[25] CHARLTON, G. (1955), 'Direct antagonism in mixed bacterial populations', *J. Bact.*, **70**, 56–59.
[26] JONES, G. E. (1963), 'Suppression of bacterial growth by sea water', *Symp. Marine Microbiol.*, Ch. 53, C. H. Oppenheimer, ed. Thomas, Springfield, Ill.
[27] ZOBELL, C. E. and FELTHAM, C. B. (1934), 'Preliminary studies on the distribution and characteristics of marine bacteria', *Scripps Inst. Oceanog. Tech. Ser. Bull.*, **3**, 279–96.
[28] BENTON, ANNE G. (1935), 'Chitinovorous bacteria – a preliminary survey', *J. Bact.*, **29**, 448.
[29] HESS, E. (1937), 'Chitinovorous bacteria on live lobsters', *Biol. Bd. Can. Prog. Repts.*, 19.
[30] HOCK, C. W. (1941), 'Marine chitin-decomposing bacteria', *J. Mar. Res.*, **4**, 99–106.
[31] HOCK, C. W. (1940), 'Decomposition of chitin by marine bacteria', *Biol. Bull.*, **79**, 199–206.
[32] ZOBELL, C. E. and RITTENBERG, S. C. (1938), 'The occurrence and characteristics of chitinoclastic bacteria in the sea', *J. Bact.*, **35**, 275–87.
[33] WOOD, E. J. F. (1964), 'Studies in the microbial ecology of Australasian waters, IV', *Nova Hedwigia*, 7, III–IV (in press).
[34] WOOD, E. J. F. (1963), 'Some relations of phytoplankton to environment', *Symp. Marine Microbiol.*, Ch. 28, C. H. Oppenheimer, ed. Thomas, Springfield, Ill.

[35] LOHMANN, H. (1908), 'Untersuchung zur Feststellung des vollstandigen Gehaltes des Meeres an Plankton', *Wiss. Meeresf.*, Kiel, n.f. **10**, 131–370.

[36] PARKE, MARY, MANTON, I., and CLARKE, B. (1955), 'Studies on marine flagellates, II', *J. Mar. Biol. Ass. U.K.*, **34**, 579–609.

[37] PARKE, MARY, MANTON, I., and CLARKE, B. (1956), 'Studies on marine flagellates, III', *J. Mar. Biol. Ass. U.K.*, **35**, 387–414.

[38] PARKE, MARY, MANTON, I., and CLARKE, B. (1959), 'Studies on marine flagellates, V', *J. Mar. Biol. Ass. U.K.*, **38**, 169–88.

[39] PARKE, MARY and MANTON, I. (1962), 'Studies on marine flagellates, VI', *J. Mar. Biol. Ass. U.K.*, **42**, 391–404.

[40] WOOD, E. J. F. and DAVIS, P. S. (1956), 'Importance of smaller phytoplankton elements', *Nature*, **177**, 436.

[41] BERNARD, F. (1963), 'Density of flagellates and Myxophyceae in the heterotrophic layers related to environment', *Symp. Marine Microbiol.*, Ch. 22, C. H. Oppenheimer, ed. Thomas, Springfield, Ill.

[42] ZOBELL, C. E. (1954), 'The occurrence of bacteria in the deep sea and their significance for animal life', *Publ. Int. Union. Sci.*, B16, 20–29.

[43] WISEMAN, J. D. H. and HENDEY, N. I. (1953), 'The significance of diatom content of a deep floor sea sample from the neighbourhood of the greatest oceanic depth', *Deep Sea Res.*, **1**, 47–59.

[44] MCHUGH, J. L. (1954), 'Distribution and abundance of the diatom *Ethmodiscus rex* off the west coast of North America', *Deep Sea Res.*, **1**, 216–23.

[45] KOLBE, R. W. (1962), 'Diatoms in the deep seas', *Science*, **126**, 1053–56.

[46] MANN, A. (1908), 'Report on the diatoms of the Albatross voyages in the Pacific Ocean, 1888–1904', *Contr. U.S. Nat. Mus.*, 10, 5, 221, 420.

[47] LLOYD, BLODWEN (1931), 'Muds of the Clyde Sea area, II', *J. Mar. Biol. Ass. U.K.*, **17**, 751–65.

[48] DUGGELI, M. (1936), 'Die Bakterienflora in Schlamm der Rotsee', *Rev. Hydrobiol.*, **7**, 205–363.

[49] ISSATCHENKO, B. L. (1938), 'Review of the work in microbiology of mud and marine springs', *Microbiol.*, **7**, 385–410 (Russian).

[50] RITTENBERG, S. C. (1940), 'Bacterial analyses of some long cores of marine sediments', *J. Mar. Res.*, **3**, 191–201.

[51] RUBENTSCHIK, L. and GOICHERMAN, D. G. (1935), 'On the microbiology of mud in salt lakes, I', *Mikrobiol.*, **4**, 403–20 (Russian).

[52] STONE, R. W. (1946), 'Fermentation of organic acids by marine mud cultures', *J. Bact.*, **51**, 600.

[53] THIEL, G. A. (1925), 'Manganese precipitated by micro-organisms', *Econ. Geol.*, **20**, 301–10.

[54] THIEL, G. A. (1928), 'A summary of the activities of bacterial agencies in sedimentation', *Nat. Res. Counc. Rept. Circ. Ser.*, **85**, 61–77.

[55] WAKSMAN, S. A. (1933), 'On the distribution of organic matter in the sea bottom and the chemical nature and origin of marine humus', *Soil Sci.*, **36**, 125–47.

[56] ZELINSKI, N. D. (1893), 'On hydrogen sulphide fermentation in the Black Sea and Odessa estuaries', *Proc. Russ. Phys. Chem. Soc.*, **25**, 298–303.

[57] ZOBELL, C. E. (1938), 'Studies on the bacterial flora of marine bottom sediments,' *Sed. Petrol.*, **8**, 10–18.

[58] ZOBELL, C. E. (1939), 'Occurrence and activity of bacteria in marine sediments', in *Recent Marine Sediments*, Amer. Ass. Pet. Geol., 416–27.

[59] ZOBELL, C. E. (1946), 'Studies on the redox potential of marine sediments', *Bull. Amer. Soc. Pet. Geol.*, **30**, 477–513.

[60] ZOBELL, C. E. and MORITA, R. Y. (1957), 'Barophilic bacteria in some deep sea sediments', *J. Bact.*, **73**, 563–68.

[61] ZOBELL, C. E. and MORITA, R. Y. (1957), 'Deep sea bacteria', in *Galathea Repts.*, Copenhagen, 43 pp.

[62] ZOBELL, C. E. and ANDERSON, D. Q. (1936), 'Vertical distribution of bacteria in marine sediments', *Bull. Amer. Soc. Pet. Geol.*, **20**, 258–68.

[63] EMERY, K. O. and RITTENBERG, S. C. (1952), 'Early diegenesis of California Basin sediments in relation to the origin of oil', *Bull. Amer. Pet. Geol.*, **35**, 735–806.

[64] SISLER, F. D. and ZOBELL, C. E. (1951), 'Nitrogen fixation by sulphate-reducing bacteria indicated by nitrogen–argon ratios', *Science*, **113**, 511–12.

[65] RITTENBERG, S. C., EMERY, K. O., and ORR, W. L. (1955), 'Regeneration of nutrients in sediments of marine basins', *Deep Sea Res.*, **3** (suppl.), 23–45.

[66] OPPENHEIMER, C. H. and WOOD, E. J. F. (1962), 'Note on the effect of contamination on a marine slough and the vertical distribution of unicellular plants in the sediment', *Z. allg. Mikrobiol.*, **2**, 45–47.

[67] LEWIN, JOYCE C. (1953), 'Heterotrophy in diatoms', *J. Gen. Microbiol.*, **9**, 305–13.

[68] LEWIN, JOYCE C. and LEWIN, R. A. (1960), 'Autotrophy and heterotrophy in marine littoral diatoms', *Can. J. Microbiol.*, **6**, 127–34.

[69] ALEEM, A. A. (1960), 'The diatom community inhabiting the mud flats at Whitstable', *New Phytol.*, **49**, 176–88.

[70] CALLAME, B. and DEBYSER, J. (1954), 'Obsérvations sur les mouvèments des diatomées à la surface des sédiments marins de la zone intercotidiale', *Vie et Milieu*, **5**, 243.

[71] BAAS BECKING, L. G. M. and WOOD, E. J. F. (1955), 'Biological processes in the estuarine environment, I, II', *Kon. Ned. Akad. Weten. Proc.*, **B58**, 180–81.

[72] WOOD, E. J. F. (1959), 'Some aspects of the ecology of Lake Macquarie, N.S.W., IV', *Aust. J. Mar. Freshw. Res.*, **10**, 304–15.

[73] ERIKSON, D. (1941), 'Studies on some lake mud strains of *Micromonospora*', *J. Bact.*, **41**, 277–300.

[74] WOOD, E. J. F. (1953), 'Heterotrophic bacteria in marine environments of eastern Australia', *Aust. J. Mar. Freshw. Res.*, **4**, 160–200.

[75] VELANKAR, N. K. (1955), 'Bacteria in the inshore environment at Mandapam', *Ind. J. Fish.*, **2**, 96–112.

[76] OPPENHEIMER, C. H. (1960), 'Bacterial activity in sediments of shallow marine bays', *Geochim. Cosmochim. Acta.*, **19**, 244–60.

[77] DEW, BARBARA and WOOD, E. J. F. (1955), 'Observations on the periodicity in marine invertebrates', *Aust. J. Mar. Freshw. Res.*, **6**, 469–78.

[78] ZOBELL, C. E. and FELTHAM, C. B. (1942), 'The bacterial flora of a marine mud flat as an ecological factor', *Ecology*, 2369–78.

[79] WOOD, E. J. F. (1950), 'Bacteria in marine environments', *Proc. Indo-Pac. Fish. Counc.*, **69**, 214.

[80] WOOD, E. J. F. (1959), 'Some aspects of the ecology of Lake Macquarie, N.S.W., VI', *Aust. J. Mar. Freshw. Res.*, **10**, 322–40.

[81] WOOD, E. J. F. (1964), 'Studies in the microbial ecology of the Australasian region, V', *Nova Hedwigia*, **8**, III–IV (in press).

[82] FOX, D. L., UPDEGRAFF, D. M., and NOVELLI, G. D. (1944), 'Carotenoid pigments in the ocean floor', *Arch. Biochem.*, **5**, 1–23.

[83] GRØNTVED, J. (1960), 'On the productivity of microbenthos and phytoplankton in some Danish fjords', *Medd. Danmarks Fisk. Hav.*, **3**, 3, 55–92.

[84] GRØNTVED, J. (1962), 'Preliminary report on the productivity of microbenthos and phytoplankton in the Danish Wadden Sea', *Medd. Danmarks Fisk. Hav.*, **3**, 12, 55–92.

# CHAPTER 9

# Methods in Marine Microbiology

The first difficulty encountered in a study of marine microbial ecology is that of method, in fact, the whole study of the microbiology of water is limited by the available techniques. A great deal of effort is currently being spent on the evaluation of existing methods and the development of new ones. In this discipline, we are confronted by the fact that, for a greater part of our studies, we cannot take samples directly but may, as in the case of dredge samples taken by *Albatross* and *Galathea* from the ocean deeps, be separated from the sampling device by up to 30 miles of wire rope, and a sounding wire of some 6 miles is not infrequently used in abysses such as the Planet or Kermadec Trenches. We have no visual means of knowing what is going on and are dependent on electronic and other physical devices for recording the depth at which we are actually working (plates 8, 9, 10, 11). When it is realized that the effect of wind on the ship, and of ocean currents can alter the 'stray angle' of the wire when working at sea, and that in bad weather we may not get a sight for several days and have to estimate our position by dead reckoning, it can be appreciated how serious these problems can be. In one very bad instance, 4,000 m of wire were run out in an attempt to sample to the bottom, but the stray angle reduced the actual depth of the *cast* to 1,800 m as determined by physical means. On the oceans far from shore, ships' positions may be many miles out, in fact, on one occasion, I awoke in the early hours of the morning for a station only to find that we were 80 miles from our estimated position and close inshore. We had not had a sight for several days, and had been buffeted by 60 knot winds and heavy seas. In these cases, the scientist is dependent on the navigator, and may never know if a wrong position is recorded.

## Sampling
Adequate sampling is a serious difficulty that we have to overcome. ZoBell [1], Riley [2], and Wood [3] are among the many workers who have pointed out that the microscopic life in the sea may vary greatly in quantity from day to day, from week to week, and even from year to year, and that, even

in plankton swarms, the distribution of organisms may be far from uniform. One has only to observe from an aeroplane the distribution of the coloured windrows of *Trichodesmium* in the tropics or the red tides in Californian or Gulf of Mexico waters to realize this. In small lakes, ponds, rivers, and estuaries, the distribution is more uniform, and the variation tends to be one or two dimensional, but in the oceans there are always three or more properly four dimensions to be considered for, with ocean currents and upwellings, time becomes an important dimension. In the ocean, too, samples can be taken only from ships (or from the air under rare circumstances), and ships are expensive to run, are limited in size and in the facility with which large numbers of samples can be collected and studied. Further, a ship can run only on traverses and plotted courses, and cannot be in two places at once, so that sampling is essentially one or two dimensional. Storms, too, affect the regularity of sampling, often at critical times or in critical places. We must recognize that in the sea and in large bodies of water, the number of samples which can be taken will always be regrettably small. In modern oceanographic studies, it is not sufficient to collect or study material for one discipline alone, so microbiology must take its place along with other desiderata in planning oceanographic cruises. Modern ships are now fitted to take several types of samples or collect a range of data simultaneously, and it has become much easier than it used to be to correlate microbiological findings with chemical and physical properties of the environment and with other biological features. This correlation is of course essential for the marine microbial ecologist.

With the present recording systems it is possible to punch on cards all quantitative data from a ship cruise soon after the collection of the samples and to sort the data, seeking any desired correlations, in a very brief period. More and more work on samples and records is now being done at sea, and the huge back-log of collected material which cluttered and still clutters many marine laboratories is now unnecessary. This also means that it is often possible to consider cruise results while still at sea and if necessary to alter the cruise plan to cope with immediate developments, and to take supplementary samples to check a new idea or indication. I have studied the possibilities of doing marine microbiology at sea, and there is little that cannot be done by a skilled worker, except in very rough weather, in which case it is too rough to sample.

In estuaries, and in limnology, while it is easier to sample effectively because distances are less and one is not limited by expensive vessels, rapid and immediate study of the material is still an advantage in case supplementary samples are required. For estuarine studies, mobile laboratories or fixed, temporary laboratories take the place of ships. The secret of efficient microbiological work at sea or in the field is economy of space and material. The laboratory should be so designed that the researcher has everything within easy reach for the discipline in which he is working, and can himself remain in a fixed and stable position. Thus, bacteriology requires a small section, and so do phytoplankton, and microbial chemistry if they are to be studied. Bench boards and lockers with the necessary fitments can be stored ashore and fitted into place, completely equipped, before the start of a cruise. They are then dismantled at the end of the cruise and returned to the main laboratory complete with their fitments and apparatus. Methods can be made economical of space and time: roll tubes may be used for bacterial plating instead of petri dishes, or samples may be concentrated immediately after collection and stored in small vials or containers. In fine, methods should be so designed as to obviate the returning of samples to the laboratory whenever this is possible.

*Phytoplankton Sampling*
There are three recognized methods of collecting phytoplankton, nets, pumps, and traps, the same methods being available for zooplankton samples; most of the statistical analyses of sampling have been made in connexion with the latter.

Nets are usually made of fine-mesh bolting silk or nylon attached to rings of specified diameter at the open end, the smaller end being attached to a container or *bucket*, in which the plankton is allowed to settle. The net may be towed horizontally or obliquely or hauled vertically through the water. If towed horizontally, the depth can be set by boards (resembling trawl or otter boards), by depressors or paravanes. Vertical hauls may be continuous from the bottom or from a fixed depth to the surface, or divided, using a mechanism to close the net at a given depth. Several workers, notably Winsor and Walford [4], Barnes [5], Barnes and Marshall [6] have studied the implications of net hauls. Barnes [7] showed that divided hauls made vertically using the Nansen [8] principle for closing the net ('strangling' nets) give serious losses of catch by the closing. He showed the necessity for using mechanical devices in the mouth of the net such as that devised by Clarke and Bumpus [9] or Barnes [10]. Barnes and Marshall reviewed the previous work on sampling variation and suggested a non-random distribution of plankton populations. They believe that there are what might be called 'microswarms' restricted both laterally and vertically (see also Cassie [11, 12]). These authors have shown, and my findings with marine bacteria and protoplankton are in agreement, that, when population density is low, the distribution approaches that of Poisson. They give evidence that, at higher densities, Thomas' distribution fits more closely. At still higher densities, there is evidence that the distribution may be normal. On the other hand, red tides give an obvious appearance of uneven distribution. Wood [13] found considerable uniformity in the horizontal distribution of oceanic protoplankton in uniform water. The populations in these cases were not large and the samples were taken some miles apart so there could have been micro-swarms in such populations.

For protoplankton collection, the minimum size of the organisms captured depends on the mesh size of the net, and even with the finest useable mesh (No. 20 bolting cloth) the smaller forms are missed (Harvey [14]). With such fine nets, the water column tends to be pushed in front of the net and filtration becomes inefficient, so that a smaller diameter net with a coarser mesh may catch as much protoplankton in a given time as a larger net with fine mesh. The Discovery N200 phytoplankton net was found to be very inefficient from this point of view, and a 6-inch diameter net with 170 meshes per inch caught more in the same time and place. Langford [15] states:

> 'The efficiency may be fairly constant for a standard length and rate of haul with a particular concentration of organisms but the main disadvantage lies in the fact that the efficiency does not remain constant in different lengths of haul and with different concentrations of plankton. Moreover, the efficiency of such nets has been shown to change with age and the accompanying increased clogging, shrinkage, and fraying of the threads.'

See also Ricker [16], Mackay [17], Rawson [18], and Juday et al. [19].

Pumps have a theoretical advantage over nets and in addition catch the microplankton which passes through the nets. Barnes [7] showed that the variability of pump samples taken with adequate volume controls is of the same order as that of net hauls while the distribution of $Chi^2$ for paired samples with nets and pumps also indicates a variation of a similar type, i.e. a non-random variation. The usual method of treatment of pump samples is to fill a tank of known volume and filter the plankton from this, or to pump directly through a filter, using either a fine-mesh net or a Whatman or other filter; more recently, membrane filters or continuous centrifugation have been used to collect the solid material from pump samples. Pumps can certainly provide larger samples than can be obtained by other methods, but the difficulties are mainly mechanical, e.g. the storage and handling of the flexible pipes required for sampling from even moderate depths, the depth limit to which samples can be taken in practice, and the possibility of adsorption of small phytoplankters on the walls of the pipe. Evasion of the intake through the effect of the pressure gradient, while it can affect zooplankton, would not be a factor in phytoplankton collection as the rate of movement of phytoplankton is low.

Traps for capturing protoplankton stem from the work of Juday [20]. Juday's trap samples 10 litres of water from a predetermined depth, and is adequate for protoplankton samples, though some of the zooplankton such as *Daphnia* may avoid the trap to some extent. Langford criticizes the Juday trap because of the variation in abundance of plankton both in vertical and horizontal planes, since the trap operates at a given spot and many samples would be necessary to give a picture of the plankton distribution in a lake. 'In Lake Mendota, we usually obtain coefficients of variation of the order of 200% with the Juday trap. In the smaller ponds they go up to 4,000%.' If traps are used, especially in small bodies of water, it seems that it is necessary to take composite samples.

Samplers such as the all-glass sampler of Aabye Jensen and Steemann Nielsen [21], that of van Dorn [22] (plate 12), or of Niskin [23] are open to Langford's criticism, but it is found in practice that such samplers do give results which are relatively comparable. Microbial estimations are usually expressed as the logarithm of the number of organisms, and greater accuracy is not expected. Used in this way, this sampling method gives reasonably reproducible results, well within the coefficient of variation of 30% which seems to be the limit of accuracy of protoplankton distribution studies (Wood [3]). The van Dorn and Jitts [24] samplers consist essentially of a plastic tube with plastic or rubber flaps to close both ends, and the mechanism for operating these. The Niskin sampler consists of a large hinge to which is attached a plastic bag to which is fitted a tube. When the mechanism is tripped, the tube is opened aseptically, and the hinge opens, sucking in the sample. When the plastic bag is full a clamp closes the intake tube. In the van Dorn type sampler, the tube goes down open and closes *in situ* so that pressure does not affect the sampler, and, as the cast is raised, any leakage is outward so that the sample is not contaminated. The Niskin sampler goes down deflated and sterile and can be used for culture work or trace element studies.

This discussion does not exhaust the possibilities of plankton samplers, and many have been designed for specific purposes.

*Bacteriological Sampling*
Bacteriological samplers are of the trap type, such as the Niskin sampler already described or the J-Z sampler (ZoBell [1, 25]). Both of these samplers can be used on bathythermograph or 4-mm sounding wire to depths up to 10,000 m without possible contamination. The J-Z sampler is

limited to a volume of about 100 ml, but the Niskin sampler can take up to 5 litres.

## Sediment Sampling

Adequate bottom sampling is another problem for oceanographers. Two general principles are used: grab samplers and corers. The Petterson type of grab consists of two jaws which together form a half-cylinder and are held apart during descent by a messenger-controlled release; other forms have toggles. With the messenger type the grab is lowered on a releasing shackle which is opened by a heavy messenger. When the grab is hauled, two arms are pulled together by the hauling wire to close the grab; with the toggle type, the toggles are released by the grab hitting the bottom and the grab is shut by means of a spring. This type does not work well in soft sediments. Another version is the 'orange peel' grab which is hemispherical when closed, the jaws being formed by several sectors. Grabs must be heavy to ensure that they descend vertically, for if they hit the bottom at an angle no sample is taken. In limnology and in estuarine studies, small grabs can be used with considerable success, e.g. the Eckman grab, which is closed by springs.

Grabs, however, cannot be regarded as quantitative, as the depth of their bite will depend on the surface and its nature, and as, under ideal conditions, the sample will consist of a large but variable amount of material. Further, a large shell or a piece of coral will stop the grab from closing and cause the loss of the sample. For qualitative work grabs are very useful as the material will give an idea of the processes which are occurring on the bottom. For quantitative work, corers are necessary, and these vary greatly in design. I have tried a number of these for aseptic microbial sampling, but none has proved completely satisfactory. The main difficulty is that the corer requires a strong force to drive it into the bottom, and, like the grab, it must descend vertically. In the oceans where large ships are employed, the Emery and Dietz corer [27] is probably the best. It consists essentially of a long pipe with a valve at the top to allow water to pass through during descent. Around the pipe, towards the top, are weights to drive the pipe into the sediment. Rotating vanes are placed at the top to keep the machine vertical during the descent, irrespective of the angle of the sounding wire. The pipe is fitted with a celluloid or plastic lining to contain the core after removal from the pipe, and with a celluloid comb having teeth pointing upwards, the comb being sealed to the liner. When the sample has been taken, the valve at the top closes, and the weight of the core pushes the comb downwards, closing the aperture at the bottom, thus holding the sample in the tube, even if there is a slight leak in the upper valve. Corers are sent down as rapidly as possible, and there is usually a trigger consisting of a weight (sometimes a small corer) on a long wire which is connected to the main corer by a lever. When the trigger hits, it releases the lever which in turn releases a shackle and allows the heavy corer about 20 feet of free fall. Another type is the piston corer in which the coring tube is driven into the bottom by a charge acting against the inertia of the corer.

In shallow water where small boats must be used, core sampling by such means becomes difficult because insufficient force is available to drive the corer into the sediment. The Eckman corer and small toggle corers can be used in 15 m of water or more. In very shallow water a lucite tube can be pushed by hand into the sediment, a stopper inserted and the tube withdrawn with the sample. A stopper just smaller than the inside diameter of the tube is inserted from the bottom and forced up the tube so that samples can be taken without interference from the supernatant water. In water to about 12 feet such tubes, fitted with a one-way valve at the top and taped to a long pole can be used. A single cockle shell or similar object can spoil a sample and sand and gravel present serious problems owing to lack of cohesion. Very thixotropic muds are also difficult to core.

Cores can be frozen in dry ice, removed from the corer and sectioned by a diamond saw or, in clay cores, with a knife. In all core samples no matter how carefully taken, there is always a certain amount of distortion, but this is more important to the geologist than to the biologist. The microbiologist can get a reasonable idea of the population densities at different depths in a core and can determine processes that are active at such depths. It is almost impossible to sterilize a corer so the sides of the core should be aseptically removed before samples are taken. This also helps to avoid distortion and drag contamination from upper levels.

## Treatment of Samples

Water samples from the open ocean, and often from estuaries or streams, require concentration to allow of adequate examination of the sparse populations. Sediment samples often require dilution, as their populations are often too high to estimate by direct means. Dilutions can be made directly by adding known quantities of a suitable diluent, and calculations are available for determining the errors produced by such dilutions. Concentration requires certain equipment and introduces errors which are not so well known. In sediments, the microbial populations of photosynthonts, aerobic heterotrophs, and phagotrophs are concentrated at the surface and tend to decrease rapidly with depth, usually somewhat hyperbolically. Even 0·5 cm below the surface, populations are often 1% to 0·1% of those at the surface and this creates a serious error in taking sub-samples from the sample. I have not found a method of overcoming this error, freezing the cores before cutting being the best.

Concentration is usually done by filtration, sedimentation, or centrifugation. Filtration has two difficulties; blocking and drying out. Now that molecular filters are easily available, filtration is frequently used. Blocking is not always avoidable as it depends largely on the nature and number of the particles in the sample, and even the order of their number is not always predictable. This is especially true in estuaries, where the number of particles may vary through a wide range. Drying out can take place in seconds, and means that filtrations have to be very carefully watched. Some organisms tend to burst when they touch the filter and release their material which escapes through the filter. Lasker and Holmes [28] and Holmes [29] have found a considerable leakage of $C^{14}$-assimilating material through HA millepore filters due either to the existence of ultra-microscopic photosynthonts or to disintegration of the organisms. Gentle filtration tends to minimize this loss, and blocking can be reduced by relating the amount filtered to the number and nature of the particles if this is known, e.g. by a trial filtration if sufficient material is available. Organisms can be resuspended from the filters, but this is not very satisfactory due to adsorption and the difficulty of resuspension. Other methods discussed later are to examine the residue on the filter microscopically, chemically, or culturally.

Sedimentation is required for the Utermohl method of examining phytoplankton with the inverted microscope. Samples are placed in small sedimentation tubes or cylinders and allowed to stand for from 3 to 18 hours. At times, a two-stage process is adopted, a primary sedimentation in Nessler tubes or similar cylinders and a second sedimentation of the concentrate siphoned from the bottom of the primary cylinder into a small sedimentation vessel (Lovegrove [30]). Lund [31] further modified the method by using a very shallow vessel for final sedimentation so that the upright microscope could be used. It is necessary to fix the organisms in some way, and, of the available preservatives, Lund recommends Lugol's iodine (saturated iodine in potassium iodide) for fixing, staining, and at the same time raising the specific gravity of the organisms. I have found that the number of organisms determined by fluorescence counting is much greater than by sedimentation if flagellates are present.

Centrifugation has been condemned by earlier workers (Wood [33]) because discontinuous centrifuges were used, and these caused a resuspension of part of the sediment through the inertia of the liquid when the machine was stopped. This has not been clearly stated, but is obvious from the context of the papers. The criticism does not of course apply to the modern continuous centrifuge such as the Foerst, or the Sharples centrifuge. This explains why Ballantine [32], Davis [23], and Wood [33, 34] claim success from the centrifuge. It is rather amazing that the more delicate naked flagellates appear to stand up well to centrifugation at 15,000 r.p.m. and over, but it must be remembered that they are kept moist throughout. Kimball and Wood (in press) has shown that the centrifuge, which can be cheaply made from a Waring blender, retains more chlorophyll and has a lower coefficient of variation than molecular filters. Centrifugation has the advantage that the material can be examined in the living state, and is not dependent on the total number of particles as is the case with filtration. A nylon cup and other plastic parts can be used for studies of trace elements in protoplankton samples.

**Examination of Material**
The collected material containing microbes can be examined quantitatively and qualitatively.

*Quantitative Studies*
Quantitative examination can be made by direct counts of the organisms in fresh or preserved material, by cultures of the so-called 'viable' organisms, or by estimation of selected chemical parameters such as chlorophyll, particulate carbon, 'organic' phosphate, or carbon. These are measures of standing crop, i.e. the organisms existing at the time of capture. Other methods are used in an attempt to determine the rate of growth, of which 'productivity' is one of the parameters that are being studied at the present time. We can then consider the methods which are aimed at determining the microbial biomass or a defined portion thereof, and those which estimate productivity in terms of total photosynthate produced in a given time or at a given place, or of net production which is essentially the excess of anabolic over catabolic rates.

STANDING CROP. The standing crop of protoplankton is usually determined by counting, by measurement of organic carbon, or by the estimation of chlorophyll.

Counting can be combined with estimations of the average volume as is recommended by Lund and Talling [36] who cite the considerable literature on the subject. For the protoplankton of limited size-range, conductivity counters of the Coulter type may be successfully used to estimate the volume of organisms in each size group, but so far this method has been limited by the size-variation that frequently occurs in mixed protoplankton catches, and by the expense of the equipment. Lund and Talling point out the advantages of counting in that the algae are actually observed, and changes in size, form, or aggregation may be noted. Dead or dying cells may be differentiated and chlorophyll-bearing cells distinguished from pigment-less ones. With very small populations, whose reactions are weak, counting is the most accurate method, Further, microscopic examination allows the separation of cells from debris both in plankton samples and in sediments.

The most usual method of counting is the sedimentation method of Utermohl [37] or modifications of this. Material sedimented as described above is placed in its cell on the stage of an inverted microscope and the cells counted, and if desired divided into groups or species. Difficulties of the method are that quantitative sedimentation is not possible on board ship under usual weather conditions, that critical illumination cannot be used, and that it is not possible to distinguish between the smaller chlorophyll-bearing and chlorophyll-less organisms. The method is well described by Lund [31] and Lund, Kipling, and LeCren [38].

Wood [34, 39] recommends the use of fluorescent microscopy, after concentration of the sample by centrifugation. He uses a powerful incandescent light source, which he prefers as a routine to a quartz lamp, as it is easier on the eyes and can be converted rapidly and easily to ordinary illumination for the study of individual cells. The microscope can be any monocular instrument (or a binocular with a monocular attachment), provided it has a good condenser and a mechanical stage. The light passes through a BG12 sub-stage filter (passing light around 450 m$\mu$), the condenser is immersed in paraffin oil to concentrate the light, and a Petroff Hausser counting chamber is used because it has a thin slide which allows critical illumination. An OG1 (yellow) filter is used on the eyepiece. This allows chlorophyll to fluoresce bright red, and, with a little practice, organisms can be recognized by the shape and size of their chloroplasts. Identification is aided by the easy change-over to white light. Although dead organisms will fluoresce for a time, the method does give a reasonable differentiation between living and dead protoplankton. By subsequently staining another aliquot of the sample with acridine orange according to the method of Strügger (see Wood [39]) living and dead micro-organisms can be distinguished, and the total number of micro-organisms determined. Care must be used to keep the concentration of acridine orange below 1 part in 5,000. This is the only method which distinguishes photosynthetic from non-photosynthetic micro-organisms, though it is recognized that the distinction may not be absolute. It also allows the recognition of organisms that are adsorbed on 'detritus' which so often forms a large part of the total solids in protoplankton samples, even in the open ocean (Wood [13], Strickland [40]). The method is most useful in studies of sediments where most (up to 99·8%) of the smaller microbes are adsorbed on clay particles or on sand grains (Wood and Oppenheimer [41]). Another advantage of the method is that it can, and indeed must be used with living protoplankton, and is usable at sea in any weather in which samples can be taken. Any peculiarities can be studied on the spot by reverting to white light or phase microscopy, or even to fluorescent microscopy under higher magnifications. One phenomenon observed by this means was the poor fluorescence of the chloroplasts of *Rhizosolenia* spp. when parasitized by *Richelia*. It has led to the thought that this association is probably a symbiosis rather than a parasitism. Also, chloroplasts were recognized in the collar of *Ornithocercus splendidus*, the horns of *Ceratium karsteni*, and zooxanthellae in some tintinnids. Fluorescence can also be used for following the food of copepods and cladocerans and for studying faecal pellets.

If material is to be preserved, millepore filter techniques can be used. Smaller samples than are required for the above procedures are permissible. The water sample is filtered and the filter taken through carefully graded alcohols, stained with fast green, cleared in cedar oil, and mounted in Canada balsam or hyrax. This method has advantages over the Utermohl method in that the samples can be preserved after examination. Comparisons between the relative value of these methods are desirable. The three of them allow of subsequent study of the samples for the classification of the organisms, but the naked flagellates are best observed from the living material, many bursting or becoming unrecognizable in filtered or preserved material, thus giving the fluorescence method an advantage.

The measurement of particulate carbon has been considered as an estimate of standing crop, but Strickland [40] and Wood [18] both find that there is a large amount of organic 'detritus' in many oceanic samples, and this, together with the zooplankton which is captured with the protoplankton, would upset quantitative estimates. Also, an undetermined amount of dissolved organic matter could be adsorbed on this detritus. There seems at the moment to be no way out of these difficulties. Strickland [42] considered the oxidation of organic carbon to $CO_2$ was the most accurate method of estimating organic plant material once the protoplankton has been separated from detritus and animal matter. Steele and Baird [43] found that, in Scottish coastal waters, the ratio of chlorophyll to particulate carbon could best be interpreted by assuming that living plants form the most important part of the latter, but this is not so in deeper water. Gilbricht [44] found that in Baltic Sea water near Kiel only 4% of organic carbon was living. It would seem that organic carbon figures are difficult to interpret with our present limited knowledge.

The method of analysis is relatively simple. Flocculating agents, such as aluminium hydroxide, with or without potassium alum and sodium carbonate are added and the samples are filtered or centrifuged, care being taken not to introduce cellulose from the filters. A wet combustion method is used as it is simpler and quicker: a number of oxidants have been suggested. The literature has been reviewed by Strickland [42], but he did not suggest a method for removing the detritus or animal material. He also reviewed methods for estimating standing crop using the other elements such as nitrogen or phosphorus, but pointed out that they fail because of the variable composition of plant cells. Strickland does suggest, and his suggestion has merit, that the estimation of plant enzyme activity might have possibilities in assessing standing crop.

Kreps and Verbinskaya [45] and Krey [46] were the first to suggest that plant pigments might be used as an estimate of standing crop, and the method, modified and refined, has continued to occupy the attention of workers on 'productivity' whose knowledge is chemical or biochemical rather than biological. I have examined plankton samples from the Port Hacking stations occupied regularly by workers from my laboratory there and have found that a very variable proportion of the chlorophyll-containing cells was made up of fragments of Zostera, Enteromorpha, Codium, etc., thus invalidating the results as estimates of 'phytoplankton'. Such fragmentary material exists in varying quantity in the Coral and Timor Seas, and is abundant in estuaries such as Lake Macquarie, New South Wales, and Aransas Bay, Texas. I therefore concur with the Edmonsons [47], and Margalef [48], in criticizing the use of 'chlorophyll'

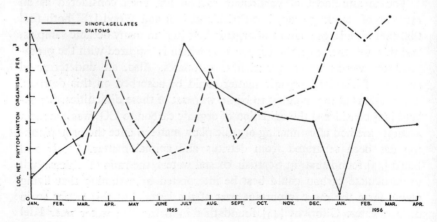

FIG. 18. The seasonal variation of diatom and dinoflagellate populations in an estuary (Lake Macquarie).

PLATE 8. Equipment for oceanographic sampling. Note winch on upper deck with wire passing to accumulator (part hidden by stanchion), thence back to meter-block on davit, past instrument-fixing position (on lower deck) into the sea. In this ship, the laboratory is directly below the winch, with a door on the deck abeam of the assistant in the chains.

PLATE 9. Meter wheel for measuring the wire as it runs out and in.

PLATE 10. Technician releasing messenger to activate samplers.

PLATE II. Weeding a form a small vessel used in case. A box deck and two a small line devices is implement the

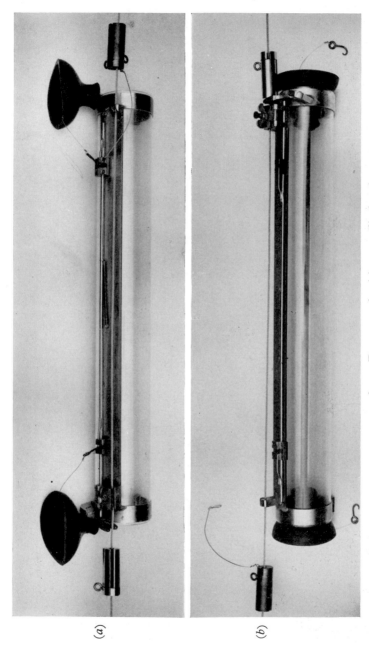

(a)

(b)

PLATE 12. A van Dorn sampler (a) open, (b) closed.

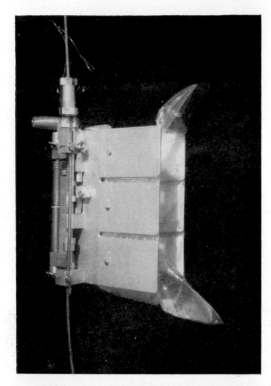

PLATE 13. Niskin sampler (a) open,

(b) closed.

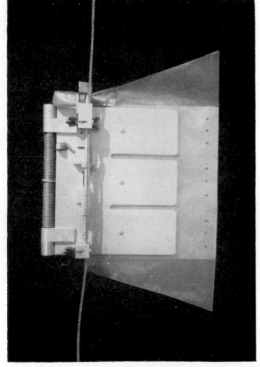

PLATE 14. Orange-peel grab.

as a measure of standing crop unless its biological implications are well understood. For example, in the Antarctic or in monospecific blooms where the composition of the plankton is known, 'chlorophyll' could give very useful information of a relative nature. Harvey [49] introduced a rapid method for estimating so-called plant pigment units, and he and Riley [50–52] made many field observations using this method. Richards and Thomson [53] developed a method for determining the quantitative spectra of acetone-extracted pigments of the protoplankton, and the expression of the results according to a formula. The Richards–Thomson equation has come in for much criticism, and is obviously inadequate. The isolation of chlorophyll c by Jeffrey (in press) will assist in the formulation of more accurate equations. Gardiner [54] considered that it might be possible to determine the group of phytoplankton present by determining the ratios of the chlorophylls and accessory pigments present. Because the pigment differences in the different groups of organisms extend to the accessory pigments, chromatographic separation of these pigments from each sample would be necessary for such a sorting. While this is theoretically possible, a direct sorting using the microscope would be quicker and probably more accurate, since pigment ratios and the ratio of pigments to the carbon content of the cell can vary with the growth phase of the organism as well as light values and other factors. Strickland points out that chlorophyll estimations are still made primarily because of the simplicity of the method and of the 'tacit assumption that an estimate correct to little better than an order of magnitude is better than no estimate at all'. This is probably true, but the same argument could apply to the counting of organisms which Strickland dismisses, though it is just as quick and easy and requires less equipment.

The method used for chlorophyll estimation is filtration of the sample (up to 5 litres) usually on millepore filters, solution of the pigments in acetone, and a spectrophotometric analysis interpreted with the aid of the Richards–Thomson equation or a modification of this. Allen [55] has suggested a chlorophyll-extraction based on the old Wilstatter method, and using a simple colorimeter. Kalle [56] proposed a chlorophyll estimation taking advantage of the auto-fluorescence of chlorophyll using a monochrometer system. It is sensitive and requires some instrumentation and has not been generally accepted. It seems worth further investigation, since it could be used at sea.

It will be obvious to anyone who considers the remarks I have made concerning standing crop estimations, or to one who reads the observations of Strickland [42], that a lot of uncritical work has been done, and I do not absolve myself from this. Most marine laboratories want an estimation of

P

plant material in the sea, usually for *ad hoc* purposes connected with fisheries, and few seem to be interested in the difficult task of correlating the various methods which have been evolved, or assessing their limitations, especially in terms of biology. This seems to me the prime task for protoplanktologists today. It is probable that none of the methods of measuring standing crop are satisfactory, and that an entirely new approach may be necessary.

DYNAMIC PRODUCTIVITY OR PRODUCTION. Dynamic measurements purport to estimate either the total biomass of plant cells produced in a given area over a given period or the photosynthetic energy converted by plants into organic matter. They are usually based on the rate of assimilation of carbon or the rate of production of photosynthetic oxygen. A criticism which may be levelled at all of them is that they take a sample in finite time, put it into unnatural conditions by placing it in a glass or plastic vessel, and treating the result as if it were directly comparable with what is happening in the sea. Thus such experiments are related to standing crop rather than to dynamic rates. The recent work described by Strickland and Terhune [57] is an earnest attempt to overcome this difficulty, but raises a number of others; it will be further considered. Gaarder and Gran [58] introduced the 'light-dark bottle' method of estimating the assimilation rate of protoplankton as a routine. In this method, oxygen is determined by the Winkler method, first on the collected sample, and after a given interval on duplicate samples which have been kept under identical conditions in black (dark) and clear (light) bottles. The bottles may be kept under constant illumination in an incubator or resubmerged at the depth from which they were taken, to simulate natural conditions. The difference between the initial oxygen and the final oxygen in the dark bottle is taken as the oxygen consumed by respiration of the protoplankton, that between the initial oxygen and the oxygen in the light bottle is assumed to be due to photosynthesis less respiration, i.e. net photosynthesis. It is assumed that the respiration in the dark bottle is the same as that in the light bottle. Strickland [42] discusses the possible errors in the Gaarder–Gran method. The accuracy of the Winkler method limits the allowable photosynthetic rate to a minimum of 20 mg C per $m^3$ per day under ideal conditions, and even this requires an incubation period of 24 hours. Such long incubation allows too much alteration in the plankton, including the microbial, population to be acceptable. Other errors are the formation of bubbles in super-saturated water, variation of $P_q$ (photosynthetic quotient) values, temperature variation, differences in respiration between light and dark bottles, and the possible growth or diminution of organisms during incubation. Steemann Nielsen [59, 60] raises the question of bacterial growth invalidating the light-dark experiments due to inhibition of the bacteria by light and antibiotics. The validity of his arguments is still controversial, as experiments on relations between protoplankton and bacteria have been contradictory, and it is probable that no constant relationship does exist.

Steemann Nielsen [59] developed a technique for assessing the uptake of carbon dioxide by photosynthesizing protoplankton. Previous methods for estimating $CO_2$ uptake, such as gas analyses, volumetric or gravimetric estimation, alkalinity changes or pH are not sensitive enough over the range required for marine studies. The Steemann Nielsen technique, which has found much favour, and has been modified by Doty [61], Doty and Oguri [62], Jitts [24] and others, relies on the introduction of a small amount of carbon[14] into the protoplankton sample, and the estimation of the amount utilized in forming cell substance during a fixed time at constant illumination. Steemann Nielsen devised it for the *Galathea* expedition in order to study the distribution of photosynthesis in the world oceans, and calculated from it the total productivity of these. It was presumed to measure gross production.

Steemann Nielsen collected his samples in the glass containers already mentioned, placed them in carefully filled bottles, and exposed them to constant light in a bath by rotating them in front of a light source for a given time (3 to 4 hours) at an illumination of 18,000 to 20,000 lux, though in practice the light fluctuated with the age of the fluorescent tubes used. After illumination, the samples were filtered through a molecular filter, rinsed with inactive sea water, and dried for 12 hours. The dry filters were treated with fuming hydrochloric acid to remove all organic carbon, dried, and the $C^{14}$ emission counted by a suitable means. Doty modified the method by keeping the bottles static in a bath in which sea water is pumped through to act as a coolant, and Jitts used a sample bottle made of plastic with plastic lids, in which the sample can be collected, injected with $C^{14}$ as carbonate, incubated and from which the plankton can be filtered directly. Doty's equipment is essentially portable and compact, that of Jitts and Steemann Nielsen rather less so. Jitts uses a light and a dark bottle on the same frame to include dark fixation in his experiments. He assumes that two samples taken simultaneously about 10 cm apart will be essentially duplicates, but this may not be strictly true, as I have found a slight bias in protoplankton samples collected in a similar manner.

Endeavours have been made to estimate diurnal productivity by the so-called *in situ* method. This consists of incubating samples for 6 hours up to or after meridian altitude at the depths from which the samples were taken, by attaching the sample bottles containing the samples plus the added $C^{14}$ to wires suspended from buoys. It can only be done in calm weather and where sudden changes are not expected. An alternative method, known as the simulated *in situ* method, is to determine the illumination in the ocean at depths to the compensation point, and to place the collected samples in a bath with filters graded so as to give illumination equivalent to that at the depths from which the samples came. The bath is cooled by running water at the prevailing surface temperature. Filters which will actually correspond actinically to ocean water at various depths are difficult to obtain.

An evaluation of the $C^{14}$ technique for measuring primary production has been made by Allen [63]. She points out that the response to light intensity and light quality vary according to the previous history of the plant cells, and there is also a variation from species to species and from one plant group to another. She doubts whether standard intensity illumination is useful even to give relative values for comparing two water masses. The *in situ* method obviates this difficulty to a large extent, but, as I have pointed out, is difficult. Allen suggests that it might be possible by using suitable mirrors and baffles to 'fold up' the light path so that the sea water in a bath could form its own filter, thus simulating natural conditions, and avoiding the use of artificial filters, which introduce factors that are difficult to assess. A difficulty here is the variation in extinction coefficient of light at different levels even in the photic zone, i.e. the water for the bath pumped from near the surface might have a low $E_k$ but a narrow band of water with a high $E_k$ at, say, 5 or 6 m could seriously reduce the light for most of the protoplankton which would be below this level in many cases. It would be difficult to reproduce this in simulated *in situ* experiments. McAllister and Strickland [64] have also tried to reduce the light in a bath by means of monel metal screens so as not to alter its actinic properties. This method might be used if the extinction coefficients at various depths were known. The diurnal periodicity of protoplankton recorded by Doty and Oguri [65], Yentsch and Ryther [66], Shimada [67], and Wood [13] which has already been mentioned is a serious problem even for *in situ* tests as the maxima and minima do not occur at the same time each day. Allen also points out the possible variation in retention of $C^{14}$ photosynthesized by the plant cell, e.g. between *Chlorella* (Myers and Johnston [68], Spoehr and Milner [69]). *Chlamydomonas* (Allen [70], Lewin [71]), and the blue-green algae (Fogg [72]) and considers that soluble products may cause discrepancies in estimates for the different algae. Such discrepancies could be very large for algae such as *Katodinium* and others which excrete up to 50% of their total assimilate. The effect of respiration is another difficulty. Steemann Nielsen claimed that his method measures gross photosynthesis, Ryther and Yentsch that it measures net photosynthesis, while, from the fact that confinement in bottles has a somewhat unpredictable effect on micro-organisms (and on larger organisms too for that matter), one could conclude that the method, as well as other methods depending on incubation, merely gives relative values for standing crop, while the rate may or may not have a relation to that in natural environments. Wood [13] found an excellent correlation between phytoplankton counts made by the fluorescence method and the assessment of $C^{14}$ assimilation made by the Jitts method, but of course as the water mass and species composition of the water were the same, the count would be expected to bear a relationship to the rate of production (fig. 13). In other water masses the correlation was much poorer. Strickland [42], commenting on the interpretation of $C^{14}$ results states: 'it is perhaps regrettable that the enthusiasm and effort initially directed towards amassing data was not diverted towards a critical evaluation of the method being used'.

There seems no doubt that valuable information regarding the relative standing crop and production can be obtained from the methods just described, especially for a particular area, but there is no evidence to show that any of them has absolute significance or even an approximation to it. Both Allen and Strickland have shown their awareness of the nature and extent of the problem, but the solution is still far to seek.

CULTURE METHODS. Knight-Jones [73] and Knight-Jones and Walne [74] suggested the applicability of culture methods for phytoplankton estimations by using dilution cultures similar to those used by bacteriologists for counting bacteria in water. The method is to set up 15 tubes of 'erdschreiber', i.e. Pringsheim's modification of Schreiber's fluid by the addition of soil extract, to make three tenfold dilutions of the sample within a suitable range and to inoculate 5 tubes of each dilution. The incubation period was 3 weeks to 6 months after which the population was estimated by the number of tubes of each dilution showing growth, applying the statistical tables prepared by the British Ministry of Health [75] with Swaroop's [76] standard errors. Erdschreiber, though a very useful medium, does not suit all micro-organisms and will to an extent act as an enrichment medium for some species. This means that certain species will outgrow others, and there is no guarantee that the dominant organism in the culture was equally represented in the protoplankton. In my own experience, of neritic protoplankton cultures, the dominant organism was frequently difficult to culture: e.g. if *Nitzschia closterium* were present in minimal amounts it was usually dominant in the cultures in a few days, while the originally dominant species such as *Schroederella delicatula* did not grow.

## Qualitative Studies

Qualitative studies are made for taxonomic, physiological, or ecological purposes, accurate taxonomy being vital for both of the latter two.

TAXONOMIC METHODS. Taxonomic studies of the larger phytoplankters, diatoms, and dinoflagellates can be made directly with the microscope. Some are best cleared before examination, e.g. diatoms by acid treatment, and dinoflagellates by treatment with hypochlorite. This applies only to the sturdier species and most of them have to be examined without treatment to avoid breaking them up. Naviculoid diatoms and *Coscinodiscus* and its allies require to be boiled with strong acid to destroy cell contents and display the structure of the siliceous tests or frustules on which the taxonomy depends. The peridineans require treatment with hypochlorite to separate the individual plates which form their armour. Diatoms such as *Chaetoceros* and *Rhizosolenia* break up with acid treatment, and the species of the former are defined by the position and number of the chloroplasts. Phase contrast, particularly anoptral phase, is very useful for the more delicate forms.

I have prepared an atlas of the species occurring in the areas in which I have worked and this is used as a rapid aid to identification, especially by trained assistants who can then work at sea and identify most planktonic and some benthic species with sufficient accuracy for ecological studies. If a form cannot be recognized, a drawing is made and compared with the literature later. Identifications can be made at sea using a simple device. This consists of a ring about 1 mm high, cemented to a microscope slide; the ring has a small groove filed across it at some point on its circumference. The sample is placed in the ring until the meniscus is convex, a cover glass put on and excess moisture removed by applying a tissue to the groove until the cover glass sits firmly on the ring. Surface tension between the slide, water, and cover minimizes movement of the material due to the ship's motion and reduces vibration to a minimum. This method allows the organisms to be studied in the living condition. The species found are listed on edge-punched cards together with latitude, longitude, salinity, temperature, and other available data. The cards used can cope with 200 species, and are typed up at sea so that anomalies can be continually checked. Samples are preserved only if they require further study in the laboratory. Coccolithophores, tintinnids, silicoflagellates, euglenids, and foraminifera may also be examined in this way or can be pipetted into smaller ringed slides with shallower cells for high power work. If necessary, they can be stained with acridine orange to demonstrate living cell contents and examined under fluorescence. Millepore filters prepared as recommended above can also be used for taxonomic studies of the larger and more robust organisms, but these cannot be turned over or moved about if this should be necessary for identification. One should learn to recognize the more important organisms in various profiles, as some of them look very different in different aspects.

The organisms of the smaller groups, e.g. the so-called μ-flagellates, may at times be fixed to a slide, stained by iodine vapour, giemsa, or acridine orange, and examined microscopically. It is frequently more satisfactory to cultivate them in stock media, especially as their morphology may alter greatly during their life history.

### Culture Methods for Phytoplankton and Benthic Plants

Physiological, ecological, life-history, and phylogenetic studies frequently require cultures; many of the protoplankton show a considerable variation in morphology, so even the time-honoured taxonomy may be full of errors; for example, the variety of *Chaetoceros* forms often found in one sample, the very different habitats of the tropical and Antarctic clones of *Corethron*, and the varying morphology of the naked flagellates (including dinoflagellates) present problems that can only be solved by culture, and a study of their life-histories *in vitro*. The physiology and nutrition of protoplankton is far too little known despite a great deal of effort. Cultures are our means of attack, but alas, the cultivation of protoplankton is not always easy! Many, particularly of the truly oceanic and tropical forms, have never been cultured. In designing culture experiments, it may be taken as a general rule that the natural environment is not the optimum of the organism involved; thus sulphate-reducing bacteria grow better when additional sulphate is added to their natural milieu, while Gran [77] found that plankton in bottles grew more rapidly with additional nitrate or phosphate. Cysteine or sodium sulphide assists the growth and reproduction of diatoms, and iron is also beneficial.

Most marine organisms will respond to a slight rise in temperature by increased metabolic rate. On the other hand, great excess of nutrients tends to be toxic, and as the sea is a very dilute solution of many salts, a toxic excess may be produced by very small amounts expressed in gram mols. Many of the difficulties in culture experiments are no doubt due to the presence of trace elements in the chemicals used in nutrient solutions even in reagent or CP grades. A very large number of culture solutions have been devised for growing photosynthetic micro-organisms and it is impossible to list them here. Two of the best media are erdschreiber, formulae for which are given by Pringsheim [78] and Galtsoff [79] and Allen and Nelson's modification of Miquel's solution [80, 81]. Both these media are improved for many purposes by adding a small amount of soil extract (Pringsheim [82], Gran [83, 84], Barker [85], Sweeney [86]) or by addition of garden soil or peat (Pringsheim [78]). With some algae, cyanocobalt-amine or thiamine can be used to replace soil extract (Droop [87]). However, no single substance or group of substances will completely replace soil extract for algae; and analyses show that it is the humic acid fraction that is effective. Matudaira's [88] comments have been mentioned earlier. Many delicate flagellates can be cultivated by adding a gram or so of actual soil to a test tube of nutrient solution and sterilizing by heating for an hour at 90°C. This method is effective for primary isolation, but will not give bacteria-free cultures. As Pringsheim [78] points out, it is best, and often necessary, to make preliminary gross isolations before attempting pure cultures so as to accustom the organisms to experimental conditions by a hardening process.

Micro-organisms which are mainly or obligatorily phagotrophic, such as *Ochromonas* and many of the dinoflagellates, will not multiply without the bacteria on which they feed and a pure culture of such an organism is manifestly impossible. Pringsheim also showed that many photosynthetic and presumably autotrophic micro-organisms will grow better in media containing organic matter, either starch or protein. If starch is used in the medium, calcium carbonate is needed to prevent undue acidity developing. More recently, Hutner and Provasoli [89], Provasoli and Pintner [90], Droop [87, 91], and many others have shown that a number of photo-autotrophs are auxotrophic.

For organisms which will grow on solid surfaces, agar or filter membrane plating methods may be used to obtain pure cultures. The surface is prepared and the required organisms are sprayed or streaked on the surface in suitable dilutions so that individual colonies may be expected. If the organisms to be cultured are motile, they will tend to move away from the centre of the colony and also away from contaminating bacteria or fungi. Selection from the edge of the expanding colony will reduce the number of contaminants, and a repetition of the treatment will often produce pure (axenic) cultures. Phototactic migrations are often used to separate photosynthetic organisms by varying the illumination across the plate. A more certain though at times tedious method of purification is the pipetting or washing method. Single organisms are selected under the microscope, either from a dish or a hollow-ground slide, and taken up in a finely drawn capillary pipette. They are then ejected into a few drops of fluid in a watch glass which is supported by a triangle in a petri dish, this assembly being sterile. The organism is again picked up from the watch glass with a sterile pipette (usually the original pipette broken off and redrawn) and the process repeated 4 to 6 times, the organism being finally transferred to a culture tube. The washing fluid should be a balanced mineral solution, e.g. Schreiber's or Miquel's solution. Another method of purification is to make use of the differential toxicity of antibiotics or antiseptics (ZoBell and Long [92], Provasoli et al. [93]). Provasoli and his co-workers have used this method to isolate a large number of organisms in axenic culture, but it is not applicable to some of the more sensitive species. Pitfalls and difficulties of pure culture study are dealt with by Pringsheim [78] who gives many valuable hints and ideas. A recent survey of axenic culture is that of McLaughlin [94].

Cultures of phytoplankton have been used for physiological studies by Pringsheim [95–102], Barker [85], Sweeney [103], Fogg [104], Droop [91, 105], Provasoli and co-workers [90, 93, 106], Hutner [107] and many others, and the reader is referred to the papers cited for the applications of such methods. Braarud and his colleagues at Oslo have used pure cultures of dinoflagellates and coccolithophores for taxonomic studies (Braarud [108], Braarud and Rossavik [109], Braarud and Pappas [110], Hasle and Nordli [111]). They have been able in certain cases to show a parallelism in form between cultures and free-living forms of the same species, to describe life histories and separate some species into clones with different norms of variation. This method of determining taxonomic relationships by life history and physiological studies is an important advance in the technology of phytoplankton ecology, while the purely phytological studies made in vitro of micro-organisms assist the ecologist in determining the function of each actor in the drama of life in the water. Braarud and his colleagues stress the importance of correlating in vitro studies with in vivo phenomena. The prime importance of this is often overlooked in the design of experiments. Curl and McLeod [112] studied the effects of light, temperature, salinity, phosphorus, and nitrogen on the growth and reproduction of Skeletonema costatum in culture and in inshore and offshore waters, and endeavoured to predict blooms of this species in marine environments. This is a method of study which could be of great assistance to marine microbial ecologists.

A very important contribution to protoplankton methods is due to Strickland and Terhune [57]. I have commented on the errors that may be expected when samples of microbial populations are studied in small vessels, and the danger of extrapolating from such experiments to the open sea. These workers have attempted to overcome this difficulty by confining plankton populations in large plastic bags 20 feet in diameter, containing some 32,000 gallons of sea water. The water in the bag is stirred by a piston driven by a water motor raising and lowering an umbrella-like device within the bag. Access was obtained through a fibreglass liner in the neck of the bag, which was buoyed by a cylindrical tank through which the fibreglass liner passed. Samples were taken through the liner when required. The authors recommend the apparatus for studying plant productivity, grazing, zooplankton growth rates, and it could also be used for observations on protoplankton succession or physiological phenomena. While observations made in such an apparatus might not be directly applicable to the open ocean, they would avoid the effects of adsorption to a very large extent, as most of the volume of the sphere would be insulated from surface effects. It would also allow some escape movements by larger organisms, e.g. copepods, and give a truer picture of marine microbial ecology.

**Bacteriological Technique**
Three aspects of bacteriology have to be considered: quantitative estimations, pure culture study, and mixed culture study.

*Quantitative Estimations*
Four general techniques are available for the quantitative study of bacterial populations: (a) direct counts of bacteria; (b) viable cell (colony) counts; (c) attachment counts; (d) estimation of relative populations by chemical activity or by nephelometry.

DIRECT COUNTS. These are made by placing an aliquot of the sample on a slide and counting the organisms seen in a field, a series of fields or on the squares of a counting chamber such as a hemacytometer slide or Petroff Hausser counting chamber, using high power, phase contrast, or fluorescence microscope. There are a number of variations of this technique among which may be listed those of Breed [113], Breed and Brew [114], Jones and Mollison [115], and Strügger [116]. Breed's method, devised for milk, is to place 0·01 ml of the material from a blood sugar pipette on to a slide on which a square centimetre has been ruled with a diamond. The drop is smeared to the limit of the square and a statistically significant number of fields counted. Since 0·01 ml covers 1 $cm^2$ the number of bacteria can be estimated once the area of a field has been determined. Hanks and James [117] used the Breed technique for soil micro-organisms with formolized milk as a fixative. Jones and Mollison [115] devised a method for counting soil bacteria in weak agar, a block of which, containing a uniform suspension of bacteria, was placed in a slide to cover a given area, dried, and stained. This gives a volume–area ratio so that the original population can be estimated. The method is limited in scope by the bacterial population of the raw agar which can at times be high. Another modification of the Breed method is due to Olson and Warren [118] in which a slide is marked with a circle enclosing a square centimetre and cut by a simple instrument; the test drop from a blood sugar pipette is smeared to the inner edge of the circle. Hanks and James calculated that reasonable accuracy is obtained by counting equidistant fields in two directions at right angles, diagonally to the direction of the smear. If the count is 6 to 20 organisms, 22 fields are enough, if over 20, 11 fields are sufficient. Criticisms of the direct method are that it includes all bacteria, whether viable or not, that it is only useful if the number of bacteria is reasonably high (of the order of $1 \times 10^5$ per ml or more), that it tells nothing regarding function, and that the bacteria which are adsorbed on particles are difficult or impossible to detect, especially in sediments. As most bacteria in aqueous environments are adsorbed, the last criticism is serious. An exceedingly useful suggestion was made by Strügger [116] who used acridine orange as already described. He claimed that the living bacteria fluoresce green, dead bacteria red. Chlorophyll fluoresces a different shade of red, but considerable experience is necessary in interpreting counts made by this method. These difficulties notwithstanding, this method, using a Petroff Hausser counter, is in my opinion the most accurate means of direct counting available at the present time. It does meet to a great extent the first and last criticisms of the direct counting method.

VIABLE COUNTS. Two methods are available, 'plating' and dilution cultures. In both cases, dilution blanks are used, aliquots are pipetted from the material to the first dilution blank, from there to the second and so on, and then to the plates or tubes so that they contain the required dilutions of the original material. Errors of sampling and dilution have been calculated by Jennison and Wadsworth [119]. In the plate method, which makes use of solid media or at least grows the bacteria on a solid surface, the number of colonies formed after incubation for 3 to 5 days is counted on suitable plates, i.e. those with 10 to 100 colonies per plate. In liquid cultures, the tubes of the greatest dilution containing the required organism is noted and the total population calculated from such tables as those of McCrady [120], the British Ministry of Health [75], or Halvorson and Ziegler [121]. The last-named and Swaroop [76] have calculated the errors of the methods which are considerable. The greater the number of plates or tubes which can be counted, the greater the accuracy, but practical considerations limit the number, usually to 2 plates of 5 liquid tubes of each dilution. In plating, the agar is melted and cooled to about 40°C, the test sample (usually 1 ml) put in a sterile petri dish and the agar poured upon it; the plate is rocked and rotated to mix the sample and allowed to set, inverted, and incubated at the required temperature.

A variant of the plate method is the roll-tube method, in which 0·1 ml of inoculum is introduced into a 6 inch × ¾ inch test tube containing 1·5 to 2 ml of melted and cooled agar or 1 ml of inoculum to 1 ml of double-strength agar, and the tube held horizontally and rolled until the agar sets in a thin film around the sides of the tube. This method is economical of media, glassware, and space and usually gives a higher count than the petri dish method. It is excellent for field work and essential for shipboard as the setting of the roll tubes is not affected by the ship's motion. In counting, a line is drawn with a marking pencil parallel with the axis of the tube, and the tube then ringed with parallel lines. Clegg and Sherwood [122] have adapted the roll-tube method for coliform counts using Mac-Conkey agar. Wood [123] used the method for fish spoilage and general marine investigations. His field kit consisted of pipettes, including blood sugar pipettes, 1 gross of 6 inch × ¾ inch test tubes for roll tubes and dilution blanks, a roll of cotton, a 1·5 litre dumpy flask, a small chemist's autoclave, a small gasoline stove, and the usual tools (scalpels, platinum loop, pestle and mortar, etc.). An incubator can be made by fitting two 30-watt lamp globes inside an insulated box, the heating current being supplied by an automobile battery (or with different globes) from a light point. A simple make-and-break activated by a long copper rod and a screw adjustment controls the temperature. The light from the globes is screened from the cultures if necessary.

Pure culture isolations can be made from the plates or roll tubes for taxonomic or physiological studies. Both dilution and plating methods give counts only of the types of organisms that will grow on the particular medium supplied, and do not give a true 'total count'.

A method of making viable counts of bacteria or protoplankton is to use a membrane filter (see Fox et al. [124], Oppenheimer [125]). The filter is placed on a sintered glass pad or a millepore pad and the liquid to be tested drawn through by suction. The concentrated precipitate can be examined microscopically or culturally. An alternative and more acceptable method is to dilute the suspension of organisms appropriately and then filter, retaining the organisms on the filter membrane according to the procedure of Oppenheimer. In this method, the filter is removed from the pad and placed on an absorbent sterile pad which has been saturated with double or triple strength medium in a sterile petri dish. The samples can then be incubated under aerobic or anaerobic conditions. The filter membrane gives an inert surface, and this is a distinct advantage.

ATTACHMENT COUNTS. This method was devised by Henrici [126] who correlated it with plate counts of lake bacteria. Slides are immersed in the water and left for a given period for the bacteria to attach, after which they are removed, dried, stained, and examined under the microscope. Henrici claims with justification that forms such as his sessile bacteria (Caulobacteriales) appear under these conditions, but cannot be cultivated by the usual bacteriological methods. Wood [127] found a very few stalked bacteria in marine environments in Australia, but some arborescent forms attached to slides immersed in sea water in some east Australian harbours; such forms were not found in cultures made by laying the slides on agar plates. However, as artificial media alter the behaviour and form of some micro-organisms, I am not prepared to say whether these peculiar forms may not grow in culture in another guise.

Henrici found his method useful in assessing bacterial activity in the Wisconsin lakes. ZoBell and Allen [128] and Wood [127] have used the method for assessing bacterial and algal attachment during the fouling of submerged surfaces. It is possible to cultivate bacteria from sparsely populated slides and follow morphological changes by placing the slides face down on an agar plate and observing the position of individual cells under the microscope. It was in this way that Wood [3] followed some of the changes from pleomorphic *Mycoplana* forms to the *Pseudomonas* and *Vibrio* forms that so often appear in culture. More recently, Kriss and his colleagues have used the slide technique on a grand scale to count and observe marine bacteria in the oceans. It can be used to study relative populations in different waters, but only for certain groups. It is possible that all attaching forms are not bacteria and there are no easy means of deciding the identity of strange organisms.

ESTIMATIONS BY CHEMICAL METHODS OR NEPHELOMETRY. Such methods are useful only for large populations, as the effects to be measured must be within the range of the assay, and the population must not change appreciably during the experiment, i.e. must be in equilibrium. The commonest parameter is respiration, but the production of characteristic substances such as hydrogen sulphide, ammonia, and nitrogen have also been used. The use of a photoelectric densitometer as suggested by Longworth [130] also requires large initial numbers of organisms. Both this and the chemical methods are useful for determining the activity (especially that of a specific enzyme) under certain conditions particularly of cultures. Conductivity counters, e.g. the Coulter counter, can be used if the volume differences of the organisms to be counted are not too great.

*Pure Culture Study*
In this technique, bacteria are isolated by plating them out on agar or other solid media, by dilution in liquid cultures, by enrichment and subsequent plating according to the methods used in other bacteriological investigations (see, for example, Salle [131]). For specific organisms such as coliform bacteria, nitrogen fixers, thiobacilli, or sulphate reducers, media are prepared which exclude the majority of bacterial species and allow only the required species and perhaps a few of its allies to grow; thermophils are obtained by raising the temperature to exclude most mesophils and psychrophils; anaerobes are cultivated by exclusion of oxygen, though this does not exclude the facultative anaerobes, and so on. The number of enrichment techniques which have been proposed is legion and the reader is referred to the manual of methods prepared by the American Society of Microbiology [132], Standard Methods for the Examination of Water and Sewage [133], and Waksman [134] for more detailed information.

Studies of the capabilities of marine organisms generally parallel those from other sources, and general biochemical and physiological principles apply, with the difficulty that sea water interferes with a number of reagents and tests, and ways round this have to be found.

*Mixed Culture Study*
Apart from pathogens, micro-organisms rarely occur naturally in pure cultures, and even when they do, as occasionally happens in plankton blooms, it is part of a succession. Thus, a pure culture growing on artificial media is an artefact that at most tells us something about a momentary phase in nature. This can be used to tell us what organism in a milieu has certain potentialities, for example that sulphate reduction may be due to *Desulphovibrio*. It does not tell us that this organism is the cause of any hydrogen sulphide observed, as that may in fact be due to sulphide-producing heterotrophs. Winogradsky was the great protagonist of the study of mixed cultures and came in for severe criticism by the Koch school of pure culture study. However, he described a number of hitherto unheard-of microbiological reactions, and correctly designated their agents. His method of attack on problems of general microbiology has not been readily accepted by microbiologists, but gives us a mine of information. Experiments are not easy to plan or to control, but by starting with simple systems, such as enrichment media, analysing the reactions and conditions in these systems, and proceeding gradually to more complex systems which approximate to the natural environment, this environment may be

better understood. This method is particularly applicable to sediments and can be applied in two ways; one is to take a column of natural sediment by means of a corer, and to study the microbial activity therein without disturbing the core. The distribution of photosynthetic organisms, sulphate reduction, sulphur oxidation, and other microbial activities can be observed, and by inserting probes, measurements can be made at required levels. The other way is to make a synthetic core of known ingredients, inoculate it with the required organisms and study the reactions, migration of organisms, and other factors. Such synthetic cores can be simple or complex to study components of the sediment system, or to build up ideal systems.

*Microbiological Assays*

An important, but as yet little used tool of the marine biologist and oceanographer is the microbiological assay, as suggested by Belser [135]. This method has been used for many years in soil studies, e.g. for phosphate estimations, trace elements, or growth factors. Hutner, Provasoli, and Baker [136] have summarized the present position in regard to its use for marine studies. They point out that so far there is a lack of adequate test organisms. This can best be overcome by greater attention to the physiology of easily cultured marine microbes. Microbial assay could be of the greatest use, not only in studying nutrition and the limitation of growth by such substances as cyanocobaltamine, but also in analyses of sea water for trace elements and in the detection of exocrines. The fact that microbial assays are at least as sensitive as the best micro-analytical methods would mean that, even in a medium as dilute as sea water, concentration would be unnecessary for a number of analyses.

## REFERENCES

[1] ZOBELL, C. E. (1946), *Marine Microbiology*, Chronica Botanica Press, Waltham, Mass., 240 pp.
[2] RILEY, G. A. (1938), 'The measurement of phytoplankton', *Int. Rev. ges. Hydrobiol. Hydrog.*, **36**, 371.
[3] WOOD, E. J. F. (1953), 'Heterotrophic bacteria in marine environments of eastern Australia', *Aust. J. Mar. Freshw. Res.*, **4**, 160–200.
[4] WINSOR, C. P. and WALFORD, L. A. (1936), 'Sampling variation in the use of plankton nets', *J. Cons. Int. Expl. Mer*, **11**, 190–204.
[5] BARNES, A. (1949), 'A statistical study of the variation in vertical hauls with special reference to the loss of catch with divided hauls', *J. Mar. Biol. Ass. U.K.*, **28**, 429–46.
[6] BARNES, H. and MARSHALL, S. M. (1951), 'On the variability of replicate plankton samples and some applications of "contagious" series to the distribution of catches over restricted periods', *J. Mar. Biol. Ass. UK.*, **30**, 233–63.

228 · MARINE MICROBIAL ECOLOGY

[7] BARNES, H. (1949), 'On the volume of water filtered by a plankton pump with some observations on the distribution of planktonic animals', *J. Mar. Biol. Ass. U.K.*, **28**, 651–61.

[8] NANSEN, F. (1915), 'Closing nets for vertical hauls and for horizontal towing', *Publ. Circ. Cons. Int. Expl. Mer*, **67**, 1.

[9] CLARKE, G. L. and BUMPUS, D. F. (1940, revised, 1950), 'The plankton sampler – an implement for quantitative plankton investigation', *Limnol. Soc. Amer. Spec. Publ.* **N5**.

[10] BARNES, H. (1953), 'A simple, inexpensive closing net', *Mo. Ital. Idrobiol.*, **7**, 189–98.

[11] CASSIE, R. M. (1959), 'An experimental study of factors inducing aggregation in marine plankton', *N.Z. J. Sci.*, **2**, 339–65.

[12] CASSIE, R. M. (1959), 'Micro-distribution of plankton', *N.Z. Oceanogr. Inst. Contr.*, 70.

[13] WOOD, E. J. F. (1963), 'Some relations of phytoplankton to environment', *Symp. Marine Microbiol.*, Ch. 28, C. H. Oppenheimer, ed. Thomas, Springfield, Ill.

[14] HARVEY, H. W. (1955), *The Chemistry and Fertility of Sea Water*, Cambridge University Press.

[15] LANGFORD, R. R. (1953), 'Methods of plankton collection and a description of a new plankton sampler', *J. Fish. Res. Bd. Can.*, **10**, 238–52.

[16] RICKER, W. E. (1933), 'The utility of nets in fresh water plankton investigations', *Trans. Amer. Fish. Soc.*, **62**, 292 (1932).

[17] MACKAY, H. H. (1924), 'A quantitative study of the plankton of the shallow bays of Lake Nipigon', *Univ. Toronto Stud. Biol. Ser.*, **25**, 169.

[18] RAWSON, D. S. (1930), 'The bottom fauna of Lake Simcoe and its role in the ecology of the lake', *Univ. Toronto Stud. Biol. Ser.*, **34**, 1.

[19] JUDAY, C., RICH, W. H., KEMMERER, G. I., and MANN, A. (1932), 'Limnological studies of Karluk Lake, Alaska, 1920–1930', *Bull. U.S. Bur. Fish.*, **27**, 417.

[20] JUDAY, C. (1916), 'Limnological apparatus', *Trans. Wisconsin Acad. Sci. Lett.*, **18**, 566.

[21] JENSEN, A. and STEEMANN NIELSEN, E. (1952), 'A water sampler for biological purposes', *J. Cons. Int. Expl. Mer*, **18**, 196–99.

[22] VAN DORN, W. G. (1956), 'Large volume water samplers', *Trans. Amer. Geophys. Union*, **37**, 6.

[23] NISKIN, S. J. (1962), 'A water sampler for microbiological studies', *Deep Sea Res.*, **9**, 501–3.

[24] JITTS, H. R. (1957), 'The 14C method for measuring $CO_2$ uptake in marine productivity studies', *C.S.I.R.O. Div. Fish. Oceanog. Rept.*, **8**, 12 pp.

[25] ZOBELL, C. E. (1941), 'Apparatus for collecting water samples from different depths for bacteriological analysis', *J. Mar. Res.*, **4**, 173–88.

[26] ZOBELL, C. E. (1954), 'Some effects of high hydrostatic pressure on apparatus observed on the Danish *Galathea* expedition', *Deep Sea Res.*, **2**, 24–32.

[27] EMERY, K. O. and DIETZ, R. S. (1941), 'Gravity coring instrument and mechanics of sediment coring', *Bull. Geol. Soc. Amer.*, **52**, 1685–1714.

[28] LASKER, R. and HOLMES, R. W. (1957), 'Variability in retention of marine phytoplankton by membrane filters', *Nature*, **180**, 1295–96.

[29] HOLMES, R. W. and ANDERSON, G. C. (1963), 'Size fractionation of $C^{14}$ labelled natural phytoplankton communities', *Symp. Marine Microbiol.*, Ch. 25, C. H. Oppenheimer, ed. Thomas, Springfield, Ill.

[30] LOVEGROVE, T. (1961), 'An improved form of sedimentation apparatus for use with an inverted microscope', *J. Cons. Int. Expl. Mer*, **25**, 279–84.

[31] LUND, J. W. G. (1951), 'A sedimentation technique for counting algae and other organisms', *Hydrobiol.*, **3**, 390.

[32] BALLANTYNE, DOROTHY (1953), 'Comparison of different methods of estimating phytoplankton', *J. Mar. Biol. Ass. U.K.*, **32**, 129–48.

[33] WOOD, E. J. F. (1963), 'The relative importance of groups of algae and protozoa in marine environments in the south-west Pacific', *Symp. Marine Microbiol.*, Ch. 24, C. H. Oppenheimer, ed. Thomas, Springfield, Ill.

[34] WOOD, E. J. F. (1962), 'A method for phytoplankton study', *Limnol. Oceanog.*, **7**, 32–35.

[35] KIMBALL, J. F. JR. and WOOD, E. J. F. 'A simple centrifuge for phytoplankton spectres,' *Bull. Mar. Sci.* (in press).

[36] LUND, J. W. G. and TALLING, J. F. (1957), 'Botanical limnological methods with special reference to the algae', *Bot. Rev.*, **23**, 453–89.

[37] UTERMOHL, H. (1931), 'Neue Wege in der quantitativen Erfassung des Planktons mit besonderer Berücksichtingung des Ultraplanktons', *Verh. int. Verein. theor. angew. Limnol.*, **5**, 567–96.

[38] LUND, J. W. G., KIPLING, C., and LECREN, E. D. (1958), 'The inverted microscope method of estimating algal numbers and the statistical basis of estimations by counting', *Hydrobiol.*, **11**, 143–70.

[39] WOOD, E. J. F. (1955), 'Fluorescent microscopy in marine microbiology', *J. Cons. Int. Expl. Mer*, **21**, 6–7.

[40] STRICKLAND, J. D. H. 1961 (1963), in *A.I.B.S. Interdisciplinary Conference on Marine Biology*, I, Ecology.

[41] WOOD, E. J. F. and OPPENHEIMER, C. H. (1962), 'Note on fluorescence microscopy in marine microbiology', *Z. allg. Mikrobiol.*, **2**, 164–65.

[42] STRICKLAND, J. D. H. (1960), 'Measuring the production of marine plankton', *Fish. Res. Bd. Can. Bull.*, **122**, 1–72.

[43] STEELE, J. H. and BAIRD, I. R. (1961), 'Relations between primary production, chlorophyll, and particulate carbon', *Limnol. Oceanog.*, **6**, 68–78.

[44] GILBRICHT, M. (1952), 'Untersuchungen zur Produktionsbiologie des Planktons in der Kieler Bucht, II. Die Produktionsgrösse', *Kieler Meeresf.*, **9**, 51–61.

[45] KREPS, E. and VERBINSKAYA, N. (1930), 'Seasonal changes in the Barents Sea', *J. Cons. Int. Expl. Mer*, **5**, 329.

[46] KREY, J. (1939), 'Die Bestimmung des Chlorophylls im Meerwasser Schöpproben', *J. Cons. Int. Expl. Mer*, **14**, 201.

[47] EDMONSON, W. T. and EDMONSON, Y. H. (1947), 'Measurements of production in fertilized salt water', *J. Mar. Res.*, **6**, 228.

[48] MARGALEF, R. (1956), 'Considerations on the quantitative determination of phytoplankton through the pigment method, and on the factors that modify the relation between pigments and dry weight', *Publ. Inst. Biol. Appl. Barcelona*, 16, 17.

[49] HARVEY, H. W. (1934), 'Measurement of phytoplankton population', *J. Mar. Biol. Ass. U.K.*, 19, 761–73.

[50] RILEY, G. A. (1938), 'Plankton studies, I', *J. Mar. Res.*, 1, 335.

[51] RILEY, G. A. (1939), 'Plankton studies, II', *J. Mar. Res.*, 2, 145–62.

[52] RILEY, G. A. (1941), 'Plankton studies, III', *Bull. Bingham Oceanog. Coll.*, 7, 3, 1–93.

[53] RICHARDS, F. A. with THOMSON, T. G. (1952), 'The estimation and characterization of phytoplankton populations by pigment analyses, II', *J. Mar. Res.*, 11, 156–72.

[54] GARDINER, A. C. (1943), 'Measurement of the phytoplankton population by the pigment extraction method', *J. Mar. Biol. Ass. U.K.*, 25, 739.

[55] ALLEN, MARY BELLE, 1961 (1962), in *A.I.B.S. Interdisciplinary Conference on Marine Biology*, I, Ecology.

[56] KALLE, K. (1951), 'Meereskundlich-chemische Untersuchungen mit Hilfe des Pulfrich Photometer von Zeiss, VII', *Deutsche Hydrograph.*, 4, 92.

[57] STRICKLAND, J. D. H. and TERHUNE, L. D. B. (1961), 'The study of *in situ* marine photosynthesis using a large plastic bag', *Limnol. Oceanog.*, 6, 93–96.

[58] GAARDER, T. and GRAN, H. H. (1927), 'Investigations on the production of plankton in the Oslo Fjord', *Rapp. et Proc. Verb. Cons. Int. Expl. Mer*, 42, (3).

[59] STEEMANN NIELSEN, E. (1952), 'The use of radioactive carbon ($C^{14}$) for measuring organic production in the seas', *J. Cons. Int. Expl. Mer*, 18, 117–40.

[60] STEEMANN NIELSEN, E. (1955), 'The production of antibiotics by plankton algae and its effect upon bacterial activities in the sea', *Deep Sea Res.*, 3 (suppl.), 281–86.

[61] DOTY, M. S. 'Current status of carbon-14 method of assaying productivity of the ocean', *Rept. U.S.A.E.C.* to April, 1955.

[62] DOTY, M. S. and OGURI, M. (1957), 'The carbon-fourteen technique for determining primary plankton productivity', *Publ. Stat. Zool. Napoli.*, 31 (suppl.), 70–94.

[63] ALLEN, MARY BELLE (1961), 'Evaluation of the $C^{14}$ technique for measurement of primary production', *1st Radioecol. Symp. Fort Collins, Colorado*, Sept. 15.

[64] MCALLISTER, C. D., PARSONS, T. R., STEPHENS, K., and STRICKLAND, J. D. H. (1961), 'Measurements of primary production in coastal sea water using a large-volume plastic sphere', *Limnol. Oceanog.*, 6, 237–58.

[65] DOTY, M. S. and OGURI, M. (1957), 'Evidence for a photosynthetic daily periodicity', *Limnol. Oceanog.*, 2, 37–40.

[66] YENTSCH, C. S. and RYTHER, J. H. (1957), 'Short-term variations in phytoplankton and their significance', *Limnol. Oceanog.*, 2, 140–142.

[67] SHIMADA, B. M. (1949), 'Diurnal fluctuation in photosynthetic rate and chlorophyll-*a* content of phytoplankton from eastern Pacific waters', *Limnol. Oceanog.*, **3**, 336–39.

[68] MYERS, J. and JOHNSTON, J. (1949), 'Carbon and nitrogen balance of *Chlorella* during growth', *Plant Physiol.*, **24**, 111–119.

[69] SPOEHR, H. A. and MILNER, H. W. (1949), 'The chemical composition of *Chlorella*; effect of environmental conditions', *Plant Physiol.*, **24**, 120–49.

[70] ALLEN, MARY BELLE (1956), 'Excretion of organic compounds by *Chlamydomonas*', *Arch. Mikrobiol.*, **24**, 163–68.

[71] LEWIN, R. A. (1956), 'Extracellular polysaccharides of green algae', *Can. J. Microbiol.*, **2**, 665–72.

[72] FOGG, G. E. (1952), 'The production of extracellular nitrogenous substances by a blue-green alga', *Proc. Roy. Soc. Ser. B*, **13**, 372–97.

[73] KNIGHT, JONES, E. W. (1951), 'Preliminary studies of nannoplankton and ultraplankton systematics and abundance by a quantitative culture method', *J. Cons. Int. Expl. Mer*, **17**, 140.

[74] KNIGHT, JONES, E. W. and WALNE, P. R. (1951), '*Chromulina pusilla* Butcher, a dominant member of the ultraplankton', *Nature*, **167**, 445–

[75] BRITISH MINISTRY OF HEALTH (1940), *The Bacteriological Examination of Water*, Repts. Publ. Health, Med. Subj. 71.

[76] SWAROOP, S. (1938), 'Numerical estimation of *B. coli* by dilution method', *Ind. J. Med. Res.*, **26**, 353.

[77] GRAN, H. H. (1927), 'The production of plankton in coastal waters off Bergen', *Rept. Norwegian Fish.*, Inv. 8.

[78] PRINGSHEIM, E. G. (1946), *Pure Culture Studies of Algae*, Cambridge University Press.

[79] GALTSOFF, P. S., LUTZ, F. E., WELCH, P. S., and NEEDHAM, J. C. (1937), *Culture Methods for Invertebrate Animals*, Comstock, New York.

[80] ALLEN, E. J. and NELSON, E. W. (1910), 'On the artificial culture of marine plankton organisms', *J. Mar. Biol. Ass. U.K.*, **80**, 421–74.

[81] ALLEN, E. J. (1914), 'On the culture of the plankton diatom *Thalassiosira gravida* Cleve in artificial sea water', *J. Mar. Biol. Ass. U.K.*, **10**, 417–39.

[82] PRINGSHEIM, E. G. (1912), 'Die Kultur von Algae in Agar', *Beitr. Biol. Pfl.*, **11**, 305.

[83] GRAN, H. H. (1931), 'On the conditions for the production of plankton in the sea', *Rapp. et Proc. Verb. Cons. Int. Expl. Mer*, **75**, 37–46.

[84] GRAN, H. H. (1932), 'Phytoplankton methods and problems', *J. Cons. Int. Expl. Mer*, **7**, 343–55.

[85] BARKER, H. A. (1935), 'The culture and physiology of marine dinoflagellates', *Arch. Mikrobiol.*, **6**, 157–181.

[86] SWEENEY, B. M. (1951), 'Culture of the dinoflagellate *Gymnodinium* with soil extract', *Amer. J. Bot.*, **38**, 669–77.

[87] DROOP, M. R. (1954), 'Cobaltamine requirement in the Chrysophyceae', *Nature*, **174**, 520.

[88] MATUDAIRA, T. (1942), 'On organic sulphides as growth-promoting ingredients for diatom', *Proc. Imp. Acad. Sci. Tokyo*, **18**, 107–116.

[89] HUTNER, S. H. and PROVASOLI, L. (1955), 'Comparative biochemistry of flagellates in *Biochemistry and Physiology of the Protozoa*, II', 17–44, Academic Press, New York.

[90] PROVASOLI, L. and PINTNER, IRMA J. (1953), 'Ecological implications of *in vitro* nutritional requirements of algal flagellates', *Ann. N.Y. Acad. Sci.*, 56, 839.

[91] DROOP, M. R. (1955), 'A pelagic marine diatom requiring cobaltamine', *J. Mar. Biol. Ass. U.K.*, 34, 229–31.

[92] ZOBELL, C. E. and LONG, J. H. (1938), 'Studies on the isolation of bacteria-free cultures of marine phytoplankton', *J. Mar. Res.*, 1, 329–34.

[93] PROVASOLI, L., PINTNER, I. J., and PACKER, L. (1951), 'Use of antibiotics in obtaining pure cultures of algae and protozoa', *Proc. Amer. Soc. Protozool.*, 2, 6.

[94] MCLAUGHLIN, J. J. A. (1960), 'Axenic Culture' in *Encyclopedia of Science and Technology*, 698–701.

[95] PRINGSHEIM, E. G. (1913), 'Zur Physiologie der *Euglena gracilis*', *Beitr. Biol. Pfl.*, 12, 1.

[96] PRINGSHEIM, E. G. (1914), 'Zur Physiologie der Schizophyceen', *Beitr. Biol. Pfl.*, 12, 49.

[97] PRINGSHEIM, E. G. (1914), 'Die Ernährung von *Haematococcus pluvialis*, Flot.', *Beitr. Biol. Pfl.*, 12, 413.

[98] PRINGSHEIM, E. G. (1920), 'Zur Physiologie der *Polytoma uvella*', *Ber. deut. Bot. Ges.*, 38, 8.

[99] PRINGSHEIM, E. G. (1921), 'Zur Physiologie saprophytischer Flagellaten (*Polytoma, Astasia*, and *Chilomonas*)', *Beitr. allg. Bot.*, 2, 88.

[100] PRINGSHEIM, E. G. (1926), 'Über das Ca-Bedürfnis einiger Algen', *Planta*, 2, 555.

[101] PRINGSHEIM, E. G. (1934), 'Über Oxythrophie bei *Chlorogonium*', *Planta*, 22, 146.

[102] PRINGSHEIM, E. G. (1942), 'Contributions to our knowledge of saprophytic algae and flagellates, III. *Astasia, Distigma, Monoidium*, and *Rhabdomonas*', *New Phytol.*, 41, 171.

[103] SWEENEY, B. M. (1954), '*Gymnodinium splendens* a marine dinoflagellate requiring vitamin $B_{12}$,' *Amer. J. Bot.*, 41, 821–24.

[104] FOGG, G. E. (1957), 'Relationships between metabolism and growth in plankton algae', *J. Gen. Microbiol.*, 16, 294–97.

[105] DROOP, M. R. (1954), 'A note on the isolation of small marine algae and flagellates for pure cultures', *J. Mar. Biol. Ass. U.K.*, 33, 511–14.

[106] PROVASOLI, L. (1937–1938), 'Studi sulla nutrizione dei protozoi', *Boll. Lab. Zool. Agr. Bachic. Milano*, 8, 3.

[107] HUTNER, S. H. (1961), 'Plant-animals as experimental tools for growth studies', *Bull. Torrey Bot. Club*, 88, 339–49.

[108] BRAARUD, T. (1945), 'Morphological observations on marine dinoflagellate cultures (*Porella perforata, Goniaulax tamarensis, Protoceratium reticulatum*)', *Avh. Norske Vidensk-Akad.*, 1, 11, 1–18.

[109] BRAARUD, T. and ROSSAVIK, E. (1951), 'Observations on the marine dinoflagellate *Prorocentrum micans* Ehr. in culture', *Avh. Norske Vidensk-Akad.*, 1, 1–18.

[110] BRAARUD, T. and PAPPAS, I. (1951), 'Experimental studies on the dinoflagellate *Peridinium triquetrum* (Ehr.) Lebour', *Avh. Norske Vidensk-Akad.*, **1**, 2, 1–21.
[111] HASLE, GRETHE R. and NORDLI, E. (1951), 'Form variation in *Ceratium fusus* and *tripos* populations in cultures and from the sea', *Avh. Norske Vidensk-Akad.*, **1**, 4, 1–25.
[112] CURL, H. JR. and MCLEOD, G. C. (1961), 'The physiological ecology of a marine diatom, *Skeletonema costatum* (Grev.) Cleve', *J. Mar. Res.*, **19**, 70–88.
[113] BREED, R. S. (1911), 'The determination of the number of bacteria in milk by direct microscopical examination', *Z. Bakt.*, II, **30**, 337–40.
[114] BREED, R. S. and BREW, J. D. (1916), 'Counting bacteria by means of the microscope', *N.Y. Agr. Exp. Sta. Bull.*, **48**, 1–31.
[115] JONES, P. C. T. and MOLLISON, J. E. (1948), 'A technique for the quantitative estimation of soil micro-organisms', *J. Gen. Microbiol.*, **2**, 54–69.
[116] STRÜGGER, S. (1948), 'Fluorescent microscope examination of bacteria in soil', *Can. J. Res.*, **26**, 288.
[117] HANKS, J. H. and JAMES, D. F. (1940), 'The enumeration of bacteria by the microscopic method', *J. Bact.*, **39**, 297–305.
[118] OLSON, C. R. and WARREN, F. G. (1944), 'Mechanical aids in the direct microscopic method of counting bacteria', *J. Bact.*, **47**, 495–98.
[119] JENNISON, M. W. and WADSWORTH, G. P. (1940), 'Evaluation of the errors involved in estimating bacterial numbers by the plating method', *J. Bact.*, **39**, 389.
[120] MCCRADY, M. H. (1918), 'Table for rapid interpretation of fermentation tube results', *Publ. Health. J.*, **9**, 201–20.
[121] HALVORSON, H. O. and ZIEGLER, N. R. (1933), 'Application of statistics to problems in bacteriology', *J. Bact.*, **25**, 101–121; **26**, 331–339.
[122] CLEGG, L. F. L. and SHERWOOD, H. P. (1947), 'The bacteriological examination of molluscan shellfish', *J. Hyg.*, **45**, 504–21.
[123] WOOD, E. J. F. (1940), 'Studies in the marketing of fish in eastern Australia, II', *C.S.I.R. Aust. Pam.*, 100.
[124] FOX, D. L., OPPENHEIMER, C. H., and KITTREDGE, J. S. (1953), 'Microfiltration in oceanographic research', *J. Mar. Res.*, **12**, 233–43.
[125] OPPENHEIMER, C. H. (1952), 'The membrane filter in marine microbiology', *J. Bact.*, **64**, 783–86.
[126] HENRICI, A. T. (1933), 'Studies on fresh water bacteria, I', *J. Bact.*, **25**, 277–86.
[127] WOOD, E. J. F. (1950), 'The role of bacteria in the early stages of fouling', *Aust. J. Mar. Freshw. Res.*, **1**, 85–91.
[128] ZOBELL, C. E. and ALLEN, E. C. (1933), 'Attachment of bacteria to submerged slides', *Proc. Soc. Exper. Biol. Med.*, **30**, 1409–11.
[129] KRISS, E. A. (1959), *Marine Microbiology*, Izd. Akad. Nauk, S.S.S.R., Moscow, 455 pp.
[130] LONGWORTH, L. G. (1936), 'The examination of bacterial populations with the aid of a photo-electric densitometer', *J. Bact.*, **32**, 307.
[131] SALLE, A. J. (1954), *Fundamental Principles of Bacteriology*, McGraw-Hill, New York, 782 pp.
[132] American Society for Microbiology. *Manual of Methods.*

[133] American Public Health Association (1936), *Standard Methods for the Examination of Water and Sewage.*

[134] WAKSMAN, S. A. (1932), *Principles of Soil Microbiology*, Williams Wilkins, Baltimore.

[135] BELSER, W. (1958), 'Possible application of a bacterial bioassay in productivity studies', *U.S.D.I. Fish. Wildl. Serv. Spec. Rept. Fish.*, **279**, 53–54.

[136] HUTNER, S. H., PROVASOLI, L., and BAKER, H. (1961), 'Development of microbiological assays for biochemical, oceanographic, and clinical use', *Microchem. J.*, **1**, 95–113.

# Index

235